Marine Engineering

Design of Propulsion and Electric Power Generation Systems

Hans Klein Woud

MSc, FIMarEST

Professor of Marine Engineering, Delft University of Technology

Douwe Stapersma

MSc, CEng, FIMarEST

Professor of Marine Engineering, Royal Netherlands Naval College

Sponsored by

Published by IMarEST
The Institute of Marine Engineering, Science and Technology
80 Coleman Street
London EC2R 5BJ

www.imarest.org

A charity registered in England and Wales
Registered Number 212992

First published 2002
This reprint 2003
The contents of this reprint are unchanged. Only some printing errors have been corrected and a few sentences have been reworded to improve the clarity of the text – *The authors*

A CIP catalogue record for this book is available from the British Library

ISBN 1-902536-47-9

Preface

This book is based on some 30 years of practical experience with the design of machinery systems, mainly for naval ships. Both authors have worked on the design of propulsion, electric power generation and auxiliary systems for frigates, submarines and patrol ships. They have lectured on marine engineering during the last 15 years at the Delft University of Technology and at the Royal Netherlands Naval College. The book is intended as study material for university and polytechnic high school students, but also as a reference for marine engineers working in the field.

Marine engineering covers the design and operation of machinery and electrical systems and much less the design of the equipment used within these systems. The main topic, consequently, is systems engineering, which involves the design of marine systems, based on the functions which have to be performed on a ship, with a certain task or mission.

It is the conviction of the authors that it is only possible to design well-functioning and cost-effective systems when the relevant fundamental sciences are understood and properly used. This involves topics such as: thermodynamics, fluid mechanics, electrical engineering, dynamics, ship resistance and propulsion. Furthermore, it is mandatory to understand the physical principles and characteristics of the applied equipment.

Nowadays, the propulsion system and the electric power generation plant are almost always integrated in some form. This integration may be limited to the application of a shaft generator, driven by the propulsion plant; but with electric propulsion, the systems are fully integrated, leading to an All-Electric Ship.

On the basis of these considerations the book covers the following subjects:

1. The basis of marine engineering: systems engineering, covering mission, functions, systems and components.
2. Underlying physical principles. A short treatment of thermodynamics and electrical engineering, as used within the following chapters, is given. The topics are treated in a condensed way, because it is assumed that the reader is familiar with them.
3. The main components of propulsion and electric power supply systems, the resistance and propulsion characteristics of ships and the electric power demand.
4. Energy conversion: an overview of different types of energy conversion and the associated equipment. Further, the energy flow diagram is introduced, which helps to visualise the energy conversions taking place in a system.
5. Power plant concepts: this chapter treats possible propulsion and electric power supply system configurations, with their advantages and disadvantages. Redundancy considerations and machinery space lay-out are also discussed.
6. Machinery: the operating principles and characteristics of the main equipment — covering prime movers, transmission equipment, propulsors and electrical equipment (electric motors, generators and converters). The equipment is described in such a way that the reader will understand their principle of operation and get sufficient background to talk with the designer of the equipment: the mechanical or electrical engineer. Also the fuels used on board ships are discussed in this chapter. Four

machinery types (diesel engines, gas turbines, electrical components and propellers), are so important for a ship power plant, that these are treated in greater detail in the following four chapters.

7. Diesel engines are the most frequently used prime movers on board ships and determine to a great extent the characteristics of the complete power plant. This chapter gives a thorough discussion of working principles, performance, turbocharging, operating envelope, power density, thermodynamic background and some information about construction and installation.

8. Gas turbines are frequently used on board naval and other fast ships. Their specific characteristics cover working principle (for both simple and advanced cycles), thermodynamic background, performance, power density, operating envelope and installation.

9. Main characteristics of electric motors, speed control and drive characteristics. This includes AC generators, frequency and voltage control as well as power sharing and reactive current sharing. Finally, the most relevant power electronic converters are discussed, along with their main fields of application.

10. Screw type propellers: working principle, performance, open water diagrams and optimal propeller diameter and speed, are covered.

11. Matching the propulsion engine to propeller. One of the most essential tasks of the marine engineer is to match the prime mover to the propulsor. This chapter covers the basic matching problem and the criteria to be satisfied. Next it discusses the off-design problem and how to solve it. All relevant off-design conditions are treated: change of speed, increased or decreased ship resistance, change of number of driving shafts, change of propeller pitch, change of number of driving engines, influence of power-take-off and the change of transmission gear ratio.

12. Ship fuel consumption and exhaust emission. This chapter details the calculations necessary to determine the fuel consumption, exhaust emissions (in the form of SO_x and NO_x), ship range and endurance.

At the end of most chapters one or a few exercises are included. The reader is encouraged to undergo these exercises because it helps to understand the contents of the book. When the exercises are a straightforward application of previously dealt with topics, there is no worked out solution, only the resulting answers. In other cases the solution to the exercise has been worked out.

The book does not cover the control, monitoring and auxiliary (cooling, lubrication, compressed air and fuel) systems necessary for the power plant. Neither does it cover the dynamic behaviour of propulsion and power generation systems or vibration analysis of drive trains. These are, however, important topics which justify thorough treatment. It is therefore the intention of the authors to publish a volume covering these subjects, together with topics such as waste heat usage, refrigeration, air conditioning, ventilation and reliability and maintainability.

The authors thank the referees, who have read and commented on the complete conceptual text. Their valuable contributions certainly have improved the quality of the book. Our heartfelt thanks go to:

- Prof Hallvard Engja, Norwegian University of Science and Technology, Trondheim, Norway.

- Hans Huisman, MSc, P&O-Nedlloyd, Rotterdam, The Netherlands.

- Jaap van den Hul, MSc, Royal Niestern Sander Shipyard, Delfzijl, The Netherlands.

- Prof Tony Roskilly, University of Newcastle upon Tyne, UK.

- Rob Viergever, MSc, Royal Schelde Shipyard, Vlissingen, The Netherlands.

- Prof Edwin Wiggins, Webb Institute, USA.

Also thanks to Ronald Dingemanse, BSc, of Imtech Marine & Offshore, Rotterdam, The Netherlands, who read the conceptual text of the electrical topics and gave valuable comments.

Last but not least the authors thank ms. Willemien Verdonk, MSc, who contributed so much to the book in her role as Editor. Frequently, she had to start with a sketchy manuscript, which she worked out to a complete, well-balanced text. In that process, she acted as a critical reader, who gave very valuable suggestions for improvement, both technically and educationally.

The authors:
Hans Klein Woud and Douwe Stapersma

About the authors

J. Klein Woud: graduated in 1966 as mechanical engineer at Delft University of Technology, with specialisation in internal combustion (diesel)engines. After military service he joined, in 1968, Stork Werkspoor Diesel where he worked as application engineer for marine diesel engines. During 1970-1986 he worked for the naval design office, Nevesbu, The Hague, where he was involved with the design and engineering of frigates, submarines and patrol craft and their machinery systems. In October 1986 he was appointed professor of marine engineering at Delft University of Technology. He lectures on marine engineering systems and conducts research with regard to condition monitoring, maintenance and design techniques. During January 1995-June 1998 he was dean of the Faculty of Mechanical Engineering and Marine Technology.

D. Stapersma: after graduating in 1973 as a mechanical engineer at Delft University of Technology in the field of gas turbines, he joined Nevesbu where he was involved in the design and engineering of the machinery installation of the Standard frigate for the Royal Netherlands Navy. He then coordinated the integration of the automatic propulsion control system for a class of export corvettes. From 1980 he was responsible for the design and engineering of the machinery installation of the Walrus-class submarines and, in particular, their machinery automation. He then became in charge of the design of the Moray-class submarines in a joint project organisation with the Rotterdam Dockyard Company. He is currently professor of marine engineering at the Royal Netherlands Naval College and a part-time professor of marine engineering and diesel engines at Delft University of Technology.

Table of Contents

Nomenclature

Roman variables

a	acceleration	m/s^2
a	Seiliger pressure ratio combustion	-
A	area	m^2
A_B	bore area	m^2
afr	air–fuel ratio	-
afr_{tot}	total air–fuel ratio (including scavenging)	-
A_S	wetted surface of a ship	m^2
b	expansion ratio combustion (3-4)	-
B	magnetic flux density	T
c	expansion ratio combustion (4-5)	-
C	capacitance	F
C	heat capacity	J/K
$\dot{C}$	heat capacity rate	J/K·s
C_{adm}	admiralty constant	$\frac{\text{ton}^{2/3}\cdot\text{knts}^3}{\text{kW}}$
C_D	delivered power coefficient	-
C_E	specific resistance	-
c_m	mean piston speed	m/s
c_p	specific heat at constant pressure	J/kg·K
CSR	continuous service rating	-
C_T	thrust loading coefficient	-
C_T	total resistance coefficient	-
C_T^{*}	thrust coefficient	-
C_Q^{*}	torque coefficient	-
c_v	specific heat at constant volume	J/kg·K
d	distance travelled	mile
D	diameter	m
D	drag force	N
D_B	bore diameter	m
e	energy per unit of mass	J/kg
ecm	energy consumption per mile	J/mile
E	energy	J
E	induction voltage	V
E	modulus of elasticity	Pa
$\dot{E}$	energy flow	J/s
E_{kin}	kinetic energy	J
EM	engine margin	-
EMF	electromotive force	V
E_{pot}	potential energy	J

ES	energy source	-
EU	energy use	-
f	frequency	Hz
f	(engine firing) frequency	Hz
F	force	N
F	fuel available on board	kg, tonnes
fcm	fuel consumption per mile	kg/mile
F_L	Lorentz force	N
Fr	Froude number $\dfrac{v_s}{\sqrt{g \cdot L}}$	-
g	gravitational constant	9.81 m/s^2
G	shear modulus of elasticity	Pa
h	height	m
h	specific enthalpy	J/kg
H	enthalpy	J
H	hydraulic energy	J
h^H	higher heat value	J/kg
h^L	lower heat value	J/kg
i	gearbox reduction ratio	-
i	number of cylinders	-
I	electric current	A
I_A	current through armature	A
I_b	base current	A
I_c	collector current	A
I_e	effective current	A
I_F	current through field windings	A
I_L	line current	A
I_m	amplitude of current	A
I_P	phase current	A
J	advance ratio	-
k	hull roughness	m
k	number of revolutions per cycle (1 or 2)	-
k_e	number of engines	-
K_E	coil constant	-
K_G	generator constant	-
K_M	motor constant	-
k_p	number of propellers	-
K_Q	torque coefficient	-
K_T	thrust coefficient	-
l	length	m
L	(self) inductance	H
L	length	m
L	lift force	N
L_s	stroke length	m

m	mass	kg
M	torque	Nm
M	molecular weight	kg/kmol
$\dot{m}$	mass flow rate	kg/s
$\dot{m}_{air,in}$	total air flow into diesel engine	kg/s
M_B	engine (brake) torque	Nm
m_{ca}	mass of combustion air	kg
$m_{ca,min}$	minimum required m_{ca}	kg
MCR	maximum continuous rating	-
M_{cyl}	effective (brake) torque/cylinder	Nm
M_D	delivered torque	Nm
m_f	mass of fuel (per cycle)	kg
$\dot{m}_f$	mass flow of fuel	kg/s
m_{pe}	mass of pollutant emission	kg
M_S	shaft torque	Nm
N	number of windings	-
n	revolutions per second	rev/s
n	rotational speed	s^{-1}
n_C	polytropic index for compressor	-
n_e	engine speed	rev/s
n_p	propeller speed	rev/s
n_s	synchronous rotational speed	rev/s
n_T	polytropic index for turbine	-
p	pressure	Pa
p	number of poles	-
P	pitch	m
P	power	W
$\bar{p}$	mean pressure	Pa
pem	pollutant emission per mile	kg/mile
P/D	pitch ratio	-
P_a	average power	W
P_A	pneumatic power	W
P_B	brake power	W
P_C	compressor power	W
p_{cxp}	pressure during expansion	Pa
P_D	delivered power (all propellers together)	W
P_E	effective towing power	W
per	pollutant emission ratio	kg/kg
P_H	hydraulic power	W
P_i	indicated power	W
P_{loss}	electrical losses	W
p_{me}	mean effective pressure	Pa
p_{mi}	mean indicated pressure	Pa

P_O	open water propeller power	W
P_P	(delivered) propeller power	W
P_S	shaft power	W
P_T	thrust power	W
P_T	turbine power	W
q	heat per unit mass	J/kg
Q	electric charge	C
Q	heat	J
Q	torque	Nm
$\dot{Q}$	heat flow	J/s
Q_{comb}	combustion heat	J
Q_f	fuel heat input	J
Q_{in}	heat input	J
q_{in}	specific heat input	J/kg
Q_{out}	heat output	J
q_{out}	specific heat output	J/kg
q_{xy}	specific heat transfer in stage x-y	J/kg
r	propeller radius	m
r	radius	m
R	electric resistance	ohm=Ω
R	gas constant ($\bar{R}/M$)	J/kg·K
R	range	miles
R	resultant force of drag and lift	N
R	ship resistance	N
$\bar{R}$	universal gas constant	8.314 kJ/kmol·K
R_A	armature resistance	Ω
r_c	geometric compression ratio (1-2)	-
r_e	effective expansion ratio (5-6)	-
Re	Reynolds number $\frac{v_s \cdot L}{v}$	-
Ro	Roughness $\frac{k}{L}$	-
R_F	electrical resistance of field windings	Ω
s	slip between stator and rotor	-
s	specific entropy	J/kg·K
S	entropy	J/K
sac	specific air consumption	kg/Ws (kg/kWh)
sfc	specific fuel consumption	kg/Ws (g/kWh)
SM	service margin	-
spe	specific pollutant emission	kg/Ws (g/kWh)
spi	specific pollutant index	-
t	thrust deduction factor	-
t	time	s

T	period	s
T	temperature	K
T	endurance	sec, hours, days
T	thrust	T
t_{on}	on-time of transistor	s
u	specific internal energy	J/kg
U	internal energy	kJ
U	potential difference	V
U	overall heat transfer coefficient	$J/s \cdot m^2 \cdot K$
U	voltage	V
U_A	voltage drop over armature	V
U_{av}	average voltage	V
U_C	voltage drop over a capacitance	V
U_{ce}	voltage drop over base-emitter	V
U_e	effective voltage	V
U_F	voltage over field windings	V
U_L	line voltage	V
U_L	voltage drop over a self-inductance	V
U_m	amplitude of the voltage	V
U_{nom}	nominal voltage	V
U_P	phase voltage	V
U_R	voltage drop over a resistor	V
v	specific volume	m^3/kg
v	velocity	m/s
V	volume	m^3
$\dot{V}$	volume flow	m^3/s
V_{BDC}	volume at BDC	m^3
v_S	ship speed	m/s
V_s	swept volume	m^3
V_{TDC}	volume at TDC	m^3
∇	displacement volume	m^3
w	specific work	J/kg
w	wake factor	-
W	work	J
$\dot{W}$	rate of work or power	J/s
W_{com}	compression work	J/cycle
W_{cxp}	expansion work	J/cycle
W_e	effective work	J/cycle
W_i	indicated work	J/cycle
X_C	capacitive reactance	Ω
X_L	inductive reactance	Ω
X_R	resistance	Ω
z	elevation	m
Z	impedance	

Greek variables

α	angle of attack	rad
α	firing angle	rad
α_P	phase displacements	rad
β	hydrodynamic pitch angle	rad
β	angle between conductor velocity vector and magnetic field	rad
β	coefficient of performance	-
β_{AB}	bore area specific power	W/m^2
$\beta_{\dot{m}}$	specific power related to mass flow	kJ/kg
β_{VS}	swept volume specific power	W/m^3
δ	diminutive	-
∂	partial derivative	-
Δ	displacement	tonne
Δ	difference	-
ε	geometric compression ratio	-
η	efficiency	-
η	dynamic viscosity	N/m^{2}s
η_c	polytropic compressor efficiency	-
η_{carnot}	Carnot efficiency	-
η_{comb}	combustion efficiency	-
η_D	propulsive efficiency	-
η_e	effective (engine) efficiency	-
η_{GB}	gearbox efficiency	-
η_H	hull efficiency	-
η_{HE}	heat exchanger efficiency	-
η_i	indicated efficiency	-
η_m	mechanical efficiency	-
η_O	open water propeller efficiency	-
η_q	input heat efficiency	-
η_R	relative rotative efficiency	-
η_S	shaft efficiency	-
η_{scav}	scavenge efficiency	-
η_{td}	thermodynamic efficiency	-
η_{trap}	trapped air efficiency	-
η_T	polytropic turbine efficiency	-
η_{TRM}	transmission efficiency	-
φ	phase difference	rad
φ	volume ratio	-
Φ	magnetic flux	Wb = kg·m^2/A·s^2

κ	isentropic index, specific heat ratio	-
λ	air excess ratio	-
λ_s	stroke/bore ratio	-
λ_{tot}	total air excess ratio	-
μ	permeability of medium	H/m
μ_0	permeability of vacuum	H/m
μ_R	permeability of medium relative to vacuum	-
υ	kinematic viscosity	m^2/s
π	pressure ratio	-
π_C	compressor pressure ratio	-
π_T	turbine pressure ratio	-
σ_b	bending stress	Pa
σ_t	tensile stress	Pa
σ_y	yield stress	Pa
θ	non-dimensional heat flow	-
θ	pitch angle	rad
ω	angular velocity	rad/s
ω	radial frequency of a voltage	rad/s
ρ	density	kg/m^3
σ	stoichiometric air/fuel ratio	-
τ	temperature ratio	-
τ_C	compressor temperature ratio	-
τ_T	turbine temperature ratio	-

Chapter 1

Introduction to Marine Engineering

1.0   Learning goals

After studying this chapter, the student should be able to:

-   *Explain the concepts of Systems Engineering, i.e. functions, systems and components, in general.*

-   *Describe the main functions and systems on board a vessel.*

1.1   Introducing Marine Engineering as Systems Engineering

Marine engineering is the field of engineering that deals with the design and operation of the machinery plant on marine structures, such as vessels and offshore platforms. The machinery plant includes mechanical and electrical systems: a few examples are given in the next list:

*   propulsion system
*   electric power generation and distribution systems
*   fuel treatment and supply systems
*   cargo heating system
*   tank cleaning system
*   fresh water systems
*   ventilation systems
*   bilge water system
*   ballast water system
*   fire fighting systems.

In general terms, the machinery plant includes systems to sail the vessel, to generate electrical power, to condition cargo, to provide living conditions for the crew, and others. To design and operate these systems, knowledge of marine structures, and the machinery and electrical equipment within those systems is required. For instance, to design a propulsion plant, the resistance characteristics of a ship need to be understood and the desired ship speed needs to be known, but also engine characteristics such as delivered power and the interaction with the load of the propeller need to be understood.

Marine engineering is the art of integrating the components into systems in order to be able to perform a specific set of functions. This is the system engineering approach to marine engineering. Design of the machinery and equipment itself is not within the field of marine engineering.

A systematic description of the machinery plant can be achieved with a functional decomposition. A functional decomposition of the vessel divides the vessel's main goal, the mission, into the main functions that need to be performed to achieve this goal. The functional approach forces the engineer to consider why the systems are on board, instead of how they are split up in components (i.e. the big picture vs. details). The coherence and interaction between systems (but also within the system, between components) would be more difficult to comprehend, if the function of the whole system is not the starting point of the analysis.

The systems approach will be used mainly to structure this book; the system analysis focuses on the machinery and equipment (and their connections and interaction). The functional approach, however, will never be out of focus. Section 1.2.1 *Ship functions* discusses the functional analysis in detail. Ship systems and their components are introduced in section 1.2.2.

A system has to provide a function, but it also has to meet requirements set by underlying principles such as physics, economics, reliability, safety, maintainability, space and weight limitations, and control. These underlying principles are mentioned in section 1.3 *Underlying principles of Marine Engineering*. The system also has to comply with rules and regulations set by national and international regulatory bodies. Regulatory bodies include governmental bodies (for example the United States Coast Guard (USCG) and the Netherlands Shipping Inspectorate (NSI)), international organisations (for example the International Maritime Organization (IMO) and the International Electrotechnical Committee (IEC)) and class societies such as Lloyd's Register of Shipping (LR), Bureau Veritas (BV), Det Norske Veritas (DNV) and American Bureau of Shipping (ABS).

1.2   Functional decomposition: functions, systems and components

A vessel or offshore platform is designed to perform a certain operational task: the mission. The mission of the vessel determines which functions are needed on board. Ship systems provide these functions. If necessary a system may be decomposed into sub-systems and ultimately into components.

1.2.1   Ship functions

The starting point for functional analysis is the main goal or purpose of the ship: the *mission*. A mission specifies which cargo to carry or which task to fulfil. Other specifications, such as the area of operation, speed and period of time at sea, build up the mission specification, or owner's requirements. Examples of missions are:

- transport of containers on intercontinental routes
- bringing fighting power to sea (naval vessels)
- exploitation of the sea in the form of fishing
- exploring the sea for gas and oil
- pipe laying on the bottom of the sea.

Realisation of the mission requires certain main functions. In general these main functions include platform functions, operational functions, hotel functions and general support functions. The *main* functions group the underlying functions, which in turn may be divided into sub-functions.

For instance, the main function *provide platform* can be divided into: *provide carrying platform, provide mobility* and *provide survivability*, as shown in Figure 1.1. As an example *provide mobility* is detailed one level deeper: in this division *propulsion, steering, navigation, mooring* and *anchoring* are sub-functions.

The operational functions are the functions that are necessary for the specific mission. *Operational functions* include functions concerning cargo handling and cargo carrying, but also pipe laying, dredging, life support for passengers, and for the Navy, threat assessment. *Hotel functions* group all hotel facilities which make life comfortable for the crew. Note that, for a cruise ship, the operational functions would, strictly speaking, include hotel functions for passengers, and not for the crew.

The main function *provide general support* groups the support for more than one function. Examples of support functions are the electric power supply, the compressed air supply, the hydraulic power supply, the fuel supply, and cooling and heating. Many functions will require the same support, for example *electric power supply* or *cooling*. This means that with a top-down approach identical general support functions are found that will be clustered in practical life. In clustered form, as the main function *provide general support*, they are attached relatively high in the functional tree. Figure 1.1 is an example of a functional tree. The tree visualises the preceding functional breakdown of the machinery plant. (Note that the tree is incomplete). The functions *propulsion* and *electric power supply* will be the main subjects of this book.

Figure 1.2 shows the operational function for three specific examples: (A) a containership, (B) a frigate and (C) an offshore support vessel.

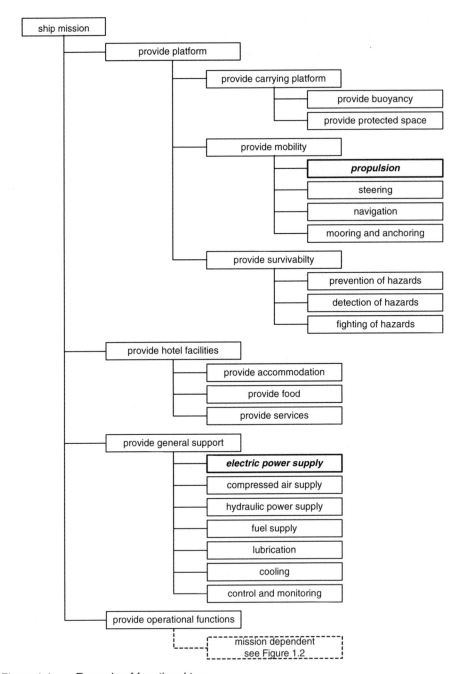

Figure 1.1   Example of functional tree.

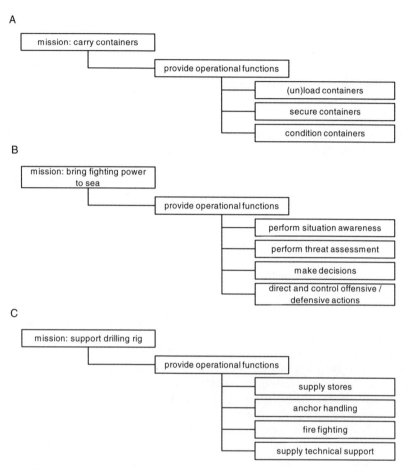

Figure 1.2   Examples of mission specific operational functions.

1.2.2   *Ship systems and components*

Systems

A system is the combination of machinery, equipment and its connections (piping, cabling) which performs the task indicated by a (sub-)function. Systems may be grouped by their function:

- *Platform systems* provide the platform functions. The hull or the offshore platform provides the carrying platform and protection against the environment. The propulsion system, the steering system, the navigation system and the anchoring and mooring systems provide mobility. Fire detection and fire-fighting systems are examples of systems that provide survivability.

- *Hotel systems* provide the hotel facilities. Examples are cabins, galley equipment, laundry equipment, drinking water systems and waste disposal systems.
- *Support systems* provide the support function, e.g: electric power supply systems, hydraulic power supply system, lubrication oil system and compressed air system.
- *Operational systems* provide the operational functions, e.g: cargo-handling and conditioning systems, combat system, fishing gear, oil drilling equipment or pipe laying system.

Systems can be divided into sub-systems and components depending on the complexity and divisibility of the building blocks and the intended purpose of the description. In some cases it may be sufficient to look at the diesel engine as a component in the propulsion system, whereas in other cases the diesel engine should be described as a sub-system, which in turn can be split up in components.

Components

A component is a building block of a system. The diesel engine is an example of a component of the propulsion system: its function is to provide mechanical power. Another example is a shaft in the propulsion system: it transfers mechanical power from the engine to the propulsor. Other common components are an electric motor, a cable, piping, a propeller, a bearing, a pump, a compressor and a turbine.

In this book, a component is generally described using a black box approach. The goal is to provide the student with sufficient technical knowledge and skill to integrate equipment and machinery into systems in a well-founded manner both technically and economically. This means that the component's function in the system, its behaviour (e.g. physical and electrical principles), its interaction with other components and the operational (control) characteristics are important. The detailed design or construction of the components will not be described.

Some commonly used components in the propulsion and electric power plants are described in Chapter 6, and the diesel engine and the gas turbine will be discussed in more detail in Chapter 7 and Chapter 8, respectively.

1.3   Underlying principles of Marine Engineering

As explained earlier in this chapter, the design of machinery systems requires knowledge of ships, machinery and equipment. More specifically, the marine engineer has to be familiar with physical principles, economics, RAMS (reliability, availability, maintainability and safety) requirements, space and weight limitations, and control and monitoring. All principles are explained briefly, not necessarily in order of importance.

Physical and electrical principles

Studying Marine Engineering requires basic knowledge of the physical principles that govern the operation of systems, machinery and components. In this book thermodynamics, fluid dynamics, heat transfer and electrical engineering are applied. It provides an effective way to understand the working principles of the machinery and it shows the commonality of different types of machinery.

Economic principles

The design of a machinery plant is not complete without economic considerations. Not only the costs of acquisition should be considered but also the operational costs, such as costs for energy, maintenance and manning and the life cycle costs.

Reliability, Availability, Maintainability and Safety (RAMS)

Systems need to comply with accepted standards for reliability, availability, maintainability and safety. RAMS considerations are important for the operation and economics of the ship, but also for crew safety and environmental impact.

Space and weight considerations

Space and weight considerations capture the naval architecture side of marine engineering. As the systems are part of a marine structure, space and weight need to be considered. The design of a ship influences the location of systems and the available space. The weight and location of a system influence a vessel's deadweight and stability.

Control and monitoring

Control and monitoring requirements influence the design of the plant directly, for instance by the number of sensors and actuators. The requirements are based on operations (remote or local and manual or automatic control), manning (skill, man hours, crew reduction) and safety (automatic shutdown, emergency stop).

1.4 Exercises

Exercise 1

Define the mission and main functions of a dredger.

Exercise 2

Construct a functional tree for a vessel of your choice. Use at least three levels in the functional breakdown: mission, main functions and functions.

Chapter 2

Underlying Physical Principles

2.0   Learning goals

It has been assumed that the student is familiar with:

Thermodynamics:

-   *The first and second laws of thermodynamics,*

-   *The application of these laws to open and closed systems,*

-   *The ideal gas model.*

Electrical engineering:

-   *The basic electrical components resistance, capacitance and inductance,*

-   *The associated relationships between current and voltage over these components,*

-   *The relations between voltage, current and power in basic electric networks,*

-   *The difference between DC and AC,*

-   *The basics of magnetic induction: Faraday and Lorentz.*

2.1   Introduction

The basic principles of thermodynamics and electrical engineering used in this book are treated in this section. This chapter is meant to introduce the terminology and symbols used throughout this book and it is meant to be used as a reference for later chapters.

2.2   Basic thermodynamic principles

2.2.1   First law of thermodynamics

Evaluation of energy and energy transfer in thermodynamic processes requires application of the conservation of energy principle. The first law of thermodynamics is based on this principle. The law will first be given in its generic form and will later be applied to closed and open systems. The generic form covers all energetic considerations in this book.

General

Figure 2.1 introduces a schematic presentation of a thermodynamic system. The system is separated from the surroundings by the chosen system boundary. Two kinds of thermodynamic systems are used in this book: closed systems (a fixed quantity of mass) and open systems (a fixed control volume). The process is characterised by the heat, work and mass flows that cross the system boundaries, and the internal energy and mass of the system.

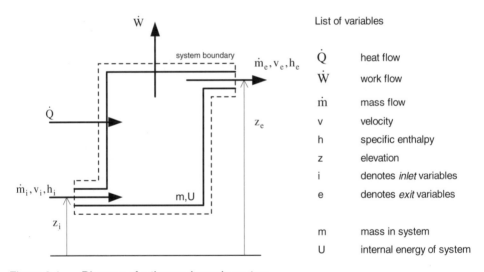

Figure 2.1   Diagram of a thermodynamic system.

The first law of thermodynamics states that the change of energy within the system equals the heat flow into the system, minus the work flow delivered by the system, plus the difference in enthalpy H, kinetic energy E_{kin} and potential energy E_{pot} of the entering and exiting mass flows. The influence of chemical reactions is not included. Equation (2.1) shows the first law in generic terms for a single inlet and a single exit flow.

$$\frac{dU}{dt} = \dot{Q} - \dot{W} + \dot{m}_i \cdot \left(h_i + \frac{v_i^2}{2} + g \cdot z_i \right) - \dot{m}_e \cdot \left(h_e + \frac{v_e^2}{2} + g \cdot z_e \right) \qquad (2.1)$$

Additionally the conservation of mass principle must be complied with; the change of mass within the system boundary is the difference between entering and exiting mass flow.

$$\frac{dm}{dt} = \dot{m}_i - \dot{m}_e \qquad (2.2)$$

Note that equation (2.1) is sometimes given with $\dfrac{dE}{dt}$ instead of $\dfrac{dU}{dt}$. In that case, energy E equals the sum of internal, kinetic and potential energy of the system:

$$E = U + E_{kin} + E_{pot}$$

In most cases, however, kinetic energy E_{kin} and potential energy E_{pot} of the system do not change and therefore can be omitted.

Closed system

A closed system is a thermodynamic system where no mass flow occurs across the system boundary. So, $\dot{m}_i = \dot{m}_e = 0$, in which case the first law according to equation (2.1) reduces to:

$$\frac{dU}{dt} = \dot{Q} - \dot{W} \; or \; dU = \delta Q - \delta W \qquad (2.3)$$

After integration for a process between state 1 and state 2 the first law becomes:

$$U_2 - U_1 = Q_{1,2} - W_{1,2}$$

Note the different differential symbols d and δ. The internal energy U is a state variable (dU is a total differential). This means that the internal energy of a system is an inherent property of the state of the system; it depends only on its current state, and is independent of the way in which the system was brought to that state. Heat and work on the other hand are not state variables. The amount of heat or work depends on the path of the process between the beginning and end states of the process. δQ and δW are not total differentials but small amounts of heat and work also called diminutives.

Frequently, closed systems are considered as cycles. A cycle is a sequence of processes of a closed system in which the initial state and the final state of the process are identical. Figure 2.2 shows an example of a cycle in a p–V diagram: the Brayton cycle. The cycle starts at point 1 and returns to that same point via 2, 3 and 4. The state variables do not change over the cycle:

$$m_{1,start} = m_{1,end} \rightarrow \Delta m = 0 \qquad (2.4)$$

$$U_{1,start} = U_{1,end} \rightarrow \Delta U = 0 \tag{2.5}$$

This means that for a cycle the total heat supplied to the process must be equal to the total work delivered by the process, because equation (2.3) reduces to equation (2.6):

$$Q_{cycle} = W_{cycle} \tag{2.6}$$

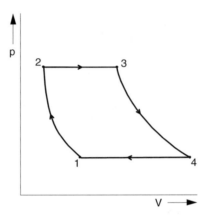

Figure 2.2   The Brayton cycle in p–V diagram.

Examples of closed systems are a refrigeration system or a steam turbine plant complete with feedwater pump, boiler and condenser. Sometimes it may be useful to consider a diesel engine or a gas turbine as a closed loop thermodynamic cycle.

Open systems

An open system is a thermodynamic system that can be referred to as a volume through which mass may flow. The general form of the first law of thermodynamics is applicable for open systems. For an open system at steady state (an open stationary system), the state variables of the mass in the system do not change with time. Consequently, the internal energy and the mass within the system do not change with time:

$$\frac{dU}{dt} = 0 \; and \; \frac{dm}{dt} = 0 \tag{2.7}$$

The mass flows entering and exiting the system must be equal in order to have no accumulation of mass:

$$\dot{m}_i = \dot{m}_e = constant = \dot{m}$$

With these assumptions the first law, refer to equation (2.1), for an open system at steady state reduces to:

$$\dot{W} = \dot{Q} + \dot{m} \cdot \left((h_i - h_e) + \frac{v_i^2 - v_e^2}{2} + g \cdot (z_i - z_e) \right) \qquad (2.8)$$

Examples of open systems at steady state

Examples of open systems are the compressor (as part of a complete refrigeration system), the turbine (as part of a complete steam turbine plant) or a diesel engine. The following examples of open systems at steady state are often found in Marine Engineering.

■ A steam turbine generates mechanical energy (work) from a steam mass flow. If the turbine is well insulated, the heat flow over the system boundary will be very low and it may be assumed that the process is adiabatic, i.e. $\dot{Q} = 0$. If the turbine is constructed in such a way that height and velocity differences between intake and exit are also of minor importance, ($z_i \approx z_e$ and $v_i \approx v_e$) the work flow can be written as:

$$\dot{W} = \dot{m} \cdot (h_i - h_e) \qquad (2.9)$$

Under similar assumptions, this relation is also valid for compressors, pumps and hydraulic motors.

■ A heat exchanger or a boiler has no transfer of work across system boundaries, i.e. $\dot{W} = 0$. Using similar assumptions as above it can be shown that the heat transfer is associated with an enthalpy difference:

$$\dot{Q} = \dot{m} \cdot (h_e - h_i) \qquad (2.10)$$

■ A nozzle, guide vane or diffuser is used to increase or decrease velocity of a fluid. There is no transfer of work and heat. If it is also assumed that height at intake and exit are equal ($z_i = z_e$) then:

$$v_e^{\,2} - v_i^{\,2} = 2 \cdot (h_i - h_e) \qquad (2.11)$$

When v_i can be considered zero this results in $v_e = \sqrt{2 \cdot (h_i - h_e)}$.

■ A throttling process involves a fluid flow over a resistance in a valve or a pipeline. As no work is performed by such a resistance and no heat transfer occurs, the first law of thermodynamics reduces to:

$$h_i = h_e \qquad (2.12)$$

This relation holds when changes in velocity or height may be neglected (i.e. $z_i \approx z_e$ and $v_i \approx v_e$).

2.2.2   Second law of thermodynamics

The second law of thermodynamics is used (1) to predict the direction of processes, (2) to establish the conditions of final equilibrium and (3) to determine the best possible theoretical performance of a process. In this section only the aspects of the second law that are necessary for understanding the processes in this book are discussed.

Direction of processes and final equilibrium state

It can be observed that processes have a natural direction. These spontaneous processes can only be reversed if other processes are added. Two examples are given:

- If two bodies, with different temperatures are brought into contact, a heat flow will occur from the high temperature body to the low temperature body. This will result in a temperature (internal energy) decrease of the first body and a temperature (internal energy) increase of the second body. The heat flow will cease at the moment that both bodies have the same temperature; this is the final equilibrium state.

- If two containers filled with air at different pressures are connected, a similar spontaneous process will take place. An air mass flow will occur from the high-pressure container to the low-pressure container. This will result in a pressure decrease in the first container and a pressure increase in the second container. The airflow will cease at the moment the pressures in the two containers are equal.

Reversibility

A process of a system is reversible if the system can be restored to the initial state without changing the surroundings. It is essential to include the surroundings in this definition, because a system can always be brought back to its initial state by changing the surrounding, for instance by increasing the ambient pressure or temperature.

The natural processes described above (heat flow between two bodies and air mass flow between two containers) are irreversible, because it is not possible to bring the bodies and the containers back to their original state without a change of state of the surroundings.

Entropy

The entropy change of a system that is subjected to a *reversible* process with heat transfer is defined as:

$$dS = \frac{\delta Q}{T} \qquad (2.13)$$

Note that entropy S [J/K], like pressure, temperature, internal energy and enthalpy is a state variable. The relation states that for a *reversible* process in which heat transfer takes place, the entropy change is equal to the heat flow divided by temperature. For an *irreversible* process, the entropy change is greater than the heat flow divided by temperature. So, a way of expressing the second law in general form is:

$$dS \geq \frac{\delta Q}{T} \qquad (2.14)$$

Or after integration,

$$S_2 - S_1 \geq \int_1^2 \frac{\delta Q}{T}$$

Work on a closed system

A closed system that undergoes a reversible process involving volumetric change is considered. An example of such a system is a cylinder filled with gas under a piston. Reversibility in this case means that (1) there is no friction between piston and cylinder and (2) that the pressure in the cylinder is equal on every location within the cylinder at every moment. The latter means in practice that compression or expansion should take place slowly. For a volumetric change the work can now be expressed as:

$$\delta W = p \cdot dV \tag{2.15}$$

Assuming a piston area A, this relation results from the general expression for work as follows:

$$\delta W = F \cdot ds = p \cdot A \cdot ds = p \cdot dV$$

The result is that for a *reversible* process of a closed system, work can be determined as:

$$W_{1,2} = \int_1^2 p \cdot dV \tag{2.16}$$

Although, compression and expansion are, in practice, never reversible due to friction, the relation found here can frequently be applied to these processes with great accuracy, because friction can be considered to be outside the system boundary and then treated afterwards.

Heat transfer

When heat is transferred in a *reversible* process the amount of heat can be determined from:

$$\delta Q = T \cdot dS \tag{ref. (2.13)}$$

$$Q_{1,2} = \int_1^2 T \cdot dS \tag{2.17}$$

In practice, heat transfer never is a reversible process. However, heat transfer can be imagined as an internally reversible process, if the heat flow takes places between two bodies with an infinitesimal small temperature difference dT. The result of this assumption is that the above relation can frequently be applied if the system boundary is suitably chosen. The heating or cooling body, with a distinct temperature difference to the process under consideration should not be included within the system boundary.

Gibbs equations

The Gibbs equations are deduced from the first and second laws of thermodynamics. The first law of thermodynamics for a closed system can be expressed as equation (2.3):

$$dU = \delta Q - \delta W \qquad\qquad \text{ref. (2.3)}$$

The expressions for reversible work and heat, derived in the preceding paragraphs are:

$$\delta W = p \cdot dV \qquad\qquad \text{ref. (2.15)}$$

$$\delta Q = T \cdot dS \qquad\qquad \text{ref. (2.13)}$$

The first Gibbs equation is obtained when those expressions are combined:

$$dU = T \cdot dS - p \cdot dV \qquad\qquad (2.18)$$

The second Gibbs equation is a formulation of enthalpy. By definition enthalpy is:

$$H \overset{\text{def}}{=} U + p \cdot V \qquad\qquad (2.19)$$

And from this follows:

$$dH = dU + p \cdot dV + V \cdot dp \qquad\qquad (2.20)$$

With equation (2.18) this leads to the second Gibbs equation:

$$dH = T \cdot dS + V \cdot dp \qquad\qquad (2.21)$$

Note that both Gibbs equations contain only state variables p, T, V, U, H and S. The equations are therefore valid for all processes, both reversible and irreversible, even though the expressions for work and heat used in the derivation (equations (2.13) and (2.15)) only apply to reversible processes.

Work for reversible stationary process of an open system

For a stationary process in an open system the first law of thermodynamics can be written as:

$$\delta W = \delta Q - dH - dE_{pot} - dE_{kin} \qquad\qquad \text{ref. (2.8)}$$

In case a reversible process is considered, heat transfer can be expressed as equation (2.13) and the expression for work leads to:

$$\delta W = T \cdot dS - dH - dE_{pot} - dE_{kin} \qquad\qquad (2.22)$$

With the second Gibbs equation (2.21), this can be rewritten as:

$$\delta W = -V \cdot dp - dE_{pot} - dE_{kin} \qquad\qquad (2.23)$$

Frequently the changes in kinetic and potential energy are minor and can be neglected. This leads to the following expression for work for a *reversible* stationary (i.e. ideal) process of an open system:

$$\delta W = -V \cdot dp \tag{2.24}$$

$$W_{1,2} = -\int_1^2 V \cdot dp \tag{2.25}$$

This is an expression to determine the work for a pump, a hydraulic motor, a compressor and a turbine if these processes are reversible. Note the difference between this expression for indicator work of an open system and equation (2.15), which is valid for a closed system.

Work in general can always be determined with the first law of thermodynamics. As an example, consider work for a well-insulated turbine as deduced in section 2.2.1 (assuming $\dot{Q} = 0$, $z_i \approx z_e$ and $v_i \approx v_e$):

$$\dot{W} = \dot{m} \cdot (h_i - h_e) \hspace{2cm} \text{ref. (2.9)}$$

Using this equation is often better than using equation (2.25), since it is applicable to both reversible and irreversible processes.

Carnot efficiency

If thermal energy is converted into mechanical work in a cycle, it can be shown that the maximum possible efficiency is obtained if the cycle is reversible and that any reversible process has the same maximum efficiency. A well-known example of such a cycle is the Carnot process. A Carnot cycle consists of four separate processes:

- Isentropic (reversible adiabatic) compression from state 1 to state 2 where the temperature is T_H.
- Reversible isothermal expansion, from state 2 to state 3. The process receives energy (heat) Q_H from the high temperature reservoir.
- Isentropic expansion from state 3 to state 4, until temperature drops to T_L.
- Reversible isothermal compression from state 4 back to state 1. The gas discharges heat Q_L to a low temperature (T_L) reservoir.

The Carnot cycle is shown in a p–V diagram and in a T–S diagram (Figure 2.3).

Because all processes of the cycle are reversible, areas in the p–V diagram represent work and areas in the T–S diagram represent heat.

$$\delta W = p \cdot dV \hspace{2cm} \text{ref. (2.15)}$$

$$\delta Q = T \cdot dS \hspace{2cm} \text{ref. (2.13)}$$

The enclosed area in the p–V diagram is the net work W_{cycle} developed by the cycle. The area is shown shaded. The area in the T–S diagram under line 2–3 indicates the heat Q_H

added to the gas during process 2–3, and the area under the line 4-1 is the heat Q_L rejected during the process stage 4–1. By definition, Q_H is positive and Q_L is negative.

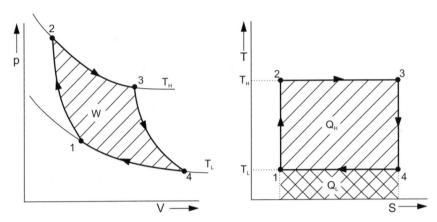

Figure 2.3   Carnot cycle in p–V and T–S diagrams.

The net amount of heat added equals the developed work:

$$Q_{cycle} = W_{cycle}$$ ref. (2.6)

Which means in this case:

$$Q_H + Q_L = W \text{ or } Q_H - |Q_L| = W$$ (2.26)

The thermal efficiency of a power cycle is defined as:

$$\eta \overset{def}{=} \frac{net\ work\ output\ W_{cycle}}{heat\ added\ Q_H}$$ (2.27)

For Carnot cycles this leads to:

$$\eta_{carnot} = \frac{W}{Q_H} = \frac{Q_H - |Q_L|}{Q_H} = 1 - \frac{|Q_L|}{Q_H}$$ (2.28)

The amounts of transferred energy Q_L and Q_H are determined with equation (2.13):

$$Q_H = T_H \cdot (S_3 - S_2)$$

$$Q_L = T_L \cdot (S_1 - S_4)$$

Because $S_1=S_2$ and $S_3=S_4$ (1–2 and 3–4 are isentropic processes), the Carnot efficiency is:

$$\eta_{carnot} = 1 - \frac{T_L}{T_H}$$ (2.29)

Note that this Carnot efficiency is valid for every reversible process in which work is produced by receiving heat at T_H and rejecting heat at T_L ($T_H > T_L$).

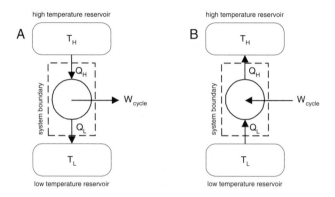

Figure 2.4   Carnot processes: (A) Power cycle and (B) Refrigeration cycle.

In a similar manner, a reversible cycle can be used to transfer heat from a low temperature T_L to a high temperature T_H. In this case, work W has to be added to the process. If we assume a cooling machine according to the Carnot process, the cycle can also be represented by the p–V and T–S diagrams of Figure 2.3, but in a reversed sense: 1–4–3–2–1.

The heat Q_L received by the gas, or taken from the low temperature reservoir (cooling at temperature T_L) is now the useful energy flow, which is achieved by delivering work W to the cycle. By definition, Q_H and W are negative and Q_L is positive. In this case, the following relations apply:

$$-|Q_H| + Q_L = -|W|$$

The coefficient of performance β for a refrigeration cycle is defined as:

$$\beta \overset{\text{def}}{=} \frac{received\ heat\ Q_L}{net\ work\ W_{cycle}} \tag{2.30}$$

For the Carnot refrigeration cycle the coefficient of performance is:

$$\beta_{carnot} = \frac{Q_L}{|W|} = \frac{Q_L}{|Q_H| - Q_L} = \frac{T_L}{T_H - T_L} \tag{2.31}$$

2.2.3   Ideal gas model

Evaluation of the properties of gases in machinery like diesel engines, compressors and turbines is important because they influence the behaviour of the machinery. The relationship among the state properties pressure, specific volume and temperature is given by an equation of state. In this section the ideal gas equation of state is reviewed. (For theoretical background and more information see also [Moran and Shapiro, 1993].) The ideal gas model suffices to describe the behaviour of the working fluid in machinery such as diesel engines, gas turbines, compressors and similar machinery.

Ideal gas

The ideal gas equation of state is as follows:

$$p \cdot v = R \cdot T \ or \ \frac{p}{\rho} = R \cdot T \tag{2.32}$$

Where p is pressure [Pa], v is specific volume [m^3/kg], ρ is density [kg/m^3], T is temperature [K] and R is the specific gas constant ($R = \bar{R}/M$, where $\bar{R} = 8.314 \ kJ/kmol \cdot K$ is the universal gas constant and M is the molecular or atomic weight). Equation (2.32) is the ideal gas equation of state given in intensive (mass specific) variables. This equation may also be written with extensive variables, volume V [m^3] and mass m [kg]:

$$p \cdot V = m \cdot R \cdot T \tag{2.33}$$

For a gas obeying the ideal gas equation of state, it can be shown that internal energy u [J/kg] and specific enthalpy h [J/kg] are functions of T alone:

$$u = u(T) \tag{2.34}$$

$$h = h(T) \tag{2.35}$$

As a result, the specific heats c_v and c_p are also functions of T alone, because the specific heats are defined as partial derivatives of u and h.

$$c_v \overset{def}{=} \left. \frac{\partial u}{\partial T} \right)_v \rightarrow c_v = \frac{du}{dT} \tag{2.36}$$

$$c_p \overset{def}{=} \left. \frac{\partial h}{\partial T} \right)_p \rightarrow c_p = \frac{dh}{dT} \tag{2.37}$$

Note that for an ideal gas it can be shown that R= c_p - c_v.

The internal energy and enthalpy for an ideal gas in intensive properties, and in extensive properties become:

$$du = c_v \cdot dT \rightarrow dU = m \cdot c_v \cdot dT \rightarrow U_2 - U_1 = m \cdot \int_{T_1}^{T_2} c_v \cdot dT \tag{2.38}$$

$$dh = c_p \cdot dT \rightarrow dH = m \cdot c_p \cdot dT \rightarrow H_2 - H_1 = m \cdot \int_{T_1}^{T_2} c_p \cdot dT \tag{2.39}$$

These deductions are only valid when mass is constant: $U = m \cdot u$, so its derivative is $dU = m \cdot du + u \cdot dm$. Only if m is constant, this reduces to $dU = m \cdot du = m \cdot c_v \cdot dT$. The same holds for enthalpy H: $H = m \cdot h$, so $dH = m \cdot dh + h \cdot dm$ and if m is constant $dH = m \cdot dh = m \cdot c_p \cdot dT$.

Perfect gas

Frequently, it is acceptable to treat the specific heats c_p and c_v as if they were constants over an interval of temperature. This introduces the perfect gas assumption: a perfect gas is an ideal gas with constant c_p and c_v. Consequently, the internal energy and the enthalpy of a perfect gas can be written as:

$$U_2 - U_1 = m \cdot c_v \left(T_2 - T_1\right) \tag{2.40}$$

$$H_2 - H_1 = m \cdot c_p \left(T_2 - T_1\right) \tag{2.41}$$

In almost every respect, the characteristic behaviour of machinery can effectively be explained with the perfect gas assumption.

Isentropic processes of an ideal gas

From the preceding, some useful relations can be derived for reversible adiabatic (isentropic) processes of an ideal gas. The first Gibbs equation reads:

$$dU = T \cdot ds - p \cdot dV \qquad \text{ref. (2.18)}$$

For an ideal gas equation (2.38) applies and for an isentropic process (i.e. a reversible adiabatic process) also $dS = 0$, which leads to:

$$m \cdot c_v \cdot dT = -p \cdot dV \tag{2.42}$$

According to the equation of state, pressure of an ideal gas is:

$$p = \frac{m \cdot R \cdot T}{V} \qquad \text{ref. (2.33)}$$

When this is inserted in equation (2.42) and both sides of the equation are divided by $m \cdot T$, this leads to:

$$c_v \cdot \frac{dT}{T} = -R \cdot \frac{dV}{V} \tag{2.43}$$

With $R = c_p - c_v$ and the specific heat ratio κ (applicable to an ideal gas):

$$\kappa = \frac{c_p}{c_v} \tag{2.44}$$

Equation (2.43) reduces to:

$$\frac{dV}{V} = -\frac{1}{\kappa-1} \cdot \frac{dT}{T} \tag{2.45}$$

In analogy, equation (2.46) can be derived from the second Gibbs equation (equation (2.21)):

$$\frac{dp}{p} = \frac{\kappa}{\kappa-1} \cdot \frac{dT}{T} \tag{2.46}$$

The preceding relations hold for an ideal gas. If the gas is assumed to be perfect (constant c_v and c_p) equations (2.45) and (2.46) can be integrated because κ is a constant. This leads to the following relations, which are only applicable to perfect gases:

$$T \cdot V^{\kappa-1} = constant \tag{2.47}$$

$$T \cdot p^{\frac{1-\kappa}{\kappa}} = constant \tag{2.48}$$

And with $p \cdot V = m \cdot R \cdot T$ this results in:

$$p \cdot V^{\kappa} = constant \tag{2.49}$$

These equations are often referred to as the Poisson relations.

2.3   Basic electric principles

2.3.1   *Electrical components*

In an electrical circuit a charge Q moves at a rate called current I. In a direct current, the charges flow in one direction and in alternating current, the charges first flow in one direction and then in the other, repeating this cycle with definite frequency.

$$I = \frac{Q}{t} \tag{2.50}$$

The work done per unit charge is the potential difference or voltage between two points; symbol U. The unit of potential difference is volts [V]. The potential difference of a source of electrical energy is often called the electromotive force *EMF*.

The power P [W] delivered or absorbed by a portion of a circuit is defined as:

$$P = U(t) \cdot I(t) \tag{2.51}$$

Note that if both voltage and current vary with time the power will also vary with time, so the power stated is the instantaneous power.

Besides a source, an electrical circuit may contain three kinds of elements: resistance, inductance and capacitance.

Resistance

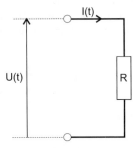

Figure 2.5   A resistor R subjected to a voltage U.

Figure 2.5 shows an electrical circuit containing only a resistor. The voltage drop over the resistor is defined by Ohm's law:

$$U(t) = I(t) \cdot R \qquad (2.52)$$

The unit of resistance R is ohm [Ω]. Resistance may be compared to friction in a mechanical system. Mechanical friction opposes a velocity, whereas electrical resistance opposes a current. The energy dissipated while opposing the current is heat. The electric power P developed in the resistance equals:

$$P(t) = U(t) \cdot I(t) = I^2(t) \cdot R \qquad (2.53)$$

Inductance

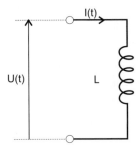

Figure 2.6   An inductance L subjected to a voltage U.

Figure 2.6 shows an electrical circuit containing only an inductance. A voltage drop will be encountered over an inductance which is proportional to the rate of change of the current:

$$U(t) = L \cdot \frac{dI(t)}{dt} \quad or \quad I(t) = \int_0^t \frac{U(t)}{L} dt \qquad (2.54)$$

Where the proportionality constant L is called the self-inductance, or inductance of an element. The unit of self-inductance is Henry [H].

Inductance can be compared to the mass of inertia in mechanical systems. A mass opposes a change of velocity, whereas an inductance opposes a change of current. The power of an inductance is:

$$P = U \cdot I = L \cdot I \cdot \frac{dI}{dt} \qquad (2.55)$$

The inductive energy stored in an inductance is:

$$E_{ind} = \int_0^t P \cdot dt = \int_0^t L \cdot I \cdot \frac{dI}{dt} \cdot dt = \int_0^I L \cdot I \cdot dI = \tfrac{1}{2}LI^2 \qquad (2.56)$$

This storage of electrical energy can be compared to the storage of kinetic energy in a mass: $E_{kin} = \tfrac{1}{2} \cdot m \cdot v^2$.

Capacitance

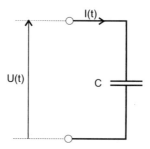

Figure 2.7   A capacitance C subjected to a voltage U.

Figure 2.7 shows an electrical circuit containing only a capacitance. As the inductive effect opposes the change of current, the capacitive effect opposes the change in voltage over the element, as given by the relations in equation (2.57).

$$I(t) = C \cdot \frac{dU(t)}{dt} \quad or \quad U(t) = \int_0^t \frac{I(t)}{C} dt \qquad (2.57)$$

Where the proportionality constant C is the capacitance of an element. It expresses the charge-storing property of an element in Farads [F].

A capacitance can be compared to a spring in mechanical systems. A spring opposes a change of force, whereas the capacitance opposes a change of voltage. The power associated with this effect is:

$$P = U \cdot I = C \cdot U \cdot \frac{dU}{dt} \qquad (2.58)$$

The energy stored in a capacitance is:

$$E_{cap} = \int_0^t P \cdot dt = \int_0^t C \cdot U \cdot \frac{dU}{dt} \cdot dt = \int_0^U C \cdot U \cdot dU = \frac{1}{2}CU^2 \qquad (2.59)$$

This stored (potential) electrical energy can be compared to the potential energy stored in a spring : $E = \frac{1}{2k} \cdot F^2$. Note that in mechanical systems the *stiffness* is used, whereas in electrical systems the capacitance, i.e. the *flexibility* is used.

2.3.2   Kirchhoff's laws

The first law of Kirchhoff states that the algebraic sum of the currents directed towards a node is zero (see Figure 2.8). In other words, the electrons will not accumulate in a junction point:

$$\sum_{i=1}^n I_i(t) = 0 \qquad (2.60)$$

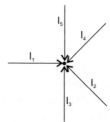

Figure 2.8   The first law of Kirchoff: the sum of the currents directed towards a node is zero.

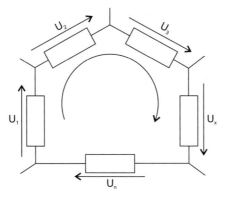

Figure 2.9   The second law of Kirchoff: the sum of the voltages around a closed path is zero.

The second law of Kirchhoff states that the algebraic sum of all the voltages taken in a specified direction around a closed path:

$$\sum_{i=1}^{n} U_i(t) = 0 \qquad (2.61)$$

This principle is illustrated by Figure 2.9.

2.3.3   Voltage and current in basic electrical networks

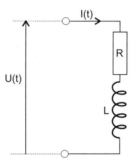

Figure 2.10   Series connection of a resistance and an inductance.

Series connection of a resistance and an inductance

Figure 2.10 shows a circuit which consists of a series connection of a resistor with resistance R and a self-inductance L, subjected to an external voltage $U(t)$. The externally applied voltage varies harmonically as:

$$U(t) = U_m \cdot \cos \omega t \qquad (2.62)$$

Where,

$\qquad U_m$ = *amplitude of the voltage [V]*

$\qquad \omega$ = *radial frequency of the voltage = $2 \cdot \pi \cdot f$ [1/s]*

$\qquad$ f = *frequency [Hz]*

$\qquad$ t = *time [s]*

The resulting current $I(t)$ is also assumed to be a harmonic function with the same frequency but with a phase lag angle φ:

$$I(t) = I_m \cos(\omega t - \varphi) \qquad (2.63)$$

Where,

$\qquad I_m$ = *amplitude of the current [A]*

$\qquad \varphi$ = *phase lag angle*

Both the voltage and the current can be drawn in a vector diagram. The voltage amplitude vector $\overline{U}_m$ and the current amplitude vector $\overline{I}_m$ rotate with an angular velocity ωt. This is shown in Figure 2.11.

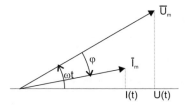

Figure 2.11   Current and voltage vector diagram of a R-L series connection.

The projections of the vectors $\overline{U}_m$ and $\overline{I}_m$ on the horizontal axis give the instantaneous magnitudes of the voltage $U(t)$ and the current $I(t)$.

Over the resistor R a voltage drop will occur (refer to equation (2.52)):

$$U_R = I \cdot R = I_m \cdot R \cdot \cos(\omega t - \varphi) \tag{2.64}$$

The voltage drop over the self-inductance L is (refer to equation (2.54)):

$$U_L = L \cdot \frac{dI}{dt} = -I_m \cdot \omega \cdot L \cdot \sin(\omega t - \varphi) = I_m \cdot \omega \cdot L \cdot \cos\left(\omega t + \frac{\pi}{2} - \varphi\right) \tag{2.65}$$

And according to Kirchhoff's second law (refer to equation (2.61) it follows that:

$$U = U_R + U_L \tag{2.66}$$

$$U_m \cos(\omega t) = I_m \cdot R \cdot \cos(\omega t - \varphi) + I_m \cdot \omega \cdot L \cdot \cos\left(\omega t + \frac{\pi}{2} - \varphi\right) \tag{2.67}$$

In vector notation this leads to:

$$\overline{U}_m = \overline{I_m \cdot R} + \overline{I_m \cdot \omega \cdot L} \tag{2.68}$$

which is shown in the vector diagram of Figure 2.12.

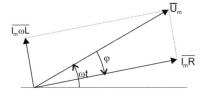

Figure 2.12   Vector diagram of the voltages in a R-L series connection.

The amplitudes are now related as follows:

$$U_m = I_m \cdot Z = I_m \sqrt{X_R^2 + X_L^2} = I_m \sqrt{R^2 + \omega^2 \cdot L^2} \tag{2.69}$$

Where,

$\qquad X_R = R = resistance\ [\Omega]$

$\qquad X_L = \omega \cdot L = inductive\ reactance\ [\Omega]$

$\qquad Z = impedance\ [\Omega]$

The phase lag angle φ can be derived from Figure 2.12:

$$\tan \varphi = \frac{\omega L}{R} \rightarrow \varphi = \arctan\left(\frac{\omega L}{R}\right) \tag{2.70}$$

This evaluation of an inductive load, i.e. a combination of a resistor and an inductance, leads to the conclusion that the current has a phase lag relative to the applied voltage. It also becomes clear that the current and the voltage over the resistor do not have a phase difference, whereas the voltage over an inductance has a phase advance of 90° relative to the current.

Series connection of a resistance and a capacitance

In case of a series connection of a resistance and a capacitance (see Figure 2.13), the vector diagram and the relations between voltage and current can be derived in the same way.

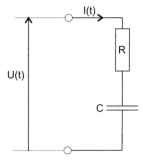

Figure 2.13   Series connection of a resistor and a capacitance.

Again the circuit is subjected to an external voltage and now the current is assumed to have a phase *advance* φ, see Figure 2.14:

$$U(t) = U_m \cos \omega t \ \ and \ \ I(t) = I_m \cos(\omega t + \varphi)$$

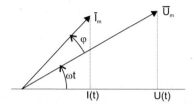

Figure 2.14   Voltage and current vector diagram of R-C series connection.

The voltage relation now becomes:

$$U = U_R + U_C$$

$$U_m \cos(\omega t) = I_m \cdot R \cdot \cos(\omega t + \varphi) + \frac{I_m}{\omega C} \cdot \cos\left(\omega t - \frac{\pi}{2} + \varphi\right) \tag{2.71}$$

Or in vector notation:

$$\overline{U}_m = \overline{I_m \cdot R} + \overline{\left(\frac{I_m}{\omega \cdot C}\right)} \tag{2.72}$$

These vectors are shown in Figure 2.15.

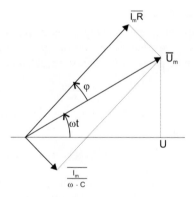

Figure 2.15   Vector diagram of the voltages in an R-C series connection.

The amplitudes are related by:

$$U_m = I_m \cdot Z = I_m \sqrt{X_R^2 + X_C^2} = I_m \sqrt{R^2 + \frac{1}{\omega^2 \cdot C^2}} \tag{2.73}$$

Where,

$$X_C = \frac{1}{\omega \cdot C} = \textit{capacitive reactance } [\,\Omega\,]$$

The phase advance angle is:

$$\varphi = \arctan\left(\frac{1}{\omega \cdot R \cdot C}\right) \qquad (2.74)$$

This evaluation of a capacitive load, leads to the conclusion that the current now has a phase advance relative to the applied voltage. Furthermore, the voltage over a capacitor has a phase lag of $90°$ relative to the current.

2.3.4   Direct and alternating current

Direct current (DC)

Direct current is used for control and monitoring on board ships. Sometime direct current systems are used as main electric power supply system in special applications such as submarines and offshore platforms. The power of a DC-user can be calculated from:

$$P = U \cdot I = I^2 \cdot R \qquad\qquad \text{ref. (2.53)}$$

Though it seems like capacitors and self-inductance are not of influence in a DC-network, it should be recognized that this is only true in stationary conditions. During transients, capacitors and self-inductance should not be neglected.

Single phase alternating current (AC)

The simplest form of alternating current is single phase AC. In marine applications single phase current is used as a secondary power supply system for small users. The instantaneous power of a single phase user can also be calculated by equation (2.51) :

$$P = U(t) \cdot I(t)$$

For an alternating current, both current and voltage are periodic functions of time as defined in the previous section:

$$U(t) = U_m \cos \omega t \ \ and \ \ I(t) = I_m \cos(\omega t - \varphi) \quad \text{ref. (2.62) and (2.63)}$$

If inductive or capacitive loads are present in the electrical circuit, a phase displacement will occur between voltage and current. In power supply systems there are almost always inductive loads: primarily due to AC-motors, transformers and fluorescent lighting. They lead to a phase lag of current relative to voltage.

The average power developed by a single phase alternating current is:

$$P_a = \frac{1}{T}\int_0^T U \cdot I \cdot dt = \frac{1}{T}\int_0^T U_m \cdot I_m \cdot \cos \omega t \cdot \cos(\omega t - \varphi) \cdot dt \qquad (2.75)$$

$$\rightarrow P_a = \frac{1}{2} \cdot U_m \cdot I_m \cdot \cos \varphi \qquad (2.76)$$

Where,

P_a = *average power [W]*

T = *period* $= 1/f = 2 \cdot \pi / \omega$ *[s]*

In practice, the effective voltage U_e and effective current I_e are used instead of the maximum voltage U_m and maximum current I_m. The effective voltage is the virtual DC-voltage that would develop the same power in a resistor as the applied AC-voltage would. The effective variables are defined as the root mean square values of voltage and current:

$$U_e = \sqrt{\frac{1}{T} \cdot \int_0^T (U_m \cdot \cos \omega t)^2 \, dt} = \frac{U_m}{\sqrt{2}} \qquad (2.77)$$

$$I_e = \sqrt{\frac{1}{T} \cdot \int_0^T (I_m \cdot \cos(\omega t - \varphi))^2 \, dt} = \frac{I_m}{\sqrt{2}} \qquad (2.78)$$

Where,

U_e = *effective voltage [V]*

I_e = *effective current [A]*

With equation (2.76) this leads to the following expression for average power:

$$P_a = U_e \cdot I_e \cdot \cos \varphi \qquad (2.79)$$

In AC-systems, it is common to use the effective values instead of the amplitudes of voltage and current. For this reason, the indices *a* for average and *e* for effective are left out, which leads to:

$$P = U \cdot I \cdot \cos \varphi \qquad \text{ref. (2.79)}$$

The term *cos φ* is called the power factor. Equation (2.79) shows the importance of the phase lag angle φ: a larger phase lag angle means a smaller power factor *cos φ*. Consequently, the current would have to increase inversely proportional to the power factor in order to transmit the same power in the circuit. Larger currents imply an increase of cable dimensions and of windings in a generator or motor. This increases the costs of a system. Large currents also create high resistance losses in cables ($P_{loss} = I^2 \cdot R$).

Power and current definitions

In networks the following powers can be defined:

$$U \cdot I = \textit{apparent power [VA]}$$
$$U \cdot I \cdot \cos \varphi = \textit{real power or active power [W]} \qquad (2.80)$$
$$U \cdot I \cdot \sin \varphi = \textit{reactive power [VA]}$$

And by analogy, three types of current can be defined:

$$I = current\ [A]$$
$$I \cdot \cos \varphi = load\ current\ or\ active\ current\ [A] \tag{2.81}$$
$$I \cdot \sin \varphi = blind\ current\ or\ reactive\ current\ [A]$$

The blind current does not contribute to real power supply, but increases resistance losses.

Three-phase alternating current (AC)

Three-phase alternating current is used for transfer of electrical energy. The main electric power supply system on most ships is a three-phase system. In a three-phase system, there are three phase-windings in the generators and the electric motors. These three windings may be connected in star or in delta configuration. Most electric motors are connected in delta but they may start-up in star, and most generators are connected in star.

Figure 2.16 and Figure 2.17 show the phase voltages and phase currents for connection in star and delta respectively. They also show the relations between currents and voltages in the phase windings and those in the supply lines. Assume that the phase windings have equal loads.

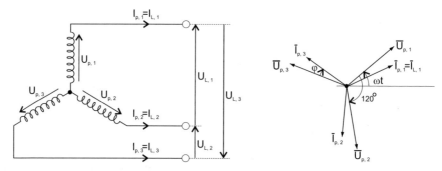

Figure 2.16   Relation between phase current and phase voltage, and line current and line voltage for star configuration.

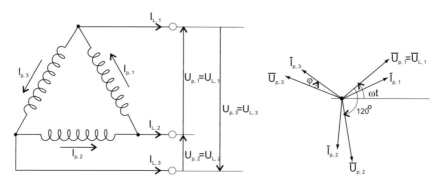

Figure 2.17   Relation between phase current and phase voltage, and line current and line voltage for delta configuration.

The phase displacements between the phase voltages in a three-phase system are 120°, or:

$$\alpha_{P,1} = 0 \ and \ \alpha_{P,2} = \frac{2\pi}{3} \ and \ \alpha_{P,3} = \frac{4\pi}{3}$$

This results in the following expressions for phase voltages in a three-phase system:

$$U_{P,1}(t) = U_m \cdot \cos \omega t$$

$$U_{P,2}(t) = U_m \cdot \cos\left(\omega t - \tfrac{2\pi}{3}\right) \tag{2.82}$$

$$U_{P,3}(t) = U_m \cdot \cos\left(\omega t - \tfrac{4\pi}{3}\right)$$

Note that the vector sum of the phase voltages is zero. The phase current has a phase lag angle relative to the phase voltage of φ, so the phase currents can be written as:

$$I_{P,1}(t) = I_m \cdot \cos(\omega t - \varphi)$$

$$I_{P,2}(t) = I_m \cdot \cos\left(\omega t - \tfrac{2\pi}{3} - \varphi\right) \tag{2.83}$$

$$I_{P,3}(t) = I_m \cdot \cos\left(\omega t - \tfrac{4\pi}{3} - \varphi\right)$$

In analogy with single phase AC current, effective voltage and current may be defined. Note that for the remainder of the text effective values will be used without the index e:

$$U = U_e = \frac{U_m}{\sqrt{2}} \ and \ I = I_e = \frac{I_m}{\sqrt{2}} \qquad \text{ref. (2.77) and (2.78)}$$

The figures also show the line properties. Line currents and voltages are the properties that can be measured in the cables connecting the electrical machines to the switchboards.

For a star connection (Figure 2.16), the phase currents relate to the line currents as follows:

$$I_{L,1} = I_{P,1} \ and \ I_{L,2} = I_{P,2} \ and \ I_{L,3} = I_{P,3} \tag{2.84}$$

The voltage difference between lines equals the vector difference between two phases. As it has been assumed that the windings are equally loaded, i.e. $|U_{P1}| = |U_{p2}| = |U_{p3}|$, the following can be shown using basic trigonometry as in Figure 2.18:

$$\overline{U}_{L,1} = \overline{U}_{P,1} - \overline{U}_{P,2} \rightarrow U_L = U_P \sqrt{3} \tag{2.85}$$

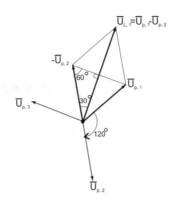

Figure 2.18   Line voltage of three *equally loaded* phase windings in star connection.

In a similar way, the line and phase variables of a delta connection (Figure 2.17) can be determined if an electrical machine is connected in delta. The following relation holds for the line voltages:

$$U_L = U_P \tag{2.86}$$

And as shown in Figure 2.17 and Figure 2.19, the following relationship exists between line and phase current provided that the phase currents are equal in magnitude.

$$\overline{I}_{L,1} = \overline{I}_{P,1} - \overline{I}_{P,3} \rightarrow I_L = I_P \sqrt{3} \tag{2.87}$$

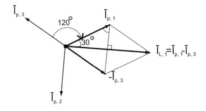

Figure 2.19   Line current of three *equally loaded* phase windings in delta connection.

The (average) power developed in one phase, expressed in effective phase values, equals:

$$P = U_P \cdot I_P \cdot \cos \varphi \qquad\qquad \text{ref. (2.79)}$$

For three equal phases in star or delta connection this leads to a total power of:

$$P = 3 \cdot U_P \cdot I_P \cdot \cos \varphi \tag{2.88}$$

Usually, however, the line values are used, which results in equation (2.89):

$$P = U_L \cdot I_L \cdot \sqrt{3} \cos \varphi \tag{2.89}$$

Note that this relation is valid for star and delta connected machines.

2.3.5 *Magnetic induction*

A magnetic field comes into being around a current-carrying conductor. A measure of the magnetic field caused by the current is the magnetic flux density *B*. Figure 2.20 shows the flux density as a vector in relation to the current *I* in the conductor.

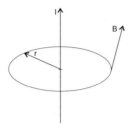

Figure 2.20   Magnetic flux density as caused by a current-carrying conductor.

The unit of flux density is Tesla [$T = Wb/m^2 = kg/As^2$]. The magnetic flux density *B* at a distance *r* of the conductor is:

$$B = \mu \cdot \frac{I}{2\pi r}$$ (2.90)

Where,

μ = *permeability of medium [H/m=Henry/m=kg×m/A^2×s^2]*

$\mu = \mu_0 \cdot \mu_R$

μ_0 = *permeability of vacuum* $= 4\pi \cdot 10^{-7}$ *[H/m]*

μ_R = *permeability of medium relative to vacuum*

Magnetic permeability is a property of the medium surrounding the conductor in which magnetic induction takes place. It is a measure of perceptiveness of the material to having magnetic flux set up in it. If the medium is not a vacuum the permeability is determined with the relative permeability. For ferrous materials μ_R may reach values of 10^5. It should be noted that the magnetic flux density cannot be increased up to any desired level, because the surrounding material may become saturated.

In case the conductor from Figure 2.20 forms a solenoid, i.e. a coil, it creates a magnetic field as shown in Figure 2.21.

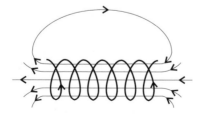

Figure 2.21   A magnetic field generated by a solenoid.

The magnetic flux density B working over an area A can be integrated to find the magnetic flux Φ:

$$\Phi = \int B \cdot dA \qquad (2.91)$$

Where,

A = *enclosed area*

Φ = *magnetic flux [Wb=Weber=kg×m²/A×s²]*

Lorentz force

A force will act on a current-carrying conductor when it is placed in a magnetic field; see Figure 2.22. This force is called the Lorentz force F_L.

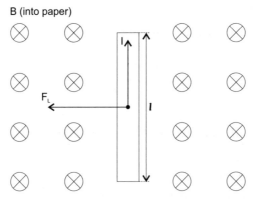

Figure 2.22   Lorentz force acting on a current carrying-conductor in a magnetic field.

If the direction of the current I in the conductor of length l is perpendicular to the direction of a magnetic field with flux density B, the Lorentz force F_L is:

$$F_L = B \cdot I \cdot l \qquad (2.92)$$

Where,

F_L = *Lorentz force [N]*

B = *magnetic flux density [T]*

I = *current through the conductor [A]*

l = *length of the conductor [m]*

(Note that, if the direction of current is not perpendicular to the direction of the magnetic field, the angle α between them should be defined and equation (2.92) should be multiplied by a factor $sin\alpha$.)

If a turn is located in a magnetic field, forces will act on both sides of the turn. The forces are equal in size but opposed in direction and will therefore create a torque. The turn is shown in Figure 2.23. The top view of the turn is also included to make the angle β visible. This is the angle between the turn and the normal of the direction of the magnetic flux.

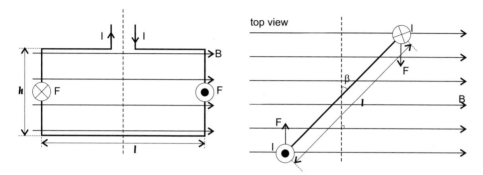

Figure 2.23   Torque acting on a turn in a magnetic field.

The forces and torque acting on the turn are:

$$F = B \cdot I \cdot h \qquad \text{ref. (2.92)}$$

$$M = F \cdot l \cdot \sin\beta = B \cdot I \cdot h \cdot l \cdot \sin\beta = B \cdot I \cdot A \cdot \sin\beta = I \cdot \Phi \cdot \sin\beta$$

Or for a N-turn coil:

$$M = N \cdot I \cdot \Phi \cdot \sin\beta$$

Electric motors convert electrical energy into mechanical energy based on the principle of the Lorentz force. The motor torque will often be given as:

$$M = K_M \cdot \Phi \cdot I \qquad (2.93)$$

Where K_M is a given constant for a certain motor. Obviously it captures the size and number of the windings and the flux density variations in the motor. Electric motors will be the subject of section 9.2.

Faraday's law

Another basic law for magnetic induction is Faraday's law. It states that an induction voltage is generated over a conductor when it is moving in a magnetic field (see Figure 2.24).

If the speed of the conductor is perpendicular to the direction of the magnetic field, the induction voltage $E[V]$ in a conductor of length l is also referred to as motional electromotive force, and is by definition:

$$E = -B \cdot l \cdot v \qquad (2.94)$$

Where,

E = *induction voltage or electromotive force (EMF) [V]*

B = *flux density of the magnetic field [T]*

l = *length of the conductor [m]*

v = *velocity of the conductor [m/s]*

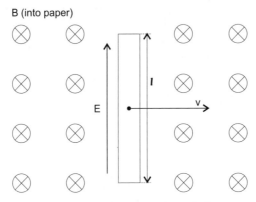

Figure 2.24   Faraday's voltage on a conductor moving relative to a magnetic field.

(If the angle between the velocity vector and the magnetic field vector is α, equation (2.94) needs to be multiplied by a factor $\sin\alpha$.)

The definition of the induced voltage contains a minus-sign because the direction of the voltage does not correspond with the direction of the original magnetic field. This can be explained if the conductor in Figure 2.24 is extended to a turn. The turn in Figure 2.25 moves horizontally into a vertical magnetic field. The induced voltage in the front end of the turn will cause a current in the turn that creates a magnetic field. This magnetic field within the turn is opposed to the magnetic field that caused the induction: the direction of this induced magnetic field is upwards.

The induced voltage may also be described as the rate of change of magnetic flux within a turn:

$$E = -\frac{d\Phi}{dt}$$

For an N-turn coil, the induced voltage also depends on the number of turns N:

$$E = -N \cdot \frac{d\Phi}{dt} \tag{2.95}$$

With Figure 2.25 the relationship between equations (2.94) and (2.95) can easily be shown:

$$E = -\frac{d\Phi}{dt} = -\frac{d(AB)}{dt} = -B \cdot \frac{dA}{dt} = -B \cdot 1 \cdot \frac{dx}{dt} = -B \cdot 1 \cdot v$$

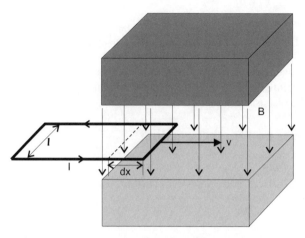

Figure 2.25   Induction in a turn when moving into a magnetic field.

For a coil rotating in a constant magnetic field, the change of magnetic field in the winding depends on the angle β between the normal of the direction of the magnetic flux density and the winding (see Figure 2.26):

$$\Phi_{max} = B \cdot A \rightarrow \Phi(t) = B \cdot A \cdot \cos\beta = B \cdot A \cdot \cos\omega t$$

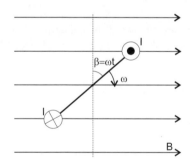

Figure 2.26   Induction in a turn rotating in a magnetic field.

With equation (2.95) the induced voltage of an N-turn coil:

$$E = N \cdot \omega \cdot B \cdot A \cdot \sin\omega t = N \cdot 2\pi n \cdot B \cdot A \cdot \sin\omega t$$

By analogy with the motor constant K_M in equation (2.93), K_E is introduced: it is a constant for a given coil. The induced EMF of a coil then equals:

$$E = K_E \cdot \Phi \cdot n \qquad (2.96)$$

Where,

  K_E = *constant, which depends on the construction of the coil*

  Φ = *magnetic flux [Wb]*

  n = *rotational speed [s^{-1}]*

Note that the coil in Figure 2.26 is rotating in a constant magnetic field. Equation (2.96), however, is also valid for magnetic fields that are not constant.

Generators convert mechanical energy into electric energy, based on the principle of Faraday's law: a voltage will be induced because windings are moving in a magnetic field. Generators will be discussed in section 9.3.

2.4   References and further reading

Black & Hartley, 1985
>   William Z. Black and James G. Hartley: *"Thermodynamics"*, Harper and Row, USA 1985.

Fitzgerald et al, 1975
>   Fitzgerald, Higginbotham and Grabel: *"Basic Electrical Engineering, 4/e"*, McGraw–Hill Kogakusha, Ltd., 1975.

Kreek, 1972 –in Dutch
>   Ir. J van der Kreek: *"Theoretische grondbeginselen der elektrotechniek"*, Nijgh & van Ditmar, Den Haag, 1972.

Moran and Shapiro, 1993
>   Michael J. Moran and Howard N. Shapiro: *"Fundamentals of engineering thermodynamics"*, John Wiley and Sons, Inc., USA 1993 (SI Version).

Chapter 3

Propulsion and Electric Power

3.0   Learning goals

After studying this chapter, the student should be able to:

- *Name and describe the main components of a propulsion system and their functions.*

- *Name and describe the main components of an electric power supply plant and their functions.*

- *Describe resistance and propulsion and give the basic definitions of hull efficiency, open water propeller efficiency, relative rotational efficiency, propulsive efficiency and transmission efficiency.*

- *Write resistance and propulsion in non-dimensional form and give the influencing parameters.*

- *Use the propulsion chain to calculate engine power or torque and speed from ship resistance and speed and vice versa.*

- *Describe how to determine the electric power demand of a vessel.*

- *Apply the concept of load and drive characteristics to ship, propeller, diesel engine and gas turbine, and determine operational points of combined characteristics.*

3.1   Introduction

Two important functions in Chapter 1 were:

- provide propulsion.

- provide electric power supply.

In conventional configurations the propulsion system is responsible for the first function, the electric power supply plant for the latter. The main components of both these systems are introduced in the first part of this chapter. In the second part, focus is on the energy demand of these systems.

The most important requirement of the propulsion system is to propel the ship at the required speed. This will be examined in section 3.4 *Resistance and propulsion*. Safety, crew capabilities (with respect to operation and maintenance), rules and regulations set by regulatory bodies, and operational requirements as specified in the mission and the specifications influence also the design of the propulsion system.

The function of the electric power plant is to supply electric power to a great diversity of electric consumers. The electric consumers, or electrical systems, include systems that are vital to the ship's operation, and safety of crew and passengers; e.g. lighting, communication, navigation and mission specific systems. Because of the importance of reliable operation of these electrical systems, regulatory bodies provide ample rules and regulations for configuration and design of electrical power plants and their components. The electrical load analysis (section 3.5) specifies the electric power required by the consumers in different operational conditions (such as in port and at sea). Number and capacity of the generators can be determined with this information.

One of the reasons why propulsion power and electric power are dealt with in one chapter is that, on board ships with electric propulsion, a combined electric power plant provides power to the propulsion motors and the other electrical systems.

3.2   Main components of the propulsion system

One of the most important systems onboard almost every marine object, is the propulsion system. The function of the propulsion system is to generate thrust, which enables the ship to move at the desired speed. Figure 3.1 shows the system's main components: prime mover, transmission and propulsor. This section discusses the functions of these components.

Figure 3.1   Main components of a propulsion system.

Prime Mover

The function of the prime mover is to deliver mechanical energy; the prime mover converts chemical energy contained in the fuel into mechanical energy. The prime mover in a propulsion system can be a diesel engine, a gas turbine or a steam turbine plant. The diesel engine is the most common prime mover in the merchant marine, mainly due to its low fuel consumption in comparison with other prime movers.

Gas turbines find their application in advanced (fast) ship types and naval vessels. The power to weight ratio of gas turbines is higher than that of diesel engines, i.e. similar power weighs less when a gas turbine is installed. This is especially advantageous for fast, advanced ships.

Some ship types, such as naval vessels and LNG carriers, may have a steam turbine plant as propulsion engine. Two kinds of steam plants can be distinguished in marine applications: fossil-fired steam plants and nuclear steam plants. Fossil-fired steam plants are frequently found on board naval vessels and LNG carriers. Submarines and aircraft carriers may be equipped with a nuclear steam plant. Prime movers will be discussed in more detail in *Chapter 6 Overview of Main Machinery, Chapter 7 Diesel Engines* and *Chapter 8 Gas Turbines.*

Transmission

Transmission is a sub-system of the propulsion system. It is a system itself built up from components such as shafts, gearboxes and bearings. The transmission's functions are (1) to transfer the mechanical energy generated by the prime mover to the propulsor (usually a propeller) and (2) to transfer the thrust generated by the propulsor to the ship's hull. The latter is done by means of a thrust bearing; a component that is found in every transmission system. The transmission components are discussed in detail in *Chapter 6 Overview of Main Machinery* (section 6.4 Transmission components).

Several types of transmissions are used. In general mechanical drives and non-mechanical drives are distinguished:

- Mechanical drive
  - *Direct:* the prime mover is coupled directly, through a shaft, to the propulsor.
  - *Geared:* the prime mover delivers its energy through a gearbox and a shaft to the propulsor. The function of the gearbox is to reduce the rotational speed of the engine to match the desired rotational speed of the propulsor. Consequently the torque generated by the prime mover is amplified by the same ratio as the rotational speed is reduced. A geared drive has the advantage of allowing the prime mover to work at a higher speed. Therefore, the prime mover will generally be smaller, lighter and cheaper than when direct propulsion is used. The additional gearbox, however, adds to the volume, weight and cost.

- Non-mechanical drive
  - *Electrical:* the prime mover powers a generator and the generated electrical energy is transported through cables, switchboards and converters to an electric motor, which in turn powers the propulsor. Usually the electric power supply to other ship systems is combined with such an electric propulsion system.
  - *Other:* Other types of non-mechanical drives, such as hydraulic drives, are seldom used.

In *Chapter 5 Power Plant Concepts* the different drives will be discussed in more detail.

Propulsor

The propulsor converts the rotating mechanical power delivered by the engine into translating mechanical power to propel the ship. The engine power is a torque M times an angular velocity ω : $P_B = M_B \cdot \omega_e$. It is converted into the thrust force T at the ship's velocity v_s: $P_T = T \cdot v_s$.

The most common propulsor is the propeller. In general, two types of propeller are distinguished, fixed pitch and controllable pitch propellers. Other types of propulsor are, for example, waterjets and Voith-Schneider propulsors. In a waterjet, water is accelerated by a pump and this generates a thrust. The Voith-Schneider propulsor consists of vertical blades making a cycloidal movement underneath the ship. Various propulsor concepts are discussed in more detail in *Chapter 6 Overview of Main Machinery* (section 6.6 Propulsors).

Propulsion support systems

Besides the main components mentioned above, the propulsion system includes propulsion support systems, also called auxiliary systems (of propulsion). The propulsion system can only function properly with these auxiliary systems, some of which are even vital to its operation. The auxiliary systems include the fuel supply and treatment systems, the engine room ventilation system (also supply of combustion air), the exhaust gas system, and lubrication, cooling and compressed air supply systems. Compressed air is used to start the engine, as is common practice.

Figure 3.2 gives an example of a propulsion system including its auxiliary systems. The propulsion system in this example consists of a diesel engine directly coupled to the propeller, and its auxiliary systems.

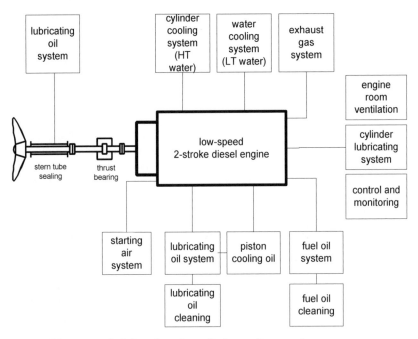

Figure 3.2   Direct-coupled diesel engine with its auxiliary systems.

3.3 Main components of electric power plant

A ship at sea cannot use an external source of electric energy, consequently its electric power plant is autonomous and generates, distributes and converts electric power. On board ships with electric propulsion a combined electric power plant provides power to the propulsion motors and the auxiliary systems.

On board ships the electric power plant converts energy in fossil fuels into electric energy. In general, this is a three-stage process in which the following conversions can be distinguished:

- Energy contained in fossil fuels into mechanical energy (prime mover),

- Mechanical energy into main electric energy (generator),

- Main electric energy into secondary electric energy (distribution and conversion).

Main electric power is used by large electrical consumers. A distinction can be made between three phase alternating current and direct current supply systems. Except for some special applications (submarines), the latter are hardly ever used nowadays but this may change in the future. Most commonly used are the three phase alternating current systems with a frequency of 60 Hz and voltages between 440-450 V or 50 Hz and 380-400 V. If very large electric power consumers, such as bow thrusters or propulsion motors, have to be supplied, the main electric power system may use a higher voltage of 3.3 kV, 6 kV, 6.6 kV, 11 kV or even 15 kV. In this case the smaller users are fed through a transformer with 50 Hz/380 V or 60 Hz/440 V at the output.

The advantage of using high voltage is that, for a given power, currents are lower. This results in smaller and less powerful circuit breakers, cables, generators, motors, etc. Obviously, better insulation of the equipment is required. High voltage systems are economically attractive for installations with powers of 8.5 MW and above. Smaller electrical loads are supplied from *secondary electric power* supply systems, usually single phase alternating current systems with a frequency of 50 or 60 Hz and voltage of 230 or 115 V, respectively. A direct current system, usually a 24 V-system, is used to supply the control and monitoring systems. Both systems are fed from the primary supply through electric energy conversion devices (transformers, rectifiers and converters are introduced later in this section).

Besides the main and secondary electric power supply systems, an electric power plant must have an emergency electric power supply system [SOLAS, 1997]. Usually this is a separate diesel generator set: the emergency/harbour generator. The location of the emergency electric power source, associated transforming equipment and emergency switchboard should be above the uppermost continuous deck and it should be accessible from the open deck. The emergency supply is an independent system that must supply electric power to equipment that is essential for safety in an emergency for at least 18 hours for cargo-ships or 36 hours for passenger vessels. According to SOLAS this equipment includes systems such as emergency and navigation lighting, communication equipment, and fire fighting and detection systems. Other examples of equipment fed from the emergency supply in case of failure of the main supply may be the steering gear and electrically operated watertight doors.

Figure 3.3 shows the main components that will be introduced in the remainder of this section: prime mover, generator, distribution and conversion and users.

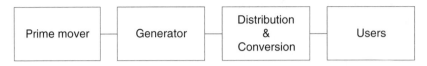

Figure 3.3 Main components of an electric power plant.

Prime mover

The prime mover in an electric power plant drives the generator. Most common is the use of a diesel engine to drive the generator due to its good performance characteristics and low fuel costs. Main electric power supply systems of 50 Hz require a prime mover with a speed of 750, 1000 or 1500 rpm, 60 Hz-systems require 900, 1200 or 1800 rpm. High-speed diesel engines need high quality fuels, whereas engines that run 750-1000 rpm can usually operate on cheaper heavy fuel. This gives them an advantage from a fuel cost point of view.

Gas turbines are also used for electric power supply systems. Compared to the diesel engine, use of a gas turbine results in a light compact plant but with high fuel costs due to expensive (high quality) fuel and lower efficiency. A steam turbine is rarely used to drive a generator (turbo-generator), nowadays. It has advantages though, when the propulsion system includes a steam plant, or when sufficient steam is generated by the energy in exhaust gases.

Generator

The generator driven by a prime mover converts mechanical energy to main electric energy. Manufacturers usually combine the generator, prime mover and auxiliary systems, such as reduction gear (if required) and lubricating oil system, to a generator set. A special kind of generator is the shaft generator, which is driven by the main propulsion engine either directly or through a gearbox.

Most common are AC generators. (If a DC main electric system is required, as on a submarine, AC generators will still be used in combination with rectifiers.) The type of generator (frequency, voltage) and number of generators are determined by the electrical load analysis, redundancy requirements and other rules and regulations provided by regulatory bodies. For electric powers up to 2500 kW, AC generators with frequency/ voltage of 50 Hz/400 V or 60 Hz/440 V (three phase) are generally installed. If the required electric power is higher, high voltage generators are implemented (voltage of 3.3 or 6 kV). Often, the generator capacity is not given as real power (kW) but as the apparent power (kVA), the product of current and voltage, because the current required from the generator determines the dimensions due to heating of the windings.

Distribution and conversion

Switchboards receive, control and distribute electric energy from generators to loads and secondary electric energy supplies. Every ship has at least one main switchboard and one emergency board. Passenger ships and some other ship types may have two or more main switchboards installed, which are connected by cables and switchgear. Main switchboards receive electric energy directly from the main generators. To keep unprotected cables (against short-circuit) between generator and generator switch as short as possible the main switchboard should be located in the immediate vicinity of the generator. The switchboard may also receive electric energy from shore when in port (or in dock). A shore power supply connection box is located on deck. When using shore power, the generators can be switched off.

The main switchboard distributes electric energy to electrical systems in its vicinity, and to distribution boards which group electrical systems that are located farther away. For example, electric energy to the winches on the foredeck may be distributed through a distribution board. Loads may be grouped by location as well as function. Sometimes all electrical systems are fed through distribution boards, and not directly from the main switchboard. Big loads such as bow thrusters are fed directly from the main switchboard.

The main switchboard also distributes energy to the secondary electric energy supplies. Between the main switchboard and the secondary electric energy supplies, the electric energy needs to be converted (from main to secondary). The electric converters are mentioned briefly:

- A transformer converts electric energy from one voltage to another, for example from 440 to 115 V. Transformers and rectifiers are usually installed in the secondary supply panel.

- A rectifier (power electronics) converts AC to DC, for example 24 V, which can be stored in a battery.

- Converters are used to alter the frequency of the electric energy. Two types can be distinguished:
  - Rotating converters (motor generator)
  - Static converters (power electronics).

When one of the secondary supply panels is a direct current supply panel, batteries are installed to ensure continuous electric energy supply to vital loads (such as operating, monitoring and control systems) during start up of the emergency system after a blackout of the primary supply system. This is called uninterrupted power supply or UPS.

Under normal conditions the main switchboard also supplies the emergency switchboard by an interconnector feeder. In case of an emergency, it is fed by the emergency generator. The switches that control the power supply to the emergency board (either from the main switchboard or from the emergency generator) are linked: only one supply may be active.

One-line diagrams

Figure 3.4 and Figure 3.5 show examples of one-line diagrams of electric power plants with primary, secondary and emergency power supplies and one or two main switchboards. The layout of an electric power plant is usually illustrated with this kind of diagram. Note that one line represents three or four conductors in case of three-phase current.

In Figure 3.4 two generators, which can operate in parallel, feed the power plant. In port, electric energy can also be supplied by the shore connection, so the generator sets may be out of service. Users in the vicinity of the main switchboard are fed directly from the board; other users are grouped in distribution panels. The one shown here has the same voltage as the main switchboard. If the voltage of the main switchboard is higher than required by the distribution panel, a transformer must be installed between the two, as shown for the secondary supplies. Also shown are the emergency board and the emergency generator.

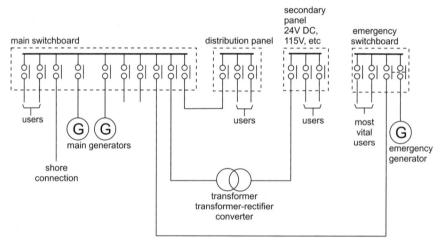

Figure 3.4   One-line diagram of electric power supply plant with primary, secondary and
              emergency power supply.

Figure 3.5 shows an electric power plant configuration with two main switchboards, as can be found on passenger vessels and navy ships, or other ship types with a large electric power plant in which the generator sets are spread out over several locations on board. Each switchboard is fed by two generator sets that are in its vicinity.

Redundancy is achieved in several ways. To a certain extent, failure of a generator set can be compensated for by the others: there are two sets on every board, and each switchboard can be fed by the other board through the interconnection. For redundant systems, one system will be connected to Switchboard 1 and the other to Switchboard 2. Consider two lubricating oil pumps for instance, when one is in service the other is on stand-by. By connecting them to different switchboards, the reliability of the system is improved. The distribution board that groups the most vital users will be connected to both switchboards.

The shore connection, emergency generator and secondary supply panels and transformers have been left out of Figure 3.5 to keep the diagram simple. They should, however, be added in the same way as in Figure 3.4 for a complete representation of the electric power plant.

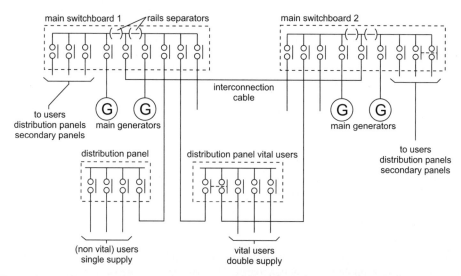

Figure 3.5   One-line diagram of power supply plant with two main switchboards.

Earthed or unearthed systems

A three-phase AC power supply system may be earthed or unearthed. In an earthed system the star point of the three phases (the central point of the three phases in Figure 2.16) is connected to the ship's hull. In an unearthed system, also called a floating system, such a connection is not made.

Both systems have some advantages and disadvantages. In an unearthed system, one phase may come into contact with the hull, e.g. due to bad cable isolation (cracks in cable isolation and moisture), without causing a short circuit. In an earthed system such a contact between one phase and the hull will lead to a single phase short circuit situation immediately. For personnel an unearthed system is safer than an earthed system. When somebody makes contact to one phase of an unearthed system accidentally, this will not lead to injury, because there is no connection made between two phases. One should realise, however, that this is only true when there is no earth fault. In an earthed system accidental personal contact with one phase, means a connection between one phase and the star point, which will lead most probably to serious injury or death.

In an earthed system the voltage of the star point is zero, because of its connection to the hull. This also means that the voltage differences between the phases and the hull are fully determined. In a floating unearthed system, the absolute voltages of the star point and phases are not determined. Theoretically this means that the voltage differences between the phases and the hull are not known. This introduces the problem that, for an unearthed system, it is not clear which cable isolation resistance should be required. In practice, this is not completely true: the cabling together with the hull form a capacity, which allows some AC current between phases and the hull. Also the harmonic filters, which are used in combination with modern electronic power converters (see section 9.4), in order to reduce harmonic distortion (see section 9.4.8) result in a form of connection between phases and the hull. Both phenomena mean that one cannot speak of a floating system really.

To prevent that in an unearthed system a phase contact with the hull remains unnoticed, which is an unsafe situation, the regulating bodies require, that an isolation resistance monitoring system is installed. Such an installation will warn when isolation resistance of the power system and its connected equipment becomes too low to be safe.

Considering the advantages, it is common practice to have a floating unearthed power supply in low voltage systems (400V, 50 Hz or 440 V, 60 Hz). For high voltage systems (1 kV and higher) it is common practice to have earthed power supplies. In that case the isolation resistance of the cables is more critical and can be accurately determined. The earthing consists of a connection between star point and the hull through a high resistance. The resistor ensures that in case of an earth fault the short circuit current does not become excessive.

Three or four wire systems

A three-phase power supply system may use cables with three or four wires. In a three-wire system only the three phases are connected to the switchboards. In a four-wire system the star point is also brought to the switchboards. The advantage of a four-wire system is that a lower voltage secondary power supply can be created without the need for transformers. This is done sometimes in 50 Hz systems, which have e.g. a 400 V three-phase AC power supply. The line voltage difference (between two phases) is 400 V. The voltage difference between a phase and the star point is then 230 V ($400/\sqrt{3}$). (see section 2.3.4) This gives the opportunity to create a 400 V three phase AC primary power supply, in combination with a 230 V single phase AC secondary power supply, without transformers.

In 60 Hz systems it is common practice to have a 440 V three phase AC primary power supply in combination with a 115 V single phase AC secondary power supply. In such a case a four-wire system makes no sense, because the voltage difference between one phase and the star point is then 254 V ($440/\sqrt{3}$), which does not match with the secondary voltage. In these systems always transformers are used for the secondary power supply.

3.4   Resistance and propulsion

Probably the most important design parameter of the propulsion system is the required speed of the ship stated in the mission or design specifications. To install the necessary propulsion power, the marine engineer needs details about ship resistance and propulsor. In this section the resistance of a ship is examined. Also, the variables that play a role in the propulsion required to overcome resistance are introduced. The matching of the propeller/ship load and delivered engine power is postponed to a later chapter.

3.4.1 *Hull resistance*

Translation of a hull through water requires a force. This force is called the *resistance*: it is the force that is required to tow the ship at a specified speed (without propulsor). The thrust developed by the propulsion system has to overcome the resistance of the ship. The total resistance consists of three components:

- *Frictional or viscous resistance* is the force that is the resultant of tangential forces acting on the hull as a result of the boundary layer along the hull.

- *Form or pressure resistance* is the force that is the resultant of the normal forces on the hull, due to the difference in the pressure in front of and behind the moving ship. The pressure losses become significant when the boundary layer separates from the hull at the stern of the ship.

- *Wave resistance* is the drag that is the result of waves generated by the moving ship. The kinetic and potential energy in the waves has to be generated by the propulsion system.

Often *air resistance* of the part of the ship above sea level cannot be neglected. The sum of frictional, form resistance and wave resistance results in the total hull resistance R of the ship. It is often acceptable to assume that the ship's resistance is roughly proportional to the square of ship speed v_s for relatively low speeds. Equation (3.1) states this assumption.

$$R = c_1 \cdot v_s^2 \tag{3.1}$$

Figure 3.6 shows various resistance-speed relations. For higher speeds, the resistance curve will be steeper; curves of type (2) may be encountered. Planing craft and swath (small waterplane area twin hull) ships may have curves that are more like (3).

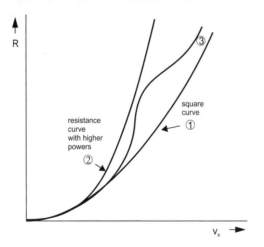

Figure 3.6   Different types of ship's resistance - speed curves.

The power required to tow the ship at ship speed v_s with resistance R is the effective (towing) power P_E (equation (3.2)). Using the assumed proportionality of resistance and ship speed squared, effective power is - as a first approximation - proportional to the cube of ship speed.

$$P_E \overset{\text{def}}{=} R \cdot v_S \tag{3.2}$$

$$P_E = c_1 \cdot v_S^{\ 3} \tag{3.3}$$

This means that if the ship speed is doubled, the required power (and ultimately fuel consumption) increases with a factor eight. Therefore, the operational requirement to sail fast is a costly affair and must be considered carefully.

The factor of proportionality c_1 is normally not a constant but contains a factor c_0 and a multiplying factor y. The nominal resistance factor c_0 is speed-dependent.

$$c_1 = y \cdot c_0(v_S) \tag{3.4}$$

The multiplier y accounts for additions to the nominal resistance due to degradation of performance in time (hull fouling) and operational conditions (displacement variations, sea state and water depth under the keel).

$$y = f(\textit{fouling, displacement, sea state, water depth}) \tag{3.5}$$

Normally c_0 is smaller at lower ship speeds: this means that for low speeds, the resistance decreases faster than the speed squared.

The propulsion power of advanced hulls may well deviate considerably from the theoretical cube law: in fact this is often a reason for the adoption of such hull forms. For a deeper insight into hull resistance, a thorough knowledge of fluid dynamics is required, in particular of (turbulent) boundary layers, (viscous) friction and wave making phenomena. This lies outside the scope of this book.

Non-dimensional resistance C_E

The speed dependency of the proportionality factor c_1 in equations (3.1) and (3.3) stems from a more general dimensionless form, which can be derived with the help of dimensional analysis. Before deriving the speed dependency of c_1 this dimensionless form of resistance is introduced.

In hydromechanics, total resistance is usually written in non-dimensional form C_T:

$$C_T \overset{\text{def}}{=} \frac{R}{\frac{1}{2} \cdot \rho \cdot A_s \cdot v_s^2} \tag{3.6}$$

In this relation, ρ [kg/m^3] is the density of water, and A_s is the wetted surface of the hull [m^2].

Usually, the wetted surface A_S is not readily available. However, it relates to displacement volume V by $A_S \propto V^{2/3}$. Then, a more practical coefficient is the coefficient used in this book: specific resistance C_E.

$$C_E \overset{\text{def}}{=} \frac{P_E}{\rho \cdot V^{2/3} \cdot v_S^3} \tag{3.7}$$

In which V is the displacement volume of the hull in cubic metres. Equation (3.7) transforms into equation (3.8) with the relation $\Delta = \rho \cdot V$:

$$C_E = \frac{P_E}{\rho^{1/3} \cdot \Delta^{2/3} \cdot v_S^3} \tag{3.8}$$

By defining specific resistance C_E, a ship is assigned a value that indicates resistance characteristics depending, amongst others on ship size, speed and hull form. Table 3.1 (see page 60) gives an idea of the order of magnitude of C_E for various ship types.

The techniques of dimensional analysis state that after writing resistance as a function of all variables on which it depends, this function can be rewritten by grouping the variables. These groups should be independent of each other and have the same dimension (most common are non-dimensional groups). In this case, specific resistance (a non-dimensional quantity) is a function of all other non-dimensional groups that play a role in the problem:

$$C_E = f\left(\underbrace{Re, Fr,}_{\text{speed, size}} \underbrace{Ro,}_{\text{fouling}} \underbrace{Hull\ form,}_{\text{geometry}} \underbrace{External\ factors}_{\text{sea state, water depth}} \right) \tag{3.9}$$

The Reynolds number Re and the Froude number Fr represent the viscous (friction) and dynamic (waves) effects on resistance (and power), respectively. They are defined as:

$$Re \overset{\text{def}}{=} \frac{\rho \cdot v_S \cdot L}{\eta} = \frac{v_S \cdot L}{\nu} \tag{3.10}$$

$$Fr \overset{\text{def}}{=} \frac{v_S}{\sqrt{g \cdot L}} \tag{3.11}$$

Therefore, the dependency of C_E on the Reynolds and Froude numbers means that C_E depends on speed and size.

Ro is a non-dimensional form of roughness. It is defined as the average hull roughness k divided by ship's length. Roughness changes in time, mainly by fouling of the hull.

$$Ro \overset{\text{def}}{=} \frac{k}{L} \tag{3.12}$$

The *Hull Form* can be described with geometrical parameters such as *L/B* and prismatic coefficient c_p. For a given ship, these are constants as long as the displacement does not change. The main *External Factors* are sea state and water depth under the keel. So, in practice equation (3.9) means:

$$C_E = f\left(v_s, \Delta, fouling, hull\ form, sea\ state, water\ depth\right)$$

This confirms the influence factors in equations (3.4) and (3.5).

Relation between c_1 and C_E

The speed-dependency of c_1 can be demonstrated by its relation to C_E. One can write:

$$P_E = \overbrace{C_E \cdot \rho^{\frac{1}{3}} \cdot \Delta^{\frac{2}{3}}}^{c_1} \cdot v_S^{\ 3} \qquad \text{ref. (3.7)}$$

By comparison with equation (3.3) it becomes clear that the original constant c_1 is the product of the specific resistance C_E and factors containing powers of density ρ and displacement Δ:

$$c_1 = C_E \cdot \rho^{\frac{1}{3}} \cdot \Delta^{\frac{2}{3}} \qquad (3.13)$$

In particular the dependency on the Froude number means that the propulsion power can change with speed more rapidly than is predicted by the cube law. The cube law is only valid for low Froude numbers (Fr = 0.1 - 0.2).

Relation between P_E and displacement

The effective power can be written as:

$$P_E = C_E \cdot \rho^{\frac{1}{3}} \cdot \Delta^{\frac{2}{3}} \cdot v_S^{\ 3} \qquad \text{ref. (3.7)}$$

This shows the basic dependencies on displacement and speed.
If C_E and v_S are assumed to be constant, a change in displacement from Δ_{nom} to Δ changes P_E according to Equation (3.14):

$$P_E = \left(\frac{\Delta}{\Delta_{nom}}\right)^{\frac{2}{3}} \cdot P_{E,nom} \qquad (3.14)$$

This means that resistance varies with displacement to the power 2/3, as long as hull form, hull fouling, and external factors such as sea state and water depth do not vary too much.

3.4.2 *Propulsion*

The function of a propulsor is to deliver a thrust force T to overcome the resistance R of the hull. The power needed to overcome resistance R at speed v_s is the effective power P_E, already defined in equation (3.2):

$$P_E \stackrel{def}{=} R \cdot v_S \qquad \text{ref. (3.2)}$$

Attention will be given to the screw propeller because it is the most common type of propulsor for ships. This section examines propulsion in a propeller–transmission–prime mover configuration. The power as delivered by the propeller in water moving at velocity of advance v_A with useful output T is the thrust power P_T (per propeller):

$$P_T \stackrel{def}{=} T \cdot v_A \qquad (3.15)$$

The required thrust of a ship propelled by a propulsor normally exceeds the resistance, which is scaled up from a towing test of a model (without propeller) in a towing tank. The main reason for this difference is that the propulsor draws its water along the hull and rudders and thus creates added resistance. On the other hand the advance velocity v_A generally is lower than the ship's speed v_s due to the wake of the ship. These two effects are discussed in this section.

Thrust deduction factor

The difference between total thrust of k_p propellers ($k_p T$) and resistance R as a fraction of the total propeller thrust is called the thrust deduction factor t:

$$t \stackrel{def}{=} \frac{k_p \cdot T - R}{k_p \cdot T} \qquad (3.16)$$

From this definition the relation between thrust and resistance is:

$$R = (1 - t) \cdot k_p \cdot T \qquad \text{ref. (3.16)}$$

The term *thrust deduction* was chosen because only a part of the thrust produced by the propellers is used to overcome the pure towing resistance of the ship, the remaining part has to overcome the added resistance: so going from thrust T to resistance R there is a deduction. The term is somewhat misleading since starting from resistance R the actual thrust T is increased:

$$k_p \cdot T = \frac{R}{(1 - t)} \qquad \text{ref. (3.16)}$$

Example A.

Assume a single-screw ship with block coefficient C_B= 0,60 and B/L=0,15. The thrust deduction is 19% (i.e. t = 0.19). Then 1-t = 0.81, or 81% of the thrust T is necessary to overcome the <u>towing</u> resistance R. The remaining 19% is the additional thrust required for the resistance in the <u>propelled</u> situation.

Wake factor

Another important effect is that the velocity of the water at the propeller location does not equal the ship's speed: the entrained water in the boundary layer around the ship has a certain forward speed. The boundary layer at the ship's stern has a considerable thickness and normally the propeller is completely within the region where the water velocity is affected by the hull's presence. As a result the advance velocity v_A of the propeller relative to the water is smaller than the ship speed v_S.

(Note that as a result of the suction of the propeller, the actual water velocity at the propeller entrance is much higher than the ship's speed: the *advance velocity*, however, is equal to the water velocity at the propeller disc area if the propeller would not be present. In other words it is the *far field* velocity that is felt by the propeller located in the boundary layer of the hull.)

The difference between ship's speed and advance velocity in front of the propeller, as a ratio of ship's speed is called the wake factor w:

$$w \stackrel{\text{def}}{=} \frac{v_S - v_A}{v_S} \tag{3.17}$$

From this definition the advance velocity as experienced by the propeller can be expressed in terms of the ship speed:

$$v_A = (1 - w) \cdot v_S \qquad\qquad \text{ref. (3.17)}$$

Example B.

Assume the wake factor is 24% (or w = 0.24). Then the advance velocity v_A for the propeller is 1 - w = 0.76 or 76% of the ship's speed.

Hull efficiency

As a result of thrust deduction and wake factor, the sum of the thrust power P_T of all the propellers does not equal the effective power P_E. The ratio of effective power to propulsive power is called the hull efficiency η_H, clearly because all differences between the towed and propelled hull are contained within this factor:

$$\eta_H \stackrel{\text{def}}{=} \frac{P_E}{k_p \cdot P_T} = \frac{R \cdot v_S}{k_p \cdot T \cdot v_A} \tag{3.18}$$

Hull efficiency can be, and often is, higher than unity. This is caused by thrust $k_p T$ normally exceeding the resistance R on one hand, and the velocity of advance v_a being lower than the ship's speed v_s on the other hand (provided that the propeller is well hidden in the boundary layer behind the ship). The propeller "thinks" that the ship is sailing slower but at a slightly increased resistance at that lower speed.

With the thrust deduction factor and wake factor as defined in equations (3.16) and (3.17) the hull efficiency η_H (equation (3.18)) can be written as:

$$\eta_H = \frac{1-t}{1-w} \tag{3.19}$$

If the wake factor exceeds the thrust deduction factor the hull efficiency is higher than unity. This is often the case in particular for single-screw ships.

Example C.

Combining Examples A and B, hull efficiency can be determined:

$$\eta_H = \frac{1-t}{1-w} = \frac{1-0.19}{1-0.24} = \frac{0.81}{0.76} = 1.066 > 1$$

So in this case the effective power of the hull would be 7% more than the power produced by the propeller.

The effect of wake can exceed the influence of the thrust deduction. The beneficial effect of the wake is the deeper reason for locating the propeller behind the ship and not in front. The physical explanation is that the location aft gives the propeller the opportunity to win back energy from the boundary layer. This is the main reason that the single propeller is preferred for merchant ships: it saves energy and thus in the end fuel.

Example D shows a numerical example for a twin-screw naval ship. Requirements for redundancy and manoeuvrability almost invariably lead to two propeller shafts. Also, it is almost impossible to deliver the relatively high power of naval ships to one single propeller: the diameter, which is important for the load carrying capacity, is limited for small ships like frigates compared to containerships for instance. A notable exception is the USN "Patrol frigate" ("Perry" class) which is a single screw frigate.

Example D.

With the figures that are typical for a twin screw naval vessel, w=0.02 and t=0.06 it follows that:

$$\eta_H = \frac{1-t}{1-w} = \frac{1-0.06}{1-0.02} = \frac{0.94}{0.98} = 0.96 < 1$$

So in this case the effective power of the hull would be 4% less than the power produced by the propeller.

Propeller efficiency

In order to deliver thrust at a certain translating speed, power must be delivered to the propeller as torque Q and rotational speed:

$$P_O \stackrel{def}{=} Q \cdot \omega_p = 2\pi \cdot Q \cdot n_p \tag{3.20}$$

The index *O* stands for *open water* and refers to the fact that propellers normally are tested in an open water tank or tunnel. During such an open water test the flow in front of the propeller is uniform. During the test the so-called open water propeller efficiency can be measured:

$$\eta_O \overset{\text{def}}{=} \frac{P_T}{P_O} = \frac{1}{2\pi} \cdot \frac{T \cdot v_A}{Q \cdot n_p} \tag{3.21}$$

The open water propeller efficiency lies in the range of 0.3 for inland ships to 0.7 for frigates.

In reality, i.e. behind the ship, the torque M_p and thus the power P_p actually delivered to the propeller are generally slightly different as a result of the non-uniform velocity field in front of the actual propeller.

$$P_p \overset{\text{def}}{=} M_p \cdot \omega_p = 2\pi \cdot M_p \cdot n_p \tag{3.22}$$

The ratio between open water power (or torque) and actually delivered power (or torque) is called the *relative rotative efficiency:*

$$\eta_R \overset{\text{def}}{=} \frac{P_O}{P_p} = \frac{Q}{M_p} \tag{3.23}$$

The relative rotative efficiency normally does not differ much from unity: values in the range of 0.98 to 1.02 may be encountered.

Propulsive efficiency

It is common practice to define the *total propulsive efficiency* to embrace all effects concerning hull and propeller discussed up to now. So, the propulsive efficiency must be defined as the quotient of the previously defined effective power P_E delivered to the hull and the power actually delivered to *all* the propellers P_D. The total propulsive efficiency is defined as:

$$\eta_D \overset{\text{def}}{=} \frac{P_E}{P_D} \tag{3.24}$$

With the definitions of effective power, thrust power, open water power and delivered power this can be written as:

$$\eta_D = \frac{P_E}{P_D} = \frac{P_E}{k_p \cdot P_p} = \frac{P_E}{k_p \cdot P_T} \cdot \frac{P_T}{P_O} \cdot \frac{P_O}{P_p} = \frac{R \cdot v_S}{k_p \cdot T \cdot v_A} \cdot \frac{1}{2\pi} \cdot \frac{T \cdot v_A}{Q \cdot n_p} \cdot \frac{Q}{M_p} \quad \text{ref. (3.24)}$$

Then, with the definitions of hull efficiency η_H, open water propeller efficiency η_O, and relative rotative efficiency η_R the following chain of partial efficiencies arises:

$$\eta_D = \eta_H \cdot \eta_O \cdot \eta_R \tag{3.25}$$

In which the hull efficiency according to equation (3.19) can further be expressed in thrust deduction t and wake factor w:

$$\eta_D = \frac{1-t}{1-w} \cdot \eta_0 \cdot \eta_R \tag{3.26}$$

As a result of the propeller–hull interaction, the propulsive efficiency η_D of the propeller(s) operating behind the ship can be better than the propeller efficiency η_0 as measured in an open water test. The propeller efficiency depends on many factors, amongst others the loading of the propeller.

During the energy conversion process at the propeller much energy is lost. Even though the propeller has been in use for more than 150 years, still a lot of research effort is put into improving its efficiency: in the first place by refining the propeller itself, but also by using the rotational energy behind the propeller (for example in a second, contra-rotating propeller or in an additional, free spinning Grimm wheel).

Non-dimensional delivered power coefficient C_D

Not only effective towing power P_E but also delivered power P_D is increasing with the cube of ship speed, if it is assumed that the total efficiency η_D remains almost constant at ship speeds other than nominal ship speed, as shown by the following relations:

$$P_E = c_1 \cdot v_S^3 \qquad \text{ref. (3.2)}$$

The power delivered to all the propellers is:

$$P_D = \frac{P_E}{\eta_D} = \frac{c_1 \cdot v_S^3}{\eta_D} = c_2 \cdot v_S^3 \tag{3.27}$$

By analogy with specific resistance C_E, the non-dimensional delivered power coefficient C_D is derived. Also the parameters on which c_2 depends are determined by defining C_D and showing its relation to c_2.

The effective power equals:

$$P_E = C_E \cdot \overbrace{\rho^{1/3} \cdot \Delta^{2/3} \cdot v_S^3}^{c_1} \qquad \text{ref. (3.7)}$$

In a similar manner, P_D can be solved from equation (3.2) and equation (3.27):

$$P_D = \frac{P_E}{\eta_D} = \frac{C_E \cdot \rho^{1/3} \cdot \Delta^{2/3} \cdot v_S^3}{\eta_D} = \overbrace{C_D \cdot \rho^{1/3} \cdot \Delta^{2/3} \cdot v_S^3}^{c_2} \tag{3.28}$$

In which the non-dimensional *delivered power coefficient* C_D is by definition:

$$C_D \stackrel{def}{=} \frac{P_D}{\rho \cdot \nabla^{2/3} \cdot v_S^3} = \frac{P_D}{\rho^{1/3} \cdot \Delta^{2/3} \cdot v_S^3} = \frac{C_E}{\eta_D} \tag{3.29}$$

Examples of values of the specific resistance, the delivered power coefficient and total propulsive efficiency are given in Table 3.1.

Ship		Container ship	Container ship	Container feeder	Inland ship	Frigate 20 knots	Frigate 30 knots
Capacity	TEU	6000	3600	340	120	-	-
V_S	knots	24	24	15	8	20	30
DWT	ton	70000	45500	3750	1520	3500	3500
η_D	-	0.75	0.75	0.65	0.40	0.70	0.70
$1000\,C_E$	-	8	9	14	28	20	22
$1000\,C_D$	-	11	12	22	70	29	31
C_{adm}	$\frac{ton^{2/3}\cdot knots^3}{kW}$	683	607	338	104	255	232

Table 3.1 Specific resistance and delivered power coefficients for various ships.

C_D is a function of C_E and η_D. This means that C_D must depend on the same variables as C_E and η_D. The previous section already showed C_E as a function of ship speed, fouling, hull form, sea state and water depth. The efficiency of the propeller η_O, which is included in the propulsive efficiency η_D, depends on the propeller geometry and is sensitive to cavitation. Cavitation occurs when local pressures at the propeller are lower than the vapour pressure due to high velocities. Locally, vapour-filled cavities arise, which collapse violently when leaving the local low pressure area, causing efficiency loss and damage to the propeller. Local pressures at the propeller depend on depth (height of water column above the propeller), thus displacement of the ship and the velocity of the water. The velocity of the water at the propeller depends on hull form, ship speed and propeller geometry and is also influenced by the sea state:

$$\eta_D = f\left(v_S, \Delta, propeller\ geometry,\ hull\ form,\ sea\ state\right) \tag{3.30}$$

Then the specific delivered propulsion power coefficient C_D depends on hull *and* propeller parameters:

$$C_D = f\left(v_S, \Delta, fouling,\ hull\ form,\ propeller\ geometry,\ sea\ state,\ water\ depth\right) \tag{3.31}$$

Now remember:

$$c_2 = C_D \cdot \rho^{1/3} \cdot \Delta^{2/3} \qquad\qquad \text{ref. (3.28)}$$

So, the constant c_2 must depend on the same variables as C_D.

Another common coefficient is the admiralty constant. The constant can be used to estimate the power to be installed when ships of similar dimensions are known.

$$C_{adm} \overset{def}{=} \frac{\Delta^{\frac{2}{3}} \cdot v_s^3}{P_D} \qquad (3.32)$$

Where Δ is the displacement of the ship in tonnes and P_D is the power delivered to the propulsors. Note that the admiralty constant is the inverse of the delivered propulsion power coefficient but that the density to the power 1/3 is missing. Consequently the admiralty constant is not dimensionless. The units chosen are Δ in kg or tonnes, v_s in m/s or knots and P_D in kW or horsepower. Table 3.1already gave values for the admiralty constant for different ship types and in case of the frigate in different operating conditions.

Propeller law

The relation between the power delivered to a propeller P_p and shaft (or propeller) speed n_P is known as the *propeller law*. From experience it is known that shaft (rotational) speed is almost linearly proportional to the ship's (translating) speed:

$$n_p = c_3 \cdot v_s \qquad (3.33)$$

With equations (3.28) and (3.33) it can be shown that the delivered power is not only proportional to the cube of ship speed but also to the cube of shaft speed. This is called the propeller law.

$$P_p = \frac{P_D}{k_p} = \frac{c_2}{k_p} \cdot v_s^3 = \frac{c_2 \cdot n_p^3}{k_p \cdot c_3^3} = c_4 \cdot n_p^3 \qquad (3.34)$$

The definition for propeller power was shown in equation (3.22) From this equation, torque can be solved as follows:

$$P_p \overset{def}{=} M_p \cdot \omega_p = 2\pi \cdot M_p \cdot n_p \rightarrow M_p = \frac{P_p}{2\pi \cdot n_p} \qquad ref. (3.22)$$

Then:

$$M_p = \frac{c_4 \cdot n_p^3}{2\pi \cdot n_p} = c_5 \cdot n_p^2 \qquad (3.35)$$

That is: *propeller torque* is proportional to the *square* of the *shaft speed*. There were two assumptions in the derivation of the propeller law:

▪ the propulsive efficiency remains constant in off-design conditions.

▪ shaft speed is linearly proportional to translating speed.

These two approximations have a common basis: the shape of the velocity triangle of the propeller and the assumption that the flow angle of attack remains constant. In fact, they only hold in case of a squared resistance–ship speed curve. This will be discussed further in *Chapter 11 Matching propulsion engine to propeller*.

3.4.3   Propulsion chain

The powers and efficiencies, part of which were introduced in the foregoing sections, can be represented as a propulsion chain: a chain of powers from ship (demand) to prime mover (supply) linked by the various efficiencies.

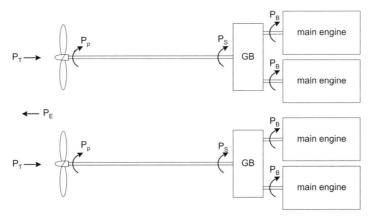

Figure 3.7   Propulsion power plant with $k_p = 2$ propeller shafts and $k_e = 2$ engines per shaft.

Figure 3.7 shows the entire propulsion chain, it is clear that to complete the propulsion chain, the theory needs to be extended to include the prime mover. To do this, the basic assumption is a simple propulsion plant configuration as given in Figure 3.1: prime mover, transmission and propulsor. In such a configuration, shafting and possibly a gearbox are found between the propulsor, in this case a propeller, and the prime mover. This transmission is responsible for power losses caused by friction in stern tube bearing and shaft bearings. Shaft losses are expressed in terms of shaft efficiency, which is defined as:

$$\eta_S \overset{def}{=} \frac{P_p}{P_S} = \frac{M_p}{M_S} \tag{3.36}$$

The shaft loss typically is 0.5 to 1 percent at nominal power. In equation (3.36) P_S is the shaft power, i.e. the power delivered to the shaft that is connected to a propeller and P_p is the power delivered to the propeller (equation (3.22)).

$$P_S \overset{def}{=} M_S \cdot \omega_p = 2\pi \cdot M_S \cdot n_p \tag{3.37}$$

Engine brake power P_B is the power developed by the engine defined by:

$$P_B \stackrel{\text{def}}{=} M_B \cdot \omega_e = 2\pi \cdot M_B \cdot n_e \tag{3.38}$$

Where M_B is the engine torque, ω_e is the angular velocity of the engine shaft and n_e is the engine speed. If there is no gearbox, brake power equals shaft power. If however, transmission includes a gearbox, gearbox losses are expressed in terms of gearbox efficiency, taking into account the number of engines per propeller shaft k_e:

$$\eta_{GB} \stackrel{\text{def}}{=} \frac{P_S}{k_e \cdot P_B} = \frac{M_S \cdot n_p}{k_e \cdot M_B \cdot n_e} = \frac{M_S}{k_e \cdot M_B} \cdot \frac{1}{i} \tag{3.39}$$

Here, i is the gearbox reduction ratio indicating the ratio of engine speed to propeller speed:

$$i \stackrel{\text{def}}{=} \frac{n_e}{n_p} \tag{3.40}$$

The gearbox losses are moderate (1% to 2%) for one-step reduction gearboxes in medium-speed diesel installations and they may be high (3% to 5%) for complex gearboxes with two or three reduction stages such as currently applied in multi-engine installations.

The total transmission efficiency is defined as the ratio of delivered power to brake power. With the definition of shaft and gearbox efficiency, total transmission efficiency can be written as the product of these two. Equation (3.41) shows this derivation.

$$\eta_{TRM} \stackrel{\text{def}}{=} \frac{P_p}{k_e \cdot P_B} = \frac{M_p}{k_e \cdot M_B} \cdot \frac{1}{i} = \frac{M_p}{M_S} \cdot \frac{M_S}{k_e \cdot M_B} \cdot \frac{1}{i} = \eta_S \cdot \eta_{GB} \tag{3.41}$$

Figure 3.8 is a schematic presentation of the propulsion chain and all powers and efficiencies that have been discussed.

To complete the power chain from the moving ship to the fuel in the tanks, the last step is effective engine efficiency. It is defined as the ratio of engine output and heat input:

$$\eta_e = \frac{P_B}{\dot{Q}_f} \tag{3.42}$$

Effective engine efficiency accounts for all engine losses in the conversion of chemical energy in fuel to the mechanical energy in the rotating output shaft of the engine.

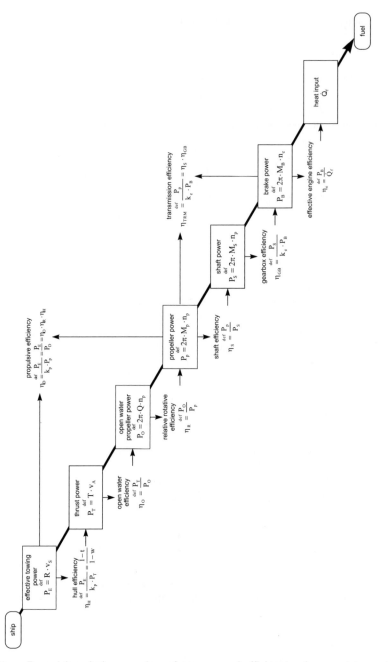

Figure 3.8   Propulsion chain: overview of powers and efficiencies from resistance to brake power.

3.5 Electric power demand

In order to determine the electric power plant capacity and configuration (generators, converters and transformers for the secondary power supplies, etc.), it is necessary to gain insight into the electric power demand of the ship under various operational conditions. The operational conditions for which the electric power demand is determined are dependent on the ship mission. For many ship types, the following operational conditions are examined:

- at sea
- manoeuvring
- in port; loading and discharging
- in port; no loading or discharging
- at anchor.

Ships with special missions (e.g. offshore installations, naval vessels) will also have special operational conditions that have to be taken into account. For certain ship missions, for example, it is necessary to make a distinction between summer and winter conditions (e.g. cruise vessels with large air-conditioning units, reefer vessels with large refrigeration units), and for naval ships the *at sea* condition is further divided into several *degrees of readiness* depending on the threat, for instance transit and action status. All things considered, this implies that the electrical power demand has to be determined for three to ten operational conditions.

There are three ways to determine the electric power demand: (1) empirical formulas, (2) electrical load analysis and (3) simulation. These three methods are described in the following. In a design process, the first estimate of the electric load is often made with empirical formulas, and as the process progresses, a more detailed calculation is made with a load analysis.

Empirical formulae

Empirical formulae can be used successfully to obtain a first estimate of the electric power demand in the pre-design stage, if the formulae are based on a sufficient number of ships with the same mission statement and comparable size. However, for the detailed design of ship and electrical systems one of the next methods is indispensable to get a more reliable result.

When empirical formulae are at hand, they can be used to determine the electric power demand or installed electric power by using, for instance, the main dimensions of the ship such as size (deadweight) or installed propulsion power. The example given here, equation (3.43), is a formula that uses the installed propulsion power to determine the electric power demand *at sea* for a conventional cargo vessel without special equipment such as a cargo refrigeration system, fishing gear, bow thrusters or deck cranes. As a rule of thumb, the electric load when manoeuvring is 130 % of the electric load at sea, and the load in port (no loading or discharging) is 30 to 40 %.

$$P_{EL} = 100 + 0.55 \times \left(P_{MCR}\right)^{0.7} \tag{3.43}$$

Be careful when using empirical formulae: only use the ones that are based on ships that are comparable in size and mission. Furthermore, be aware of the differences between the ships on which the formula is based and the one that is being designed.

Electric load analysis

The most widely used method for determining the electric power demand is the so-called electric load analysis, or electric load balance. Figure 3.9 shows an example of an electric load balance sheet. The balance sheet lists all electric power consumers vertically, sorted by power supply (main or secondary). The next columns tabulate nominal properties of the electric consumers such as:

- name

- number installed

- power at full load

- installed electric motor power (name plate power)

- nominal power absorbed from the electric net.

The second part of the sheet describes the various operational conditions in order to determine the actual electric load for each condition. In each condition, the following properties need to be determined for every electric consumer:

- number in service

- load factor

- simultaneity factor

- average absorbed power.

The power at full load is the power that has to be supplied to the flange of the machinery (as far as machinery such as pumps and compressors are concerned). The machine efficiency (e.g. pump efficiency) is accounted for. For direct electric users, such as lighting and computers, this power equals the power absorbed from the electric net. On the other hand, for electric users that are driven by an electric motor, the power absorbed from the net is the power demanded by the user divided by the electric motor efficiency. Note that, in general, the installed electric motor power is larger than the power at full load of a piece of machinery, because an electric motor has to be chosen from a manufacturer's range of motors. If, for example, a pump requires 7 kW at full load, and electric motors developing powers of 1, 2, 5 and 10 kW can be delivered, it is obvious that the 10 kW-motor will be installed. The column *number in service* speaks for itself. Some machinery will only be in service in certain operational conditions: for example loading and discharging systems only in port and the propulsion system only at sea. For machinery that has been installed redundantly, obviously the *number in service* will be less than the *number installed*.

The load factor indicates the relative (%) load of the machinery and thus specifies how much electric power is absorbed in an actual situation. A steering gear pump for example will only occasionally be fully loaded. The load factor, which varies between 0 and 1, accounts for this. A typical load factor for a steering gear pump is 0.1.

The simultaneity factor accounts for pieces of machinery that are not operated continuously but intermittently. Examples of these are air compressors, fuel pumps and ballast pumps. The simultaneity factor indicates the relative (%) mean operational time of the machinery. This factor also varies between 0 and 1. It is often possible to make a good estimation of this factor by comparing the machine capacity and the average capacity demand. In many cases no distinction is made between the load factor and the simultaneity factor, and the two factors are combined into one service factor. This does, however, not provide a clear insight into the actual load demand.

The column *average absorbed power* is the product of the absorbed power, the number in service, the load factor and the simultaneity factor. The total of this column indicates the total absorbed power for the given operational condition. The load analysis is assessed for the main and the secondary electric power supplies. The results of the load analysis for the secondary supplies, corrected for transformer efficiency, are transferred to that of the main supply.

The estimation of the load and simultaneity factors is the most difficult part of the electric load analysis. These factors are often estimated too high, in order to minimise the risk of designing a plant with a generator capacity that is too small. This results in an overestimation of the electric power demand, and consequently the chosen generator capacity is too large. Disadvantages are obvious:

- high investment

- low average load of the diesel generator sets, leading to specific fuel consumption that is not optimal and internal pollution of the engine.

A thorough study of similar ships should form the basis for load and simultaneity factor estimates.

For an example of a load balance, reference is made to Exercise 3 at the end of this chapter.

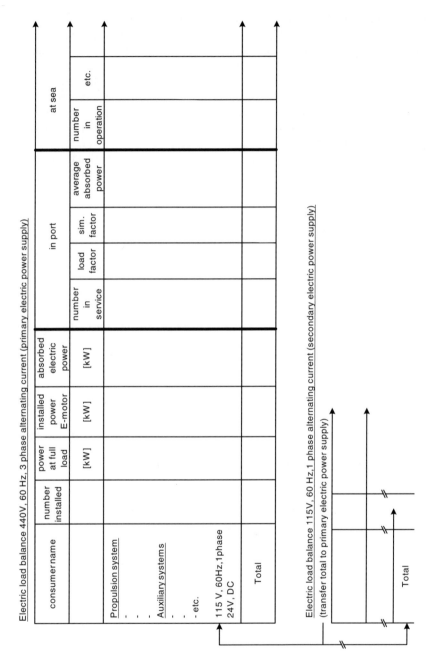

Figure 3.9   General format of load balance sheet.

Simulation of electric power demand

A more accurate electric power demand estimate can be achieved with a simulation of ship's operations under the various operational conditions. This method requires a considerable insight into the ship's operations. A simulation takes interactions between pieces of equipment into account and can model load and simultaneity factors by using stochastic probability distributions. In particular the use of probability distributions can make the method more accurate than an ordinary electric load balance.

The advantage of the stochastic probability distribution is explained with an example: the steering gear pump. The load factor was introduced in the preceding paragraph. The steering gear pump is only occasionally fully loaded; the load factor accounts for this by implying that it is partially loaded all the time. With a probability distribution the load of the pump can be modelled to be zero or full-load. After sufficiently long simulation the distribution provides insight into the expected minimum and maximum loads and the chances of exceeding a certain maximum. With this it is possible to make a well-founded choice concerning the number and capacity of the generators and transformers.

3.6 Load and drive characteristics

When resistance or effective power are viewed as demand of a ship, and propulsion power as supply, the matching of resistance and propulsion power can be viewed as a supply and demand issue. In fact, the matching of power supply and demand is not only an issue for resistance and propulsion, but for every load and its drive.

In this section, load and drive characteristics are introduced which schematically show the supply (drive) and demand (load) sides. By combining these load and drive characteristics a first step will be made towards matching the two.

3.6.1 Load characteristics

A load characteristic represents the relation between power (or torque or force) and speed (rotating or translating) required by a driven machine (or a ship). Examples of load characteristics are:

- Ship load curves: resistance or required effective power versus ship speed,

- Propeller load curves: required power or torque versus propeller speed.

The ship's load curves will be examined first. The relations between resistance R or effective power P_E and ship speed vs have been deducted in section 3.4.1, and are repeated here.

$$R = c_1 \cdot v_s^2 \qquad\qquad \text{ref. (3.1)}$$

$$P_E = c_1 \cdot v_s^3 \qquad\qquad \text{ref. (3.2)}$$

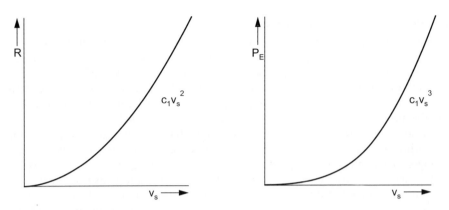

Figure 3.10   Ship load characteristics.

The diagrams in Figure 3.10 show these relations in load curves. In a similar manner, propeller load curves can be constructed. The relationship between delivered propeller power P_p or torque M_p and rotating propeller speed n_p have been derived from the previous relationship between P_E and ship speed v_s in section 3.4.2. Relationships between torque M_p or power P_p and propeller speed n_p were also deduced (equations (3.34) and (3.35)).

$$P_p = c_4 \cdot n_p^3 \qquad \text{ref. (3.34)}$$

$$M_p = c_5 \cdot n_p^2 \qquad \text{ref. (3.35)}$$

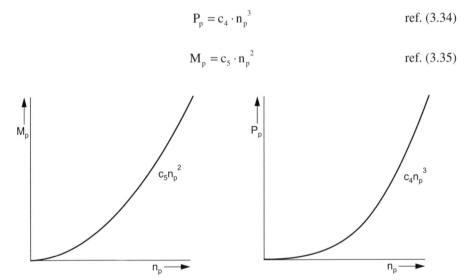

Figure 3.11 Propeller load characteristics.

3.6.2   Drive characteristics

A drive characteristic represents the relation between delivered engine power P_B (or torque M_B) and the number of revolutions n_e of a drive. Drive characteristics can be constructed for all types of driving machinery: for example diesel engines, gas turbines or electric motors. The characteristics of a diesel engine and of a gas turbine will be shown. Because working principles of these pieces of machinery have not been discussed yet, the basic drive curves are presented here and will be explained in a later chapter.

The first example shows the drive characteristics of a diesel engine. The delivered torque M_B is approximately constant in the domain between minimum and maximum number of revolutions if a constant amount of fuel is injected per engine cycle. For constant torque M_B, power P_B is directly proportional to the revolutions per second n_e, i.e.:

$$P_B = M_B \cdot 2\pi \cdot n_e \qquad\qquad \text{ref. (3.38)}$$

The power (or torque) can be regulated by controlling the fuel rack position. Figure 3.12 shows the basic drive characteristics of a diesel engine. In this diagram minimum and maximum engine speed are indicated. The fuel injection at a certain power is expressed as a percentage of the maximum injected fuel mass per engine cycle m_f.

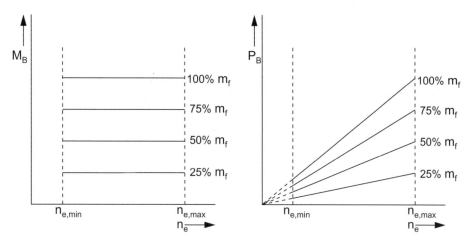

Figure 3.12   Drive characteristics of a diesel engine.

Another example of a basic drive characteristic is the power-speed curve of the free power turbine of a two-shaft gas turbine plant. This type of gas turbine approximately delivers a constant power in the domain of rotational speeds under consideration if the mass flow of fuel $\dot{m}_f$ is kept constant. This results in a rising torque for decreasing speed at constant fuel flow; see Figure 3.13.

Figure 3.12 and Figure 3.13 show that the area in which a drive can operate is restricted and depends on the type of driving machinery. This area is the operating envelope. For a given prime mover, the operating envelope is limited by a minimum and a maximum speed, and a maximum amount of the injected fuel.

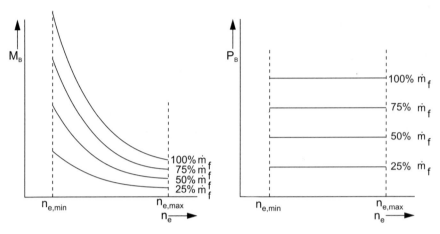

Figure 3.13   Drive characteristics of a gas turbine.

3.6.3   *Combining load and drive characteristics*

A load and a drive are in equilibrium when the power developed by the engine $P_{B,drive}$ (or $M_{B,drive}$) and the power asked for by the propeller $P_{B,load}$ (or $M_{B,load}$) are equal. When k_e engines are driving one propeller, the brake power $P_{B,load}$ per engine required by the propeller is:

$$P_{B,load} = \frac{P_p}{\eta_{TRM} \cdot k_e} \qquad\qquad \text{ref. (3.41)}$$

And the brake torque required by the propeller is:

$$M_{B,load} = \frac{M_p}{\eta_{TRM} \cdot k_e \cdot i}$$

If the system is in equilibrium, it operates under stationary conditions (no acceleration or deceleration). These equilibrium conditions result in operational points. A system may have several operational points depending on both the load and the drive, but also on operation, design and off-design conditions considered. These points must lie within the operating envelope of the driving machinery.

Figure 3.14 shows the operational point in the combined load and drive characteristics of a diesel engine and a fixed pitch propeller in torque-speed curves, and power-speed curves. The operational point defines n_{eq}, from which ship speed can be calculated.

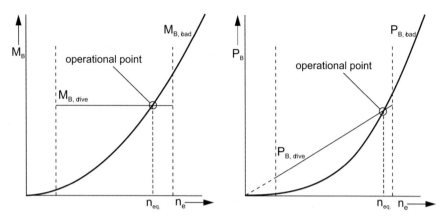

Figure 3.14   Matching of load and drive characteristics.

The combined curves are also used to determine the influence of for example fuel rack position (fuel injection) or increased ship resistance to the ship speed. Figure 3.15 shows that a decrease in fuel injection (i.e. decrease of $P_{B,drive}$) shifts the operational point to a lower engine (or propeller) speed. This demonstrates how, eventually, ship speed can be controlled by fuel injection.

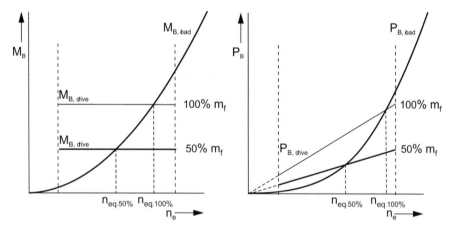

Figure 3.15   Influence of decrease of fuel injection to propeller speed.

Figure 3.16 shows the influence of increased ship resistance to propeller speed: the operational point shifts to a lower propeller speed, and consequently leads to a lower ship speed at constant torque. Chapter 11 will focus on the matching issues in more detail.

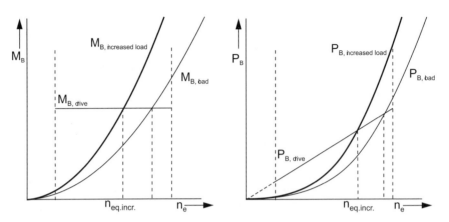

Figure 3.16   Influence of increase of resistance to propeller speed.

3.7   Exercises

Exercise 1

A ship is propelled by two identical screw type propellers (k_p=2). Each propeller is driven through a reduction gearbox by two identical high-speed diesel engines (k_e=2). In the design condition, the ship is propelled by both propellers and the following data apply:

- ship displacement $\Delta = 4000$ *tonne*

- ship speed $v_s = 28$ *knots*

- ship resistance $R = 1111$ *kN*

- propeller speed $n_p = 220$ *rpm*

- wake fraction $w = 0.04$

- thrust deduction factor $t = 0.06$

- relative rotative efficiency $\eta_R = 0.99$

- open water propeller efficiency $\eta_O = 0.71$

- shaft efficiency $\eta_S = 0.99$

- gearbox efficiency $\eta_{GB} = 0.98$

- effective engine efficiency $\eta_e = 0.40$

- engine speed $n_e = 1200$ *rpm*

- lower heating value of the fuel $h^L = 42700$ *kJ/kg*

- sea water density $\rho = 1025 \ kg/m^3$

- $1 \ knot = 1852 \ m/h$

A). Calculate the powers in the complete propulsion chain: effective power P_E, thrust power P_T, open water propeller power P_O, propeller power P_p, delivered power P_D, shaft power P_S, brake power (per engine) P_B and heat input to an engine $\dot{Q}_f$.

B). Calculate the efficiencies encountered in the propulsion chain: hull efficiency η_H, propulsive efficiency η_D, transmission efficiency η_{TRM} and the fraction of the fuel energy that is converted into towing power.

C). Calculate the specific resistance C_E and the delivered power coefficient C_D.

D). Calculate the thrust generated by one propeller T and the open water torque Q, as well as the torque delivered to the propellers M_P.

E). Calculate the shaft torque M_S and the engine torque M_B.

F). Calculate the fuel flow $\dot{m}_f$ to one engine.

Exercise 2

A ship is propelled by a fixed pitch propeller ($k_p=1$), which is driven by a single diesel engine ($k_e=1$) through a reduction gearbox with constant transmission ratio i. The ship has a square resistance ship speed relation: $R = c_1 \cdot v_s^2$ where $c_1 = constant$. Further, it may be assumed that propulsive efficiency η_D is constant and that the propeller speed is proportional to the ship's speed: $n_p = c_3 \cdot v_s$ where $c_3 = constant$.

The diesel engine delivers a torque proportional to the mass of fuel injected per cylinder cycle: $M_B = c_6 \cdot m_f$ where $c_6 = constant$. This torque can be supplied between minimum and maximum engine speed ($200 \le n_e \le 600$ rpm).

In the design condition of the ship, the diesel engine delivers maximum power at maximum engine speed. The following data apply:

- ship speed $v_s = 12 \ knots$

- ship resistance $R = 400 \ kN$

- propeller speed $n_p = 150 \ rpm$

- engine power $P_{B,max} = 4250 \ kW$

- engine speed $n_e = 600 \ rpm$

- transmission efficiency $\eta_{TRM} = 0.968$

- $1 \ knot = 1852 \ m/h$

The transmission efficiency may be assumed to be constant.

A). Calculate the following data for the design condition:
- effective power P_E and delivered power P_D
- propulsive efficiency η_D
- engine torque M_B

B). The engine fuel rack position is changed in such a way that the engine speed becomes $n_e = 400$ rpm. Calculate the following:
- ship speed v_s, propeller speed n_p
- effective power P_E, delivered power P_D, engine brake power P_B and engine torque M_B

C). The engine fuel rack position is changed to 40%. This means that 40% of the fuel at maximum engine output is injected. Calculate the following:
- engine torque M_B
- ship speed v_s, propeller speed n_p and engine speed n_e
- effective power P_E, delivered power P_D and engine brake power P_B

D). The engine fuel rack position is changed in such a way that the engine delivers a brake power of $P_B = 2125$ kW. Calculate the following data:
- ship speed v_s, propeller speed n_p, engine speed n_e
- delivered power P_D and effective power P_E
- ship resistance R

Exercise 3

For a container feeder ship an electric load analysis has to be made. Three operating conditions need to be investigated:

- Sea service: the ship is sailing at service speed and a number of containers need to be cooled.

- In port –manoeuvring and berthing: the ship is sailing at very low speeds and uses its deck machinery and bow-thruster to berth.

- In port –loading and unloading: no propulsion.

For this exercise only a limited number of electric consumers are considered. Where applicable, electric motors have to be selected from a standard range of electric motors with nameplate (nominal) powers of: 0.25, 0.5, 1, 2, 4, 7, 10, 20, 30, 40 and 50 kW. Determine the load analysis for the following consumers:

A). Propulsion system:
- High temperature (HT) cooling water pumps:

  Two centrifugal pumps will be installed, one of which will be in operation and one stand-by. The pump capacity is $\dot{V} = 85 \; m^3/h$ at a pressure head of $\Delta p = 2$ *bar*. The pump efficiency is $\eta_p = 0.75$.

- Fuel oil service pumps:

  One to be in operation and one stand-by. The pump capacity $\dot{V} = 4\ m^3/h$ at a pressure head of $\Delta p = 5\ bar$. The pump efficiency is $\eta_p = 0.65$.

- Lubricating oil pumps:

  Two screw-type pumps, one of which is in operation and one stand-by. The pump capacity is $\dot{V} = 100\ m^3/h$ at a pressure head of $\Delta p = 6\ bar$. The pump efficiency is $\eta_p = 0.80$

B). *Auxiliary systems:*

- Fuel oil separators:

  Two separators are installed. They run continuously during sea service. The excess capacity is re-circulated from the clean fuel oil day-tank, back to the fuel oil settling-tank. Each separator has a 4 kW electric motor. The motors are not fully loaded. The separators require 3 kW of mechanical power input.

- Fuel oil heater for separators:

  Two electric heaters are installed. The heaters are in operation during operation of the fuel separators. The maximum capacity of one heater is 40 kW. This capacity is based on heating of the full fuel flow (corresponding with the maximum separator capacity) from 5°C to 90°C. During normal operation approximately 50 % of the separator output is re-circulated and the fuel supplied from the settling tank will have an average temperature of 55°C.

- Fuel oil transfer pumps:

  Two screw-type pumps are provided, to pump fuel from storage tanks to the settling tank and to transfer fuel between storage tanks (for stability and trim operations of the ship). The pump capacity is $\dot{V} = 40\ m^3/h$ at a pressure head of $\Delta p = 4\ bar$. The pump efficiency is $\eta_p = 0.70$.

C). *Hotel systems:*

- Hydrophore system:

  To provide fresh water throughout the ship, a hydrophore system is provided. A hydrophore tank is kept under a pressure of 4 to 6 bar. Therefore, two hydrophore pumps are provided. Their pump capacity is $\dot{V} = 3\ m^3/h$ at a pressure head of $\Delta p = 6\ bar$. The pump efficiency is $\eta_p = 0.60$.

- Hot water heater:

  For use of hot water in the galley and for showering, two hot water heaters are provided. Each heater has a maximum capacity of 120 l/h and can heat fresh water from 10°C to 80°C. The electrical power used by one boiler is maximum 10 kW.

- Hot water circulation pump:

    Two centrifugal pumps circulate hot water through the ship, such that at every wash basin, shower and galley tap, hot water is immediately available. The pump capacity is $\dot{V} = 0.4\ m^3/h$ at a pressure head of $\Delta p = 2\ bar$. The pump efficiency is $\eta_p = 0.50$.

D). *Hull machinery:*
  - Steering gear.

    The ship is provided with an electric-hydraulic steering machine. The steering machine contains two hydraulic pumps of the controllable axial piston type. Each pump requires 24 kW at full output.

  - Captans/winches

    The ship has two winches on the fore-deck and two on the aft-deck. The installed power per winch is 30 kW.

  - Bow thruster.

    The ship has one electrically-driven bow thruster to aid manoeuvring in port. The bow thruster has a FP propeller and runs at a fixed speed. The propeller requires 280 kW and the installed motor power is 300 kW.

E). *Cargo systems:*
  - Reefer containers:

    The ship can carry 100 reefer containers. A reefer container is provided with its individual cooling system. The maximum compressor power per reefer container is 12 kW. The installed motor power is 15 kW.

Solution exercise 1

A). $P_E = 16003\ kW$ (complete ship)
  $P_T = 8172\ kW$ (one propeller)
  $P_O = 11510\ kW$ (one propeller)
  $P_p = 11626\ kW$ (one propeller)
  $P_D = 23252\ kW$ (complete ship)
  $P_S = 11743\ kW$ (one shaft)
  $P_B = 5992\ kW$ (one engine)
  $\dot{Q}_f = 14979\ kJ/s$ (one engine)

B). $\eta_H = 0.979$
  $\eta_D = 0.688$
  $\eta_{TRM} = 0.97$
  $f = 0.267$

C). $C_E = 0.021$ and $C_D = 0.031$

D). $T = 591$ *kN* (one propeller)

  $Q = 500$ *kNm* (one propeller)

  $M_P = 505$ *kNm* (one propeller)

E). $M_S = 510$ *kNm* (one shaft)

  $M_B = 47.7$ *kNm* (one engine)

F). $\dot{m}_f = 0.351$ *kg/s*

Solution exercise 2

A). $P_E = R \cdot v_s = 400 \cdot \left(12 \cdot \dfrac{1852}{3600} \right) = 2469 \ kW$ ref. (3.2)

$\quad$— $\quad P_D = \eta_{TRM} \cdot k_e \cdot P_B = 0.968 \cdot 1 \cdot 4250 = 4114 \ kW$ ref. (3.41)

$\quad$— $\quad \eta_D = \dfrac{P_E}{P_D} = \dfrac{2469}{4114} = 0,60$ ref. (3.24)

$\quad$— $\quad M_B = \dfrac{P_B}{\omega_e} = \dfrac{P_B}{2 \cdot \pi \cdot n_e} = \dfrac{4250}{2 \cdot \pi \cdot \left(\frac{600}{60} \right)} = 67.6 \ kNm$ ref. (3.38)

B). First, determine the propeller speed:

$\left. \begin{array}{l} n_p = \dfrac{n_e}{i} \\[3mm] i = \dfrac{n_{e,max}}{n_{p,max}} = \dfrac{600}{150} = 4 \end{array} \right\} \Rightarrow n_p = \dfrac{400}{4} = 100 \ rpm$

$n_{p,max} = c_3 \cdot v_{s,max} \Rightarrow c_3 = \dfrac{150}{12} = 12.5 \ \text{rpm/knot}$

$v_s = \dfrac{n_p}{c_3} = \dfrac{100}{12.5} = 8 \ \text{knots}$

The ship speed could have been determined more straight forward by recognising that $v_s \ (:) \ n_p \ (:) \ n_e$;

$v_s = v_{s,max} \cdot \dfrac{n_e}{n_{e,max}} = 12 \cdot \dfrac{400}{600} = 8 \ \text{knots}$

$\left. \begin{array}{l} P_E = R \cdot v_s \\[2mm] R = c_1 \cdot v_s^2 \end{array} \right\} \Rightarrow P_E = c_1 \cdot v_s^3$

Consequently $P_E (:) v_s^3$ and:

$$P_E = P_{E,max} \cdot \left(\frac{v_s}{V_{s,max}}\right)^3 = 2469 \left(\frac{8}{12}\right)^3 = 732 \text{ kW}$$

$$P_D = \frac{P_E}{\eta_D} = \frac{732}{0.60} = 1219 \text{ kW}$$

$$P_B = \frac{P_D}{k_e \cdot \eta_{TRM}} = \frac{1219}{1 \cdot 0.968} = 1260 \text{ kW}$$

$$M_B = \frac{P_B}{\omega_e} = \frac{P_B}{2 \cdot \pi \cdot n_e} = \frac{1260}{2 \cdot \pi \cdot \left(\frac{400}{60}\right)} = 30.1 \text{ kNm}$$

The last figure could also have been determined by realising that a square ship resistance curve leads to a *cubic* effective power curve. With constant propulsive efficiency η_D and proportionality between n_p and v_s this leads to a cubic P_B–n_p relation. This means a square M_D–n_p relation. Because η_{TRM} and i are constants this leads to a square M_B–n_e relation, i.e. M_B (:) $n_e{}^2$.

Consequently:

$$- \quad M_B = M_{B,max}\left(\frac{n_e}{n_{e,max}}\right)^2 = 67.6 \cdot \left(\frac{400}{600}\right)^2 = 30.1 \text{ kNm}$$

The load and drive characteristics show the situation. This can be done in several ways. Choose for instance M_B–n_e and P_D–n_p diagrams:

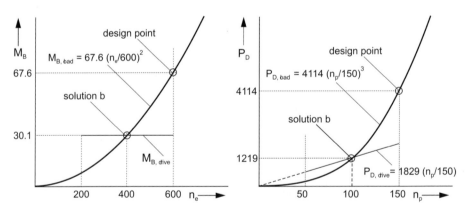

C). The mass of fuel is reduced to 40%: consequently, the delivered torque is reduced to 40%.

- $M_B = 0.4 \cdot M_{B,max} = 0.4 \cdot 67.6 = 27.1 \text{ } kNm$

- The resulting v_s and n_p can be found by drawing a diagram in which load and drive characteristics are shown. Take for example the following diagram:

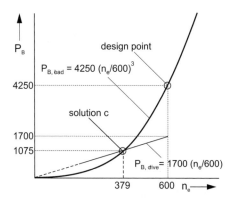

If the engine torque is reduced to 40% of maximum torque, the engine power at maximum engine speed is also reduced to 40% of its maximum: 40% of 4250 kW is 1700 kW. From the linear relation $P_B = M_B \cdot 2 \cdot \pi \cdot n_e$, it follows that the new drive characteristic becomes:

$$P_B = 1700 \cdot \left(\frac{n_e}{600} \right).$$

In the equilibrium condition $P_{B,load} = P_{B,drive}$, so

$$4250 \cdot \left(\frac{n_e}{600} \right)^3 = 1700 \cdot \left(\frac{n_e}{600} \right) \rightarrow n_e = 379 \text{ rpm}$$

With the fixed ratios it follows that:

$$n_p = \frac{379}{600} \cdot 150 = 95 \text{ rpm} \quad \text{and} \quad v_s = \frac{379}{600} \cdot 12 \text{ or } \frac{95}{150} \cdot 12 = 7.6 \text{ knots}$$

- An alternative solution to find n_e, n_p and v_s is by using an M_B–n_e diagram:

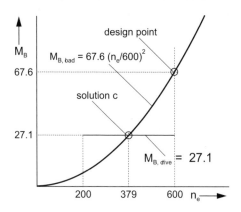

$$M_{B,load} = M_{B,drive}$$

$$67.6 \cdot \left(\frac{n_e}{600}\right)^2 = 27.1 \text{ kNm} \rightarrow n_e = 379 \text{ } rpm$$

Again n_p and v_s follow by proportionality:

$$n_p = \frac{379}{600} \cdot 150 = 95 \text{ } rpm$$

$$v_s = \frac{379}{600} \cdot 12 = 7.6 \text{ } knots$$

- For the asked powers, only the answers are given:

  $$P_E = 625 \text{ } kW \text{ , } P_D = 1041 \text{ } kW \text{ , } P_B = 1075 \text{ } kW$$

D). Only the answers are given:
   - $v_s = 9.5 \text{ } knots$, $n_p = 119 \text{ } rpm$, $n_e = 476 \text{ } rpm$

   - $P_E = 1234 \text{ } kW$, $P_D = 2057 \text{ } kW$

   - $R = 252 \text{ } kN$

Solution exercise 3

For calculation of the required power to drive a pump the following formula has been used:

- $$P_{pump} = \frac{\dot{V} \cdot \Delta p}{\eta_{pump}}$$

This formula is based on Equation 2.25: $W_{1,2} = -\int_1^2 V \cdot dp$, which gives the reversible work for an open system. Assuming incompressible fluids for pumps, this reduces to $W = -V \cdot \Delta p$ and for a real pump with a pump efficiency η_{pump} the above relation follows. The electrical power absorbed from the net is then calculated with:

- $$P_{abs} = \frac{P_{pump}}{\eta_{em}}$$

where η_{em} is electric motor efficiency which ranges from 0.85 for $P_{em} \cong 1$ kW to 0.90 for $P_{em} \cong 20\text{-}50$ kW and to 0.92 for $P_{em} \cong 300$ kW.

   The table gives the load balance for this exercise. In the following text the balance will be explained.

SYSTEMS	nr. installed	power at full load	installed E-motor power	absorbed electric power	SEA SERVICE				PORT: MANOEUVRING				PORT: LOADING/UNLOADING			
					nr in service	load factor	sim. factor	average absorbed power	nr in service	load factor	sim. factor	average absorbed power	nr in service	load factor	sim. factor	average absorbed power
	(-)	kW	kW	kW	(-)	(-)	(-)	kW	(-)	(-)	(-)	kW	(-)	(-)	(-)	kW
Propulsion																
cooling water pumps	2	6.3	7	7.2	1	1.00	1.00	7.20	1	1.00	1.00	7.20	0	-	-	-
fuel oil service pumps	2	0.9	1	1	1	0.80	1.00	0.70	1	0.80	1.00	0.70	0	-	-	-
lub oil pumps	2	20.8	30	23.4	1	0.83	1.00	19.40	1	0.83	1.00	19.40	0	-	-	-
Auxiliary systems																
fuel oil separators	2	3.0	4	3.5	2	0.90	1.00	6.30	2	0.90	1.00	6.30	0	-	-	-
fuel oil heater	2	40.0	-	40	2	0.53	1.00	42.40	2	0.53	1.00	42.40	0	-	-	-
fuel oil transfer pumps	2	6.4	7	7.4	1	0.75	0.25	1.40	0	-	-	-	0	-	-	-
Hotel systems																
hydrophore system	2	0.85	1	1	1	0.83	0.03	0.10	1	0.83	0.03	0.10	1	0.83	0.03	0.10
hot water heater	2	10	-	10	2	0.09	1.00	0.10	2	0.09	1.00	1.80	2	0.09	1.00	1.80
hot water circulation pump	2	0.05	0.25	0.1	1	1.00	1.00	0.10	1	1.00	1.00	0.10	1	1.00	1.00	0.10
Hull machinery																
steering gear pumps	2	24.0	30	27	1	0.10	1.00	2.70	1	0.40	1.00	10.80	0	-	-	-
winches	4	30.0	30	33.7	0	-	-	-	2	0.50	0.10	3.40	0	-	-	-
bow thruster	1	280.0	300	304	0	-	-	-	1	1.00	0.10	30.40	0	-	-	-
Cargo systems																
reefer containers	100	12.0	15	13.6	100	0.55	0.9	675.0	100	0.55	0.9	675.0	100	0.55	0.4	300.0

A). *Propulsion systems:*
  − HT cooling water pump:

    With $\dot{V}$ = 85 m³/h, Δp = 2 bar , η_p = 0.75 and η_{em} = 0.86 it follows: user power (P_{pump}) = 6.3 kW and the absorbed power 7.3 kW. The installed motor power should be sufficient to supply 6.3 kW, so a motor nameplate power of 7 kW is selected. During sea service and manoeuvring one of the two pumps is in operation continuously (simultaneity factor is 1) and also the load factor is assumed to be 1.

    For a centrifugal pump, the required flow will be adjusted by a suitable pressure resistance in the system. So the pump runs at its design point. In port during loading and unloading no HT cooling water pumps are running.

  − Fuel oil service pump:

    $\dot{V}$ = 4 m³/h, Δp = 5 bar, η_p = 0.65 and η_{em} = 0.84 leads to user power P_{pump} = 0.9 kW, absorbed power 1.0 kW and installed nameplate power 1 kW. The pressure difference in actual operation will be somewhat lower than at the design point. Assume 4 bar instead of 5 bar. Consequently the pump will run on average against a lower pressure; load factor: 4/5 = 0.8 and simultaneity factor is 1 (continuous operation).

  − Lubricating oil pump:

    $\dot{V}$ = 100 m³/h, Δp = 6 bar , η_p = 0.8 and η_{em} = 0.89 leads to user power P_{pump} = 20.8 kW, absorbed power 23.4 kW and installed power 30 kW. The pressure difference over the pump in actual operation will be about 5 bar. Consequently the pump will run on average against a lower pressure; load factor: 5/6 = 0.83 and simultaneity factor is 1 (continuous operation).

B). *Auxiliary systems:*
  − Fuel oil separator:

    The fuel oil separators both run continuously during sea operation and manoeuvring. They are switched of in port and during loading/unloading. The pressure head against which the pumps of the separators have to operate is in actual operation somewhat lower than in design condition; load factor 0.9. The electric motor efficiency is assumed to be 0.85.

  − Fuel oil heaters:

    The heat capacity of the heaters is equal to the absorbed power; user power = 40 kW, absorbed power 40 kW. There is no electric motor. Two heaters are continuously in operation at sea and during manoeuvring; simultaneity factor :1. The average temperature difference over the heater is 90 −55 = 45°C, whereas the heater is designed for 90-5=85°C. The load factor is consequently 45/85=0.53.

- Fuel oil transfer pump:

    One pump will be intermittently in operation during sea service to fill the settling tank from the storage tanks. With $\dot{V}$ = 40 m^3/h, Δp = 4 bar , η_p = 0.7 and η_{em} = 0.86 follows: user power P_{pump} = 6.4 kW, installed power 7 kW and absorbed power 7.4 kW. The ship's fuel consumption is in the order of 10 m^3/h.

    As the transfer pump capacity is 40 m^3/h it follows that the simultaneity factor is 10/40 = 0.25. The average pressure difference the pump has to overcome is 3 bar, whereas the pump at design point can supply 4 bar. The load factor becomes: ¾ = 0.75. These pumps will not operate during manoeuvring and very seldom in port.

C). *Hotel systems*:
  - Hydrophore tank

    $\dot{V}$ = 3 m^3/h, Δp = 6 bar, η_p = 0.6 and η_{em} = 0.84 leads to user power 0.85 kW, absorbed power 1 kW and installed power 1 kW. The pump is intermittently in operation, to fill up the hydrophore tank. The daily water consumption of the ship is assumed to be 2 m^3 /day. The simultaneity factor becomes 2/(24·3) = 0.03. The pump works on average against a pressure of 5 bar, whereas the pump is suitable for 6 bar; load factor is 5/6 = 0.83. The average absorbed power is very low, 0.025 kW is rounded of in the load balance to 0.1 kW.

  - Hot water heaters

    User power and absorbed power are both 10 kW. No electric motors. Both heaters are in operation. The average daily hot water consumption is 0.4 m^3/day. This requires as heat: $\rho \cdot \dot{V} \cdot c \cdot \Delta T = 1000 \cdot 0.4 \cdot 4.2 \cdot (80-10) = 117.6 \cdot 10^3$ kJ/day. In addition, heat is lost due to the continuous circulation of the hot water through the ship. A total heat use of $150 \cdot 10^3$ kJ/day is assumed. This leads to both heaters having a load factor of $150 \cdot 10^3/(24 \cdot 3600 \cdot 2 \cdot 10) = 0.09$, and an average absorbed power of 1.8 kW. Note that during periods of peak consumption, the absorbed power may be 20 kW.

  - Hot water circulation pumps

    $\dot{V}$ = 0.4 m^3/h, Δp = 2 bar , η_p = 0.5 and η_{em} = 0.80 leads to user power 0.05 kW, absorbed power 0.1 kW and installed power 0.25 kW. The pump is in continuous operation with load factor 1.

D). *Hull machinery:*
  - Steering gear

    User power 24 kW, absorbed power 27 kW and installed power 30 kW. One of the two steering gear pumps is running continuously (simultaneity factor 1). At sea very few rudder actions are required. The axial piston type pump will then be adjusted to deliver almost no flow. The load factor therefore is assumed to be 0.1. During manoeuvring the rudder is more intensely used. In that case the load factor is assumed to be 0.4.

–   Winches

User power and installed power are both 30 kW. With a motor efficiency of 0.89, the absorbed power is 33.7 kW. Two winches are only in operation during manoeuvring, load factor and simultaneity factor are therefore assumed to be 0.5 and 0.1. Note that though the average absorbed power is calculated only as 3.4 kW, the absorbed power at certain moments may be as high as 67 kW. The generating system should be capable of delivering that power during short periods.

–   Bow thruster

The absorbed power of the bow thruster will be at maximum 280/0.92 = 304 kW. As the bow thruster runs at constant speed and is provided with a fixed pitch propeller, the load factor will be 1. The simultaneity factor during manoeuvring will be rather low 0.1. This leads to an average power consumption during manoeuvring of 30.4 kW. This is in fact a misleading figure, because once the bow thruster is running it requires 304 kW. The generator should be capable to do so. Also starting up should be possible, this requires for instance a soft starter (see section 9.9.2).

E). Cargo systems:

–   Reefer containers

With a motor efficiency of 0.88, the absorbed power per reefer container will be 13.6 kW. It is assumed that 90 reefer containers are onboard during an average voyage; simultaneity factor 0.9. The load factor is assumed to be 0.55 as the maximum cooling capacity is only necessary in adverse climate conditions and shortly after the container has been loaded. During loading/unloading it is assumed that 40 % of the reefer containers are on board. Note again that this might lead to misleading figures.

3.8   References and further reading

Carlton, 1994

> J.S. Carlton: *"Marine propellers and propulsion"*, Butterworth Heinemann, UK 1994

Harrington, 1992

> Roy L. Harrington et al: *"Marine Engineering"*, The Society of Naval Architects and Marine Engineers, USA 1992

Kuiper, 1994

> Prof. dr.ir. G. Kuiper: *"Resistance and propulsion of ships"*, Delft University of Technology, 1994

Lewis, 1988

> Edward V. Lewis (editor): *"Principles of Naval Architecture, Volume 2: Resistance, propulsion and vibration"*, Society of Naval Architects and Marine Engineers, USA 1988.

Rawson and Tupper, 2001

> K. J. Rawson and E. Tupper: *"Basic Ship Theory Volume 2"*, Fifth edition, Butterworth Heinemann, UK 2001

SOLAS, 1997

> *"Safety of Lives at Sea, Consolidated Edition 1997"*, Chapter II-2 Part D Electrical Installations, International Maritime Organization, 1997

Watson, 1998

> D. G. M. Watson: *"Practical ship design"*, Elsevier Science Ltd, UK 1998.

Chapter 4

Energy Conversion

4.0   Learning goals

After studying this chapter, the student should be able to:

- *Name and explain the energy types onboard marine structures.*

- *Name and explain the most common energy conversions onboard.*

- *Use the energy conversion diagram to model energy transfers onboard a ship.*

4.1   Introduction

A vessel or a platform has to provide its own energy, so that it is an autonomous system. With this in mind it is evident that the design of efficient methods of energy storage and conversion are requisite for the ship's functionality. The ship's machinery systems, some of which were introduced in Chapter 1, require energy of different forms: for instance fuel, electric power and mechanical power.

Chapter 3 gave some insight into how to calculate the required propulsion (mechanical) and electrical power. In the description of the systems that supply these powers, energy conversion has already been touched upon:

- In the propulsion system, chemical energy in fuels is ultimately converted into mechanical energy.

- In the electric power supply system, chemical energy is ultimately converted into electrical energy.

This chapter focuses on the concept of energy conversion to understand the energy flows in a machinery plant. These energy flows show the connection between systems. The application of energy flows to model the machinery plant illustrates the importance of thermodynamics, energy transfer and electrical engineering as underlying physical principles of Marine Engineering.

Table 4.1 has been put together to give an idea of the order of magnitude of the energy demand onboard. For a few ship types, ranges are given for propulsion power and auxiliary power (subdivided in support and operational power). *Propulsion power* is the power needed to give a ship a translating motion. This power is an example of *mechanical* energy per unit time. The generation of this mechanical energy, provided for instance by a diesel engine, requires electric power for auxiliary systems such as the fuel system and the cooling water system. These energy needs (not necessarily restricted to electric power) are referred to as the *propulsion support power*. Together with the power needed for hotel services and other general support functions within the ship, it determines the *support power* required to sail the ship. To actually fulfil the mission, *operational power* is also needed for the operational functions, which can be considerable for some types of ship. Examples of operational power are: the power needed for reefer connections, cargo heating, cranes or dredging pumps. The support power together with the operational power forms the *total auxiliary power*.

Ship Type	*Propulsion Power [MW]*	*Auxiliary Power [MW]*		
		Hotel Services & General Support	*Operational Power*	*Total Auxiliary Power*
Container ship (± 7000 TEU)	50.0 - 70.0	2.5 - 5.0	3.5 - 6.5	6.0 - 11.5
Container ship (± 300 TEU)	2.0 - 5.0	0.3 - 1.0	0.3 - 1.0	0.6 - 2.0
Multi-purpose cargo vessel	5.0 - 10.0	0.5 - 1.0	0.5 - 1.5	1.0 - 2.5
Stern trawler	5.0 - 10.0	0.5 - 1.5	2.5 - 5.0	3.0 - 6.5
Beam trawler	0.5 - 1.5	0.1 - 0.3	0.1 - 3.0	0.2 - 3.3
DP Semi-Sub	7.5 - 12.5	1.0 - 3.0	1.5 - 3.0	2.5 - 6.0
Dredger	15.0 - 25.0	1.0 - 3.0	12.0 - 14.0	13.0 - 17.0
Cruise ship	15.0 - 40.0	0.6 - 2.0	3.0 - 8.0	3.6 - 10.0
Frigate	20.0 - 40.0	0.6 - 1.2	0.3 - 0.6	0.9 - 1.8

Table 4.1   Propulsion power and auxiliary power of different ship types (Year 2000).

The auxiliary power for container ships is growing as a result of an increase of the number of reefer connections (reefers are containers fitted with their own refrigerating units of 10-15 kW). The amount of auxiliary power for trawlers, semi-submersibles with dynamic positioning (DP Semi Subs) and dredgers should not come as a surprise either, given the energy consuming processes that these ships are designed for. Note the relatively large auxiliary power requirements of cruise ships as a result of the hotel services for the passengers (here logically included in operational power).

Table 4.2 illustrates the trend of growing energy demands on board naval vessels. The use of active sensors in combat systems increases the energy demand of the combat system (operational power). This trend is magnified because the displacement of frigates is increasing as well. Future use of electromagnetic weapons could even, for a short period of time after a salvo, increase the energy demand of the combat system to the same order of magnitude as the energy demand of propulsion.

Frigate (displacement [ton])	Propulsion Power [MW]	Auxiliary Power [MW]					
		Platform system		Combat system			*Total*
		Support	*Hotel*	*Sensors*	*Weapons*	*Command*	
Year 2000 (3000/4000)	20.0-30.0	0.6	0.3	0.1	0.1	0.1	1.2
Trend (5000/6000)	30.0-40.0	0.6	0.3	=>1.0	0.3	0.3	2.5
Future ? (6000/8000)	40.0-50.0	0.6	0.3	=>2.0	=>10.0?	0.6	13.5

Table 4.2   Power development in frigates (Year 2000).

4.2   Types of energy

The various systems on board a ship require different types of energy. In general, propulsion needs mechanical energy, lighting needs electric energy and steering needs hydraulic energy. The energy is expressed in Joule [J]. The required energy is usually characterised by a corresponding power, by definition the energy transfer rate. Power can often be defined as the product of effort (torque, force, electric potential difference, pressure difference, change of temperature) and flow (angular velocity, velocity, electric current, volume rate, heat flux). The unit of power is Joule per second, or Watt [W].

The most important types of energy and their conversion, storage and distribution will be introduced. Energy generation and conversion will be discussed in detail in the next sections.

Energy source

The Energy Source (ES) is the originating type of energy. Examples of energy sources are chemical energy, wind energy, solar energy and nuclear energy. The most common source of energy onboard is chemical energy as contained in fossil fuels. A fuel flow multiplied by the (lower) heat value h^L of the fuel represents a chemical energy flow which is released when combusted:

$$\dot{E}_{Chem} \overset{def}{=} h^L \cdot \dot{m} \tag{4.1}$$

Chemical energy can be stored in tanks (liquid or gaseous fuels) or in fuel rods and pebble beds (nuclear energy). Wind and solar energy cannot be stored as such.

Mechanical energy

Mechanical energy (M) drives machinery like propellers, pumps and compressors, and moves rudders, stabilisers and deck equipment. Gas turbines and diesel engines are responsible for *primary generation* of mechanical energy, i.e. conversion from an energy source to mechanical energy. An electric motor is responsible for *secondary generation*, i.e. conversion of electric energy to mechanical energy. Both types of generation or conversion will be discussed in the next section.

Mechanical energy can be present in the form of rotational motion and in the form of translational motion. Rotational mechanical power $P_{M,Rot}$ [Watt] is associated with an input or output shaft rotating with angular velocity ω [rad/s] and exerting a torque M [Nm] on its flanges:

$$P_{M,Rot} = \dot{W} \overset{def}{=} M \cdot \omega \tag{4.2}$$

An example is the propeller power or the engine brake power as defined in Chapter 3. Rotational power can be transferred by shafts from one place to another.

Translational mechanical power $P_{M,Trans}$ as associated with, for example, the motion of a ship or a linear motor equals a force F [N] times a velocity v [m/s]:

$$P_{M,Trans} \overset{def}{=} F \cdot v \tag{4.3}$$

See also the definitions for effective power and thrust power in section 3.4.2. Storage of mechanical energy is possible but not simple. Mechanical energy can be stored as potential energy, in a spring for example, or as kinetic energy in a flywheel or a moving mass, as for example the ship itself.

Electric energy

Electric energy (E) is required in many systems. A generator converts mechanical energy into electric energy. Electric energy can also be generated in fuel cells, i.e. conversion from an energy source (chemical energy).

Electric energy exists in two forms: direct current (DC) and alternating current (AC). Copper cables transport the electric energy. DC energy can be stored in batteries or capacitors. Both forms are characterised by the electric power P_{EL}. In general terms, the electric power equals the potential difference U [V] times current I [A]:

$$P_{EL} = U(t) \cdot I(t) \hspace{2cm} \text{ref. (2.51)}$$

The basic principles of electrical engineering have been discussed in Chapter 2 and will therefore not be repeated here.

Hydraulic energy

Energy can also be transported by fluid (oil or water) in hydraulic systems. This is called hydraulic energy (H). This energy is generated by hydraulic pumps, transported through piping systems and stored in hydraulic accumulators. The corresponding hydraulic power P_H equals the pressure difference Δp [Pa] times volume flow [m³/s]:

$$P_H = \dot{W} \overset{def}{=} \Delta p \cdot \dot{V} \tag{4.4}$$

Pneumatic energy

Energy can also be transported by air in pneumatic systems. Pneumatic energy (A) is generated by air compressors, transported through piping systems and stored in air vessels The corresponding pneumatic power P_A, like hydraulic power, equals a pressure difference Δp times volume flow:

$$P_A = \dot{W} \overset{def}{=} \Delta p \cdot \dot{V} \tag{4.5}$$

Heat

Heating of cargo space and accommodation, and cooling or refrigeration of air, equipment and cargo require yet another type of energy transfer: heat. Heaters and heat pumps generate this energy type. Heat is transferred in piping systems by means of different fluids; for example steam, hot air, thermal oil or chilled water. Storage of this energy type is not simple. Energy is easily lost by radiation or conduction, so good insulation is required.

In general, the heat transfer rate $\dot{Q}$ [J/s=W] is defined by the product of a mass flow $\dot{m}$ [kg/s] and a change of enthalpy Δh [J/kg], refer to Chapter 2 Equation (2.10):

$$\dot{Q} = \dot{m} \cdot \Delta h \hspace{3cm} \text{ref. (2.10)}$$

A change of enthalpy is associated with a change of temperature, or a phase change (heat of condensation, heat of evaporation), or both. If the medium does not change phase, the enthalpy change can be written as the product of specific heat c [J/kg·K] and change of temperature ΔT [K], which means that the heat transfer rate changes to:

$$\dot{Q} \overset{def}{=} c \cdot \dot{m} \cdot \Delta T \tag{4.6}$$

The product of specific heat and mass flow rate is sometimes called a heat capacity rate $\dot{C}$ [J/K·s]:

$$\dot{Q} = \dot{C} \cdot \Delta T \tag{4.7}$$

4.3   Types of energy conversion

As stated earlier a ship is an autonomous system. This implies that energy is generated from an energy source and converted on board. In general a vessel carries an energy source in the form of liquid fuels. Different energy types are generated (or in fact converted) from this energy source. The various types of energy conversion are discussed in this section.

4.3.1 Overview of energy conversions

Table 4.3 gives an overview of possible energy conversions. Cells in the table that represent existing energy conversions contain an example of a converter. The empty cells represent conversions that do not exist (yet).

In this book X/Y is the abbreviated notation of an energy converter: X represents the incoming energy flow and Y represents the outgoing energy flow. Examples are M/E for a generator and M/M for a propeller. A compound, i.e. a multi-stage converter, can be characterised in a similar manner: for example PE/Q/M to indicate energy conversion in a steam turbine plant.

The conversions at off-diagonal locations in the matrix are conversions from one type of energy to another type of energy. The main diagonal, however, contains conversions that do not change the energy type but changes its characteristics, such as voltage, frequency or angular velocity.

To→ From ↓	Energy source (ES)	Mechanical energy (M)	Electric energy (E)	Hydraulic energy (H)	Pneumatic energy (A)	Heat (Q)
Energy source (ES)	Reformer	Engine	Fuel cell	Free piston unit		Burner
Mechanical energy (M)		Gearbox & Propeller	E-Generator	Hydraulic pump	Air compressor	Chiller unit
Electric energy (E)	Electrolysis	Electric motor	Converter			Heater
Hydraulic energy (H)		Hydraulic motor		Hydraulic transformer		
Pneumatic energy (A)		Pneumatic motor			Reducer	
Heat (Q)		Turbine				Heat exchanger

Table 4.3   Matrix of possible energy conversions.

An example shown in the matrix is the gearbox where the angular velocity of rotating mechanical energy is converted. Another example is the propeller where rotating mechanical energy is converted into translating mechanical energy (change of form of energy, but not type). Yet another example shown in the matrix is the electric converter that can have the following functions: (1) convert AC electric energy to DC electric energy, (2) change the frequency of AC electric energy (3) change the voltage of AC electric energy, and (4) decrease harmonic distortion.

4.3.2 Energy source → mechanical energy

A common method of generating mechanical energy is conversion from an energy source by combustion of fossil fuels. In fact, it is a two-step conversion process; first from the energy source into heat and then from heat into mechanical work. For liquid fossil fuels approximately 40 to 43 MJ heat per kilogram of fuel is released during combustion. Not all this energy can be converted into mechanical energy. As stated in the second law of thermodynamics only a part of the heat can be transformed into work. The theoretical maximum of this fraction is defined by the Carnot efficiency, refer to equation (2.29):

$$\eta_{Carnot} \overset{def}{=} \frac{net\ work\ output\ W_{cycle}}{heat\ added\ Q_H} = 1 - \frac{T_L}{T_H} \qquad \text{ref. (2.29)}$$

In this equation T_L is the minimum process temperature (limited by the temperature of the surroundings, i.e. approximately 300 K) and T_H is the maximum process temperature (for machinery this is 1500-2000 K). Theoretically, the Carnot efficiency therefore is 80 to 85 percent. In practice, however, the efficiency of thermodynamic conversion is much less. This is illustrated by the following overview of ES/M converters:

- (Marine) steam turbine   25-30 %

- Gas turbine (simple cycle)   28-34 %

- Diesel engine (medium speed, turbocharged)   38-52 %

- Stirling engine   40-50 %

Other characteristics of these converters, also called thermal machines will be introduced in Chapter 6. Gas turbines and diesel engines are internal combustion machines. This means that the combustion gases also perform the power cycle, and the choice of working medium is limited. Internal combustion engines are compact. Steam turbines and Stirling engines are external combustion machines. The heat (from the combustion) is transferred in a heat exchanger from the combustion gases to a working medium. The working medium in steam turbines is water (steam) and in the Stirling engine is air or helium.

Heat transfer in a heat exchanger is defined as the product of a heat transfer coefficient U [$J/s \cdot m^2 \cdot K$], the heat exchanging surface A [m²] and the temperature difference ΔT [K] between the mediums:

$$\dot{Q} = U \cdot A \cdot \Delta T \qquad (4.8)$$

Efficient heat transfer requires a heat-exchanging surface, which requires space and weight. Due to the size of the heat exchanger, external combustion machines generally are less compact than internal combustion machines. The loss of temperature indicates a loss of the quality of the heat and according to Carnot a loss of efficiency too.

4.3.3   *Mechanical energy → mechanical energy*

Mechanical energy is transmitted, or converted, by shafting systems. If necessary, the shaft speed can be changed in a gear transmission. The transmission efficiency of shaft systems and gearboxes is high: 96 to 99 %. Examples of these systems onboard ships are the propeller shaft and main gearbox in the propulsion system. Gearboxes not only convert the speed of the shaft, they also convert torque. M/M-converters can also be employed to couple or uncouple driving machinery to or from the load. The use of flexible couplings enable relative movement, for instance between flexibly mounted engines and a rigid mounted gearbox. Flexible couplings are also used to minimise vibration transfer. Couplings, clutches and gearboxes will be introduced in Chapter 6.

4.3.4   *Mechanical energy ↔ electric energy*

Electric machines convert mechanical energy into electric energy or electric energy into mechanical energy. The first application (mechanical to electric) is exemplified by an electric generator and the second application (electric to mechanical) by an electric motor. The conversion efficiency of electric machines depends somewhat on the size of the machine, but is generally high: 92 to 98 %. The 'lost' energy is converted into heat. In case of part load the efficiency is lower.

Electric motors for general applications (like driving pumps and fans) and for propulsion and other major applications (like driving a dredging pump) are normally AC-motors. The AC-motors may be preceded by AC/AC or DC/AC converters for speed control. For (conventional) submarines DC motors are used (due to the presence of batteries). Electric generators are usually AC-generators. When direct current is needed (as aboard submarines) an AC/DC converter is required (usually directly built onto the generator). The principles of electric motors and generators are dealt with in Chapter 9.

4.3.5   *Electric energy → electric energy*

Energy conversion from one type of electric energy to another was already mentioned in the preceding section: AC/AC conversion and AC/DC or DC/AC conversion. The voltage of AC current is easily converted (AC/AC conversion) with an electric winding transformer. This is the electric equivalence of a gearbox. The conversion efficiency is very high: in the order of 99 %.

Until recently the problem of AC/DC conversion (or reverse) or conversion of AC frequency was solved by a combination of an electric motor and a generator. This was called a *rotating converter* or *motor-generator unit*. The efficiency of this conversion is the product of the efficiencies of the electric motor and the generator. As a result the efficiency is not very high: 85 to 90 %.

Development in recent years has resulted in components like diodes, thyristors and other semi-conductors, which convert AC to DC, or DC to AC, in a simple manner. The frequency of AC current is easily adjusted too. Those converters are referred to as *static converters*. Their efficiency is very high: 98 to 99 %. Although they are currently still voluminous, their size will probably decrease in the years to come.

4.3.6 *Mechanical energy → heat*

A heat pump converts mechanical energy into heat. A heat pump is considered a thermal machine like diesel engines and gas turbines. The difference is the direction of the thermodynamic process: when work is applied to the heat pump, heat is transported from a lower temperature level to a higher level. See also the Carnot processes in Chapter 2.

A corollary of the second law of thermodynamics is that the Carnot efficiency for a heat pump can be greater than one. This is why it is not called an efficiency but a coefficient of performance or *cop*. The definition of the ideal (Carnot) *cop* is different from the definition of the Carnot efficiency, refer to equations (2.31):

$$\beta_{Carnot} \overset{def}{=} \frac{received\ heat\ Q_L}{net\ work\ W_{cycle}} = \frac{T_L}{T_H - T_L} \qquad \text{ref. (2.31)}$$

When T_H is the temperature of the surroundings, and T_L is lower than T_H, the heat pump is called a cooling machine: it pumps heat at a low temperature to its surroundings at a higher temperature. An example of a cooling machine is a chiller unit. By means of mechanical energy, the chiller unit pumps heat from a low temperature level (chilled water) to a relatively high temperature (sea water). Another example is the refrigerating unit of the cool and cold stores. The *cop* of these machines is of the order of 3 or 4.

Instead of work, (waste) heat can also be used as input. The resulting heat pump is not an M/Q-converter but a Q/Q-converter. An example is the absorption cooling machine which is sometimes used in installations ashore (hospitals), but has not yet found application in ships. The use of heat pumps and calculation methods for heating, cooling and refrigeration systems will not be dealt with in this book.

4.3.7 *Energy source → electric energy*

From the previous sections it can be concluded that the conversion from energy source to electric energy normally requires at least three steps:

- ES/M conversion in a thermal machine
  - from chemical energy to heat (combustion)
  - from heat to mechanical energy

- M/E conversion with an electric generator

The theoretical maximum of the Carnot efficiency and practical obstacles cause a low efficiency in the second stage of the chain. Electrochemical converters, such as fuel cells and batteries avoid the accumulation of efficiency losses, because they convert chemical energy directly into electric energy. In other words, they are direct ES/E-converters. The ideal efficiency of electrochemical conversion can be proven to be equal to the ratio of the change in Gibbs energy and enthalpy (in practice the heat value):

$$\eta_{chemical} = \frac{\Delta G}{\Delta H} = 1 - \frac{T \cdot \Delta S}{\Delta H} \qquad (4.9)$$

For hydrogen and oxygen used in fuel cells this ideal efficiency proves to be 85%, which is comparable to the Carnot efficiency of thermal engines. As for thermal engines, the real attainable efficiencies for fuel cells are much lower; 45% to 65%, but the latter figure shows the greater potential of the fuel cell in the future.

4.4   Energy flow diagram

The need arises to model energy transfers and conversions in simple diagrams: such diagrams will be introduced in this section. It is important, as with every model of the 'real world', to give some thought to the scope of the model (i.e. the system boundaries) and the level of detail (i.e. the subdivision/clustering of energy transforming steps). The energy flow diagrams developed in this chapter will later be used to explain the architecture of present and future energy conversion systems on board ships.

4.4.1   Energy flow diagram and legend

The energy flow diagram models the chain of energy conversions from energy source (ES) to the types of energy required for the systems: the energy use (EU). ES and EU are the system boundaries in the general energy flow diagram. The precise definition of the system boundaries depends on the purpose of the diagram. System boundaries will be the subject of the next section.

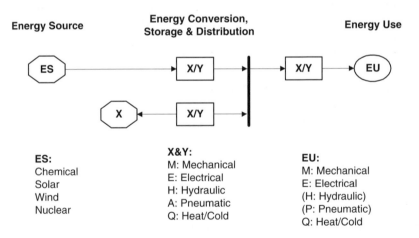

Figure 4.1   General format of energy flow diagram.

Figure 4.1 shows the general energy flow diagram. The application of this diagram to various propulsion and electric energy system concepts is the subject of Chapter 5. The legend of the diagram is defined in Figure 4.2.

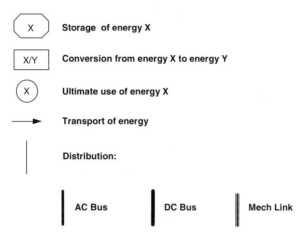

Figure 4.2   Legend of energy flow diagram.

4.4.2   *System boundaries*

The appropriate system boundaries need to be chosen to make a proper model of the input flows, output flows and intermediate conversions. The system boundaries define what part of the 'real world' is captured in the block diagram.

The input flow, one of the system boundaries, is generally chosen to be the energy source (ES) because the chain of conversions on board a ship usually starts with the conversion of chemical energy (stored in fossil fuels) to mechanical or electric energy. The output flows are the types of energy use (EU). The propulsion power is probably the most important energy use. Therefore, the power supplied to the propulsor, delivered propeller power P_p [Watt], seems the appropriate system boundary. However, the losses associated with the M/M conversion in the propeller (from rotating shaft to translating ship) are considerable. Propulsion efficiency captures these losses. To include the losses in the block diagram, the system boundary can also be defined after the propeller, thus defining effective power P_E, the power that translates the ship, as a system boundary. The two examples discussed here are shown in Figure 4.3.

The details of propulsion efficiency and other hydromechanical principles have been dealt with in *Chapter 3 Propulsion and electric power*.

Obviously, propulsion power is not the only type of energy use that needs to be considered. Large electric power demands, such as dredging pumps and thrusters, are best specified with their required rotating mechanical power. Large hydraulic users, such as the steering gear or stabilisers are described by the electric energy required at the input of the E/H conversion; the hydraulic pump. Smaller users, such as pumps and fans are also modelled by their electric power demands. (The air system is an example: the air system is modelled in terms of the electric power needed for the compressor. One may also wish to show the energy storage in air bottles and the air users connected to them.)

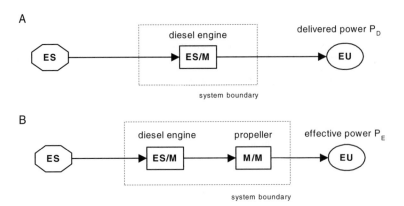

Figure 4.3   Two examples of system boundaries in the conversion of chemical energy in fossil fuels to propulsion power.

4.4.3   Level of detail

The system boundaries define which part of the 'real world' is modelled in the diagram. After these boundaries are defined, the degree of subdivision or clustering of the energy transformations in the diagram, i.e. the level of detail, needs to be considered. This will be explained by an example taken from a previous section. In section 4.3.1 the compound or multi-stage converter was introduced. Take the steam turbine plant as an example.

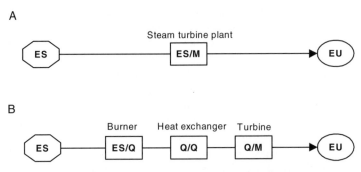

Figure 4.4   Two degrees of subdivision of the energy transformation of a steam turbine plant.

The steam turbine plant can be modelled according to the energy flow diagram. Figure 4.4 shows two energy flow diagrams. Diagram A presents the steam turbine plant as a single energy transformation from energy source into mechanical energy: it would be an appropriate level of detail if the purpose were to illustrate the overall function of the plant. Diagram B on the other hand presents the plant with a higher level of detail: it shows the different energy transformation steps of the plant, i.e. combustion, heat transfer in the boiler and power generation in the turbine. Diagram B would be the correct diagram if the purpose were to visualise the processes within the steam turbine plant.

Another example is the energy conversion in a mechanical transmission, i.e. a gearbox and a shaft line. The gearbox incorporates an energy conversion of mechanical into mechanical at a different combination of power and speed, and some friction losses. The shaft line only has (friction) losses. Often the conversion occurs in two stages and there may be a linking function. All these elements are shown in Figure 4.5-A.

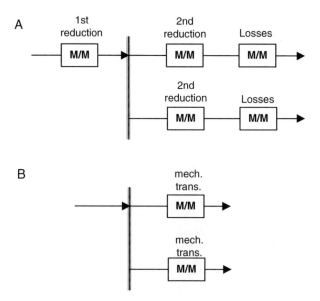

Figure 4.5   Two degrees of subdivision of the energy conversion in a 2-stage reduction gearbox.

Normally, the first and second reduction (if present), together with the losses in the adjacent shaft lines are combined into a single block *mechanical transmission*, as shown in Figure 4.5-B. The conversion into parallel branches must still be shown though.

4.5   Exercises

Exercise 1

Make an EFD for the following machinery plant:

Three diesel generators supply energy to the main switchboard. The exhaust gas of the diesel generators is used in an exhaust gas boiler to generate steam. A turbo-generator also supplies electric energy to the main switchboard.

From the switchboard there are feeds to both the propulsion system and a number of auxiliary systems:

- the propulsion system consisting of an electric motor, a shaft line and a propeller,

- a hydraulic system consisting of an electrically driven hydraulic pump,

- an electrically driven bow-thruster.

The hydraulic energy is used to drive a hydraulic winch and the steering gear. Part of the hydraulic energy is stored in an accumulator.

Chapter 5

Power Plant Concepts

5.0   Learning goals

After studying this chapter, the student should be able to:

- *Describe the different power plant concepts: mechanical direct and geared drive, partly and fully integrated electrical drive, multiple shaft configurations and combined drive.*

- *Describe the grounds on which a certain concept is chosen.*

5.1   Introduction

On board a ship, propulsion and electric power supply are two important functions that need to be performed to fulfil the ship's mission. In Chapter 3, the systems that perform those functions were highlighted: the propulsion system and the electric power plant. They were treated separately but sometimes they are tied closely together. When examining possible configurations, we will find out that the systems cannot always be viewed as separate. Obvious examples of systems that are hard to separate are (1) mechanical propulsion with a shaft generator (driven by the prime mover for propulsion) which provides (part of) the electric power, or (2) electric propulsion, in which case a combined electric power supply plant provides power for propulsion as well as other electrical systems. Therefore, the combination of the propulsion system and the electric power plant is referred to as *power plant*.

The power plant concepts can roughly be divided into two types:

- mechanical concepts

- electrical concepts.

Mechanical concepts are characterised by the mechanical transmission of energy from the prime mover to the propulsor and to other direct-driven consumers of mechanical energy. Basic components are the prime mover (diesel engine, gas turbine or steam turbine), transmission and a propulsor. The electric power supply is separate, usually by means of diesel-driven generators, but might be linked to the propulsion system by a shaft generator.

In electrical concepts the propulsor is driven by an electric motor. The power supply for propulsion motors and for the other electrical systems may be separate systems, each with their own generator sets, or an integrated system for more efficient use of the (shared) generator sets.

Within the different concepts several configurations are possible. The configurations include diesel engines, gas turbines, steam turbines, generators and electric motors which need to be combined in a satisfactory manner. The main concern when choosing one or more of these standard units are their economics. Important economic parameters are fuel consumption and procurement, installation and operational costs such as fuel, maintenance and crew costs. The choice of a power plant configuration, however, should not only depend on economics. Other important aspects that need to be considered are:

- the space and weight of the installed machinery (power density, engine room layout).

- the speeds required under different operating conditions.

- the reliability, availability and maintainability (RAM) of the machinery and the associated level of redundancy required.

- the skill of the crew and the level of automation, control and monitoring.

- the vibrations and associated noise induced in the ship.

- the signatures caused by the machinery (important for warships).

Different configurations of both mechanical concepts and electrical concepts will be introduced in this chapter. Each concept is described by its components and an energy flow diagram as introduced in Chapter 4. Applications on board merchant and naval vessels are used to illustrate design considerations and consequences for engine room layout.

5.2   Mechanical concepts

The most common power plant concept nowadays is still the mechanical drive. Mechanical drives can be divided into two types that are characterised by the transmission system: direct drive and geared (indirect) drive. In a direct drive, the transmission consists of a shafting system between prime mover and propulsor, so the rotational speed of the propulsor and the output speed of the engine are the same. Only low-speed diesels are suitable for this concept. In a geared drive, on the other hand, the transmission also includes a reduction gearbox between prime mover and propulsor, thus enabling the use of a prime mover with an output speed higher than the propulsor speed. High and medium-speed diesel engines, gas turbines and steam turbine plants require a geared drive.

If a power plant includes multiple prime movers, it is referred to as a combined drive. In a combined drive, diesel engines, gas turbines or steam turbines may be used alternatively or combined. The mechanical concepts discussed in sections 5.2.2 and 5.2.3 have one propulsion engine and are single-shaft configurations. Multiple-shaft configurations and combined drive will be discussed in section 5.2.4.

5.2.1   *Energy flow diagram*

Although direct and geared drives are two different power plant concepts, an energy flow diagram (EFD) that covers the mechanical concept in general terms can be drawn up. Figure 5.1 shows this general EFD. In a conventional mechanical drive, the power plant consists of separate propulsion and electric power systems. The propulsion system is powered by the main engine(s), delivering mechanical energy, which, after transmission, is delivered to the propulsor. The electric plant is powered by auxiliary engines and generators. A link between the two systems can be established by a power take off (PTO) of the main engine to power the electric system by means of a shaft generator. This shaft generator, or propulsion engine-driven alternator, can be mounted on the shaft or fed through a gearbox. Apart from its extra supply from the shaft alternator, the auxiliary power system is an autonomous system. If functions are vital, energy storage in the form of electric batteries provide uninterrupted power supply (UPS).

In this diagram, a gearbox has been indicated. If the EFD were to indicate a direct drive, note that the mechanical transmission (M/M) between main engine and propulsor should be left out, and that the PTO may be fed through a gearbox or directly by a shaft. The shaft generator may also be connected (through a step-up gearbox) to the free end of the engine.

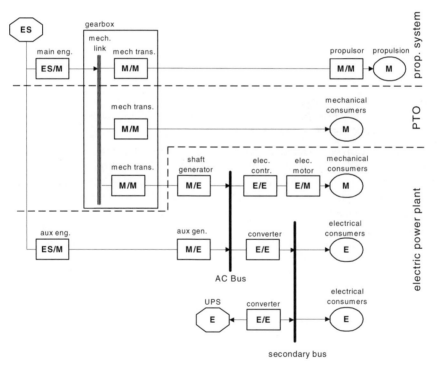

Figure 5.1   EFD of mechanical drive with optional Power Take Off (PTO).

Figure 5.1 shows the propulsion system, electric power system and PTO. The PTO is included in the diagram because, although it is optional, it is commonly used for directly driven consumers of mechanical energy such as attached pumps, and it is often found in the form of a shaft generator. The system boundary of the diagram is defined by input and output energy: the primary energy stored in fossil fuels (input) and the mechanical or electric energy used by consumers (output).

5.2.2   *Direct drive*

The majority of large conventional cargo vessels such as large container ships and bulk carriers are equipped with a diesel direct drive. In this configuration the prime mover, a low-speed diesel engine, is directly linked to a propeller, see Figure 5.2. A low-speed diesel operates on the cheapest fuel (HFO), has a high thermal efficiency and there is no need for a gearbox, so its overall economy is good. Additionally, it is reliable and the space and weight required by the engine are acceptable for the large vessels.

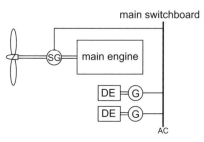

Figure 5.2   Basic diesel direct drive with one main engine for propulsion and electric power supply by a shaft generator (at sea) and auxiliary engine driven-generators (in port, standby).

The engine can be coupled directly to the propeller because, in order to operate efficiently, a propeller has to rotate at a low speed of 80 to 200 revolutions per minute, and this is the range in which a low-speed diesel engine can operate. The propeller can either be a fixed pitch propeller (FP propeller) or a controllable pitch propeller (CP propeller). In general, low-speed engines are reversible so, the engine drives a conventional FP propeller, and the speed of the ship is controlled by adjusting the speed and the direction of rotation of the diesel engine. The FP propeller is a simple, relatively cheap construction. The CP propeller, on the other hand, is more complex, and more expensive than the FP propeller. The advantage of a CP propeller is that it enables very low ship speeds and a smooth reversal of the speed due to the controllable positioning of the propeller blades.

The electrical requirements of a direct drive concept are met by diesel generator sets and possibly a shaft alternator. If a shaft generator is installed, it can usually supply the electric power needed while the ship is at sea, sailing at nominal speed and the diesel generator sets are on standby. Note that, since a direct drive normally features a FP propeller, a shaft generator would produce a voltage with varying frequency which must be converted by power electronics before connecting to the electric distribution network. When the ship is sailing at lower speed, the drop of shaft revolutions may make it impossible to maintain the rated output voltage. In that case, and under other operating conditions (for instance in port and manoeuvring) the generator sets will provide electric power.

The combination of diesel generator sets will be chosen in such a way that the electrical demand can be met with efficiently running generator sets, in every operational condition. Effort should be made to avoid generator sets running in low load conditions because of their decreasing efficiency at part load and fouling of the engine.

The electric power supply system contains a certain degree of redundancy: a minimum of two diesel generator sets is installed, one of which may be an emergency generator (driven by an emergency engine). A shaft generator, on the other hand, is not installed for redundancy reasons but for better overall efficiency and lower operational costs:

▪ The bigger main engine has a better overall efficiency than smaller auxiliary engines due to its size, and it uses cheaper fuel.

▪ The maintenance costs are lower because the auxiliary engines need less operating hours.

Table 5.1 gives a few numerical examples of diesel direct drive taken from *Significant Ships of 1998* and *1999* [RINA, 1999/2000]. The type of propeller, and the output power and revs per minute of the main engine, auxiliary engines and shaft generator (if installed) are stated.

Ship		*Main Engine*	*Shaft gen.*	*Propeller*	*Aux. Engines*
Tarquin Loch	LPG carrier 6270m^3	3590 kW 170 rpm	400 kW	CPP	3×450 kW 1800 rpm
Kanata Spirit	Oil tanker 128993m^3	14700 kW 105 rpm	-	FPP	3×720 kW 720 rpm
Black Marlin	Heavy lift vessel 98500dwt	9550 kW 127 rpm	-	CPP	4×990 kW 720 rpm
P&O Nedlloyd's Southampton	Container ship 6690TEU	66845 kW 100 rpm	3500 kW	FPP	4×3600 kW 600 rpm

Table 5.1   Examples of diesel direct configurations: main engine, shaft generator (if installed), fixed pitch or controllable pitch propeller (FPP or CPP) and auxiliary engines [RINA, 1999/2000].

5.2.3   Geared drive

In a geared drive, engine speed and propeller speed are not coupled directly, because the output speed of medium- and high-speed diesel engines, gas turbines, and steam turbines is higher than the speed that is required for efficient operation of a propeller. So, when one of these prime movers is used, a reduction gearbox reduces the rotational speed of the prime mover output to that required for the propeller.

A gearbox is not only used to reduce speed, it may also be used to combine the power of two prime movers to one shaft, or to divide the power between one or two shafts or PTOs. The gearbox is sometimes used to provide reversal of the ship speed. In that case the gearbox is provided with an astern gear train. However, in most cases, reversal of the ship speed is achieved with a CP propeller. In some cases, the diesel engine may have two directions of rotation in order to reverse the ship speed. A steam turbine plant may have a separate reverse turbine.

The electric power supply is provided by generator sets (usually diesel-driven) and possibly a shaft generator. The main engine driven shaft generator can be mounted on the output shaft of the main engine, or be powered through an output shaft of the gearbox. Since a geared drive normally features a CP propeller the shaft speed can be kept constant and the shaft generator will develop a voltage of constant frequency. Thus the complication of installing power electronic devices to keep the frequency constant is avoided. Also, the shaft generator can be used during any sailing speed, i.e. including during manoeuvring.

Diesel geared drive

The diesel geared drive finds its application on board many vessels, for instance on ferries, chemical tankers and container ships. A diesel geared drive is an option when smaller powers are needed, or when propulsion power is divided between multiple prime movers, or when space and weight requirements weigh heavily. Medium- and high-speed engines are smaller than low-speed engines: they have a higher power density, which results in low weight and volume for a required power. Mainly due to this high power density, high-speed engines are installed in small and fast ships, such as fast ferries, fast patrol boats and frigates. Often, the power plant of these ship types is a combined drive, for instance two engines that power one shaft line.

The diesel geared drive consists of a medium- or a high-speed diesel engine, a gearbox, a shafting system and a propulsor; usually a CP propeller. Medium- and high-speed engines are usually not reversible, so the propulsion chain requires either a reversible gearbox or a CP propeller. The configuration can be represented by the diagram in Figure 5.3. A few examples of ships with a diesel-geared drive are given in Table 5.2.

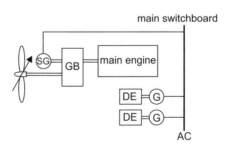

Figure 5.3   Diagram of a diesel geared drive with a shaft generator.

Ship		Main Engine	Gearbox	Shaft gen.	Propeller	Aux. Engines
Makiri Green	General cargo 12000 dwt	7800 kW 500 rpm	134 rpm	800 kW	CPP	3×485 kW 1200 rpm
Isola Gialla	Chemical tanker 43157 dwt	8775 kW 500 rpm	112.5 rpm	1800 kW	CPP	3×880 kW 900rpm
Mrs Sonja	General cargo 4930 dwt	1800 kW 750 rpm	175 rpm	-	CPP	2× 210 kVA

Table 5.2   Examples of diesel geared configurations [RINA, 1999/2000].

Steam turbine geared drive

Today, steam turbines are hardly ever used in the merchant marine. Steam turbine plants do, however, find their application on board naval vessels (aircraft carriers and nuclear submarines) and LNG (liquefied natural gas) carriers.

A steam turbine plant consists of one or two boilers and a number of turbines. Steam is generated in the boilers; it then expands in the turbines. The boilers can be powered by any of a variety of fuels (poor-quality oil, coal, or in case of LNG carriers, LNG) or by a nuclear reactor (naval applications). A steam turbine rotates at high speed (in the order of 6000 rpm), so it cannot drive a propeller directly, only geared.

The power plant concept of an LNG carrier is used as an example. Figure 5.4 shows a diagram of the configuration: two gas-burning boilers power the steam turbine that drives the propeller through a reduction gearbox. This example has a diesel generator set, and two steam turbine-driven alternators (turbo-generators), which are also fed by the two boilers [Nurmi, 1998].

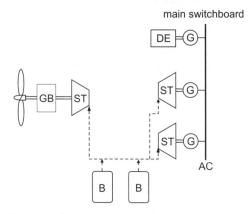

Figure 5.4   Diagram of a steam power plant on board an LNG carrier, consisting of two boilers, a steam turbine, two turbo-generators and a diesel generator set.

In general, the fuel economy of a steam plant is worse than that of the diesel engine. Despite high fuel consumption, however, it is a successful prime mover for LNG carriers due to their ability to burn boil-off gases as well as fuel oil in their boilers. Boil-off refers to the gases that vaporise in order to keep cargo pressure (and thus temperature) constant. LNG carriers are fitted with a specialised cargo containment system in which LNG is carried in unpressurised, insulated cargo tanks. The cargo temperature is kept constant (at -165 °C) by free vaporisation of the LNG. When the natural boil-off is insufficient or not available (on a ballast voyage) a forced boil-off is created by vaporising LNG by heat exchangers.

Other disadvantages of a steam plant are its low power density and high initial costs. A steam turbine plant is a voluminous installation, but because an LNG carrier is rather large in relation to her deadweight (due to the low specific gravity of LNG), weight and volume of the machinery are not as important. Also, an LNG carrier requires a high speed for efficient operation; the ship is expensive and is boiling-off cargo during the voyage. This may justify the expensive installation. Table 5.3 shows examples of steam turbine-geared drives.

Ship: LNG Carrier		Steam tur.	Boiler(s)	Turbo-alt.	Propeller	Aux.Engines (DE-driven)
Hanjin Muscat	138366m³	28610 kW	2×68 tonnes/h	2×3450 kW	FPP 83 rpm	3450 kW
Aman Sendai	18928m³	5516 kW	2×17 tonnes/h	1450 kW	FPP 125 rpm	1450 kW

Table 5.3   Examples of steam turbine-geared configurations [RINA, 1998/2000].

5.2.4   *Multiple shafts and combined drive*

Any combination of mechanical drive, i.e. multiple prime movers, is considered a combined drive. Diesel engines, gas turbines and steam turbines may be installed and used alternatively or combined. In combination with a multiple shaft configuration, the propulsion system becomes quite complex but it may offer a wide choice of operating modes.

Many aspects may result in the choice for a multiple shaft configuration or a combined drive. First consider the grounds on which a multiple shaft configuration may be chosen:

- The desired degree of redundancy: in case of failure of part of the system (propeller, shafts) the ship will be likely to have propulsion power left.

- Manoeuvring characteristics: with two propellers the ship needs less tug assistance when manoeuvring and mooring in narrow waterways and it can manoeuvre without rudders in case of emergency.

- The required propulsion power is too large for one propeller of given diameter (determined by aftship): the maximum propeller load has been reached or it generates too much noise.

- The propulsion engine does not develop enough power and a direct drive is desirable: two diesel-direct shaft lines may be installed. This may become a solution for the fourth generation containerships reaching 10,000 TEU which require more power than delivered by the largest available low-speed diesel engine.

More than one engine may be installed for one of the following reasons:

- The desired degree of redundancy.

- The required propulsion power cannot be developed by one engine of limited size: in ships such as ferries, it is desirable to keep the engine room as low as possible. This will limit the height of an engine. Consequently, multiple engines may be necessary to meet the propulsion demands.

- To accommodate a wide variety in operating conditions, two engines (per shaft) may be used: one diesel engine for low speed and two for high speed or a diesel engine and a gas turbine for high speed, as found in frigates, ferries and cruise liners. The engines may also be used alternatively: for example one engine (usually a diesel engine) for a low service speed and the other for a high service speed (a diesel engine or a gas turbine), as is found in some ferries and warships.

The possible configurations are numerous. Only some examples will be given next. Figure 5.5 shows the combined diesel-direct drive of large containerships that require more propulsion power than one low-speed diesel engine can develop.

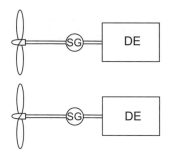

Figure 5.5   Diagram of a combined diesel direct drive with two shaft lines.

Figure 5.6 shows the power plant configuration of a ferry that consists of: two diesel engines per shaft to keep the engine room low in order to meet space requirements, and two propeller shafts (1) to split the propulsion power that is too high for one propeller and (2) to meet manoeuvring requirements. This configuration has a high degree of redundancy: the installation is functionally redundant starboard and port side.

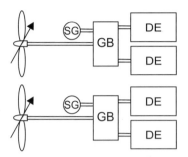

Figure 5.6   Diagram of a combined diesel geared drive with two CP propellers and
                    two diesel engines per shaft and shaft generators.

Figure 5.7 shows the power plant of the Norsun, a ferry between the UK and the Netherlands, that has been optimised for two different economical service speeds for east and westbound voyages because of the 1 hour time difference between the UK and the Netherlands [The Naval Architect, May 1987]. In this so-called "father-and-son" engine arrangement, the service speed can be chosen 18.5 or 16.5 knots. This arrangement ensures the availability of some propulsion and electrical power in case of emergency. The two auxiliary diesel engines, each driving an alternator are for use in port only.

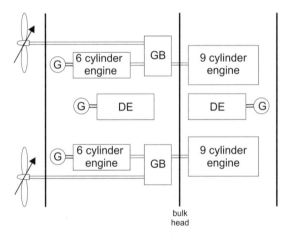

Figure 5.7   Diagram of a combined diesel geared drive with two CP propellers and
                    two diesel engines of different size per shaft as seen on board Norsun
                    and Norsea of North Sea Ferries [The Naval Architect, May 1987].

Figure 5.8 shows the possible power plant of an advanced fast ship. In this concept, the diesel engines and gas turbines each drive a waterjet. The jets driven by the diesel engines may be steerable and will be used for manoeuvring and low speed. The jets driven by the gas turbines may be fixed water jets and will be used to boost the ship to maximum speed together with the diesel driven jets.

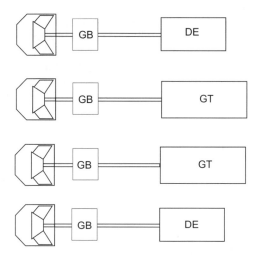

Figure 5.8   Diagram of the mechanical drive of a fast ferry: the diesel engines and
                  gas turbines drive water jets through gearboxes (CODAG).

The typical power plant configuration of a frigate, Figure 5.9, includes four prime movers, two shafts and two propellers for propulsion, and four auxiliary engines to meet the electrical demand.

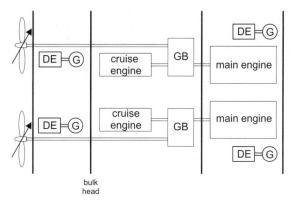

Figure 5.9   Typical mechanical drive for a frigate (CODOG or COGOG).

Note the main differences with the conventional mechanical drives on board merchant vessels: (1) there are two identical propulsion chains, (2) both chains have two engines connected to the gearbox, (3) the gearbox reduction is in two steps, and (4) there is no shaft generator.

The two-propeller configuration has resulted from requirements for manoeuvrability, propeller load and low underwater noise (i.e. propeller design) and the required high power. Considerations of fuel economy rather than redundancy have resulted in two engines per shaft: one for high speed (usually a gas turbine) and one for cruise speed (a gas turbine or a compact high-speed diesel). The main gas turbines have a low efficiency when developing power needed for cruise speed, so smaller prime movers with better fuel economy are used for the lower (cruise) speed. Gas turbines and high-speed diesel engines are usually not reversible, so this concept has CP propellers. Figure 5.10 shows the frigate's EFD.

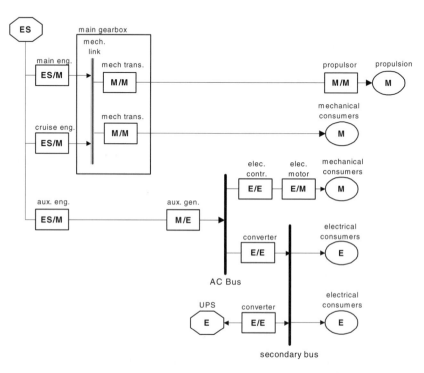

Figure 5.10   The EFD of a combined mechanical drive for a frigate: the main and cruise engines power the propulsion system and the auxiliary engines power the electrical system.

There is no shaft alternator installed as a result of frequent operation at relatively low speed (compared to the maximum boost speed). So, the electric power supply system is separate from the propulsion system. Four generator sets are favoured to ensure complete back-up redundancy, as is clear from the following considerations. An electrical blackout on a naval vessel is unacceptable, so if one operating generator fails, another should still be able to feed the vital consumers after disconnecting non-vital users. Consequently, two generator sets should always be in service. A third stand-by generator has to be started to replace the one that failed. Sometimes, it is also required that it is possible to take one generator out of service for longer periods of time for maintenance or repair, and still meet the first two requirements. When these considerations are taken into account, the electrical system will have to be powered by four generators.

For naval and fast merchant ships, the combined drive is often referred to by an acronym that describes the prime mover-side of the drive. In these acronyms *CO* stands for combined drive, and *D*, *G* and *S* stand for diesel engine, gas turbine or steam turbine, respectively. Consider the installation in Figure 5.9. If we assume that the main engines are gas turbines and the cruise engines medium-speed diesel engines, the installation is either CODOG or CODAG. The first prime mover in the acronym, in this case a diesel engine, is the cruise engine, which delivers the power required to sail at cruise speed. In the CODOG drive, the gas turbines are the drivers for high speed, whereas in CODAG both the diesel engines and the gas turbines are the drivers for high speed. So, in these acronyms: the second *O* stands for 'or'; either cruise engine(s) *or* main engine(s), and the *A* stands for 'and'; either cruise engine(s) or cruise engine(s) *and* main engine(s). Combined drives like CODAG (Figure 5.8), CODOG (Figure 5.9) and CODAD (Figure 5.11) have been used on board fast ships and in naval applications.

The CODOG or COGOG configuration as shown in Figure 5.9 is a common power plant for corvettes, frigates and destroyers. Figure 5.11 shows a similar configuration, a CODAD drive, where machinery has been arranged in separate engine rooms in a different manner. The power plant consists of four identical diesel engines and no gas turbines because of economical reasons (the efficiency of a diesel engine is better, fuel is cheaper and the investment costs are lower). When sailing at boost speed (a typical value would be 28 knots) all four engines are in service and at cruise speed (less than 23 knots), only one engine per shaft. Consequently, CP propellers and sometimes a two-speed gear are fitted. On board large US destroyers, this configuration is installed with gas turbines, i.e. a COGAG drive.

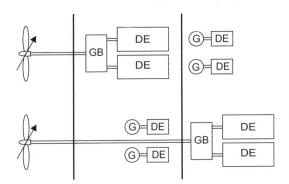

Figure 5.11   Diagram of a CODAD and the engine room layout.

5.3   Electrical concepts

In an electric drive, a prime mover drives a generator and the generator feeds a propulsion (electric) motor through a switchboard and converters. In general, electric drive may be attractive when space in the aft ship is limited, or when a large non-propulsion electrical load is to be expected (such as on a passenger ship), or when a number of propulsors are spread throughout the ship, such as thrusters for dynamic positioning on an offshore vessel. Another consideration may be a requirement for reconfigurable power supply as in a naval vessel.

The early electric drives consisted of separate systems: an electric propulsion system and an electric power system for other electric consumers. In these early drives each system would have its own separated generator sets and switchboards and no link would exist between the switchboards. Nowadays, however, propulsion and its auxiliaries, and other consumers of electric energy draw from a common supply of electric energy: the integrated electric power plant (IEP) or All Electric Ship (AES) concept.

At least two generator sets are installed for the main power supply. Under conditions with high load all sets are on line and operating at full load, and under conditions with low load one or more engines can be taken off line. Ideally, the number and capacity of the generator sets are chosen in such a way that, under each operating condition, the engines that are on line are operating at near peak efficiency. This flexibility in operation consequently decreases the fuel consumption at part load, when compared to diesel mechanical drive with less possibilities to switch off engines. In practice however, the flexibility in operation (and thus fuel saving) is limited due to the finite number of generator sets that will be installed on board.

Before treating other advantages that an electric drive may have over other concepts, it is worthwhile to realise that these advantages have to offset the disadvantages. The components in electrical drive; generators, electric motors, distribution systems and converters, add to the overall cost. Further, the total efficiency of the energy conversions from prime mover to propulsor may decrease. In many cases, the total efficiency of the electrical drive will be lower due to the efficiencies of the electric motor, the generator and the converters.

The main advantage of an electric concept is that a number of generator sets provide efficient and flexible operation, they also ensure reliability in the system under operating conditions that do not require the maximum power available: under those conditions, the required power can still be developed if one or more generator sets have failed. On the other hand, the reliability of the system may be less under conditions that require maximum power, when compared to a diesel mechanical drive.

A very practical advantage of electrical propulsion is the flexibility in the arrangement of the equipment because the prime mover is not mechanically linked to the propeller shafting. This means that the prime mover and generator may be placed at more convenient locations. In a multi-hull, for instance, the space in front of the propeller is limited; by using electric drive, only an electric motor has to be installed in the slender hull, and the generator sets may be located higher in the structure.

The flexibility of arrangement also affects the noise and vibration control of the power plant. The vibrations and noise that originate at the engine are more controllable as the location of the engine can be chosen more freely, and the engine can more easily be resiliently mounted, and/or fitted in an acoustical enclosure.

Other advantages lie in the fields of the installation of the system at new building of a ship and the maintenance. Maintenance of the generator sets can be done while one is out of service and the others are running. The size of the generator sets may also permit maintenance by exchange. The electrical equipment does not add significantly to the maintenance tasks on board.

An electric drive may result in cost benefits at new building when compared to conventional diesel-direct drives. The delivery of a large diesel engine of a diesel mechanical drive has to be planned in an early stage of the building process and will be assembled on site. In an electric drive, the components may be smaller and the generator set can be assembled in a workshop and put on board at a later stage. The procurement can therefore be postponed. If propulsion is delivered by means of a podded propeller (which can also be assembled in a workshop instead of on site), the installation of the propulsion plant has been simplified and can be postponed until the latest stages of building.

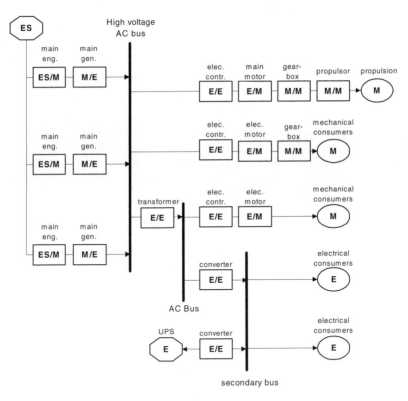

Figure 5.12   The EFD of the integrated electric power plant concept.

5.3.1   All electric ship concept

Figure 5.12 shows the EFD of an integrated electric power plant: a number of engines, not necessarily of the same size, feed one net and the propulsion system and ship services draw energy from one primary net. This way all engines can be used more efficiently under all operating conditions. (If the engines are gas turbines a reduction gearbox may be necessary between engine and generator.)

The high voltage system is usually a three phase alternating current system with a voltage in the range of 3 to 6 kV. The E/E converters after the main switchboard adapt the electric energy supply to the local needs and act as a buffer against electric distortion in the net.

Many configurations are possible. Diesel-electric drives often include more than two medium-speed diesel engines and they drive the electric motor of a FP propeller. They may be found in all kinds of ship types; amongst others cruise ships, ferries and chemical tankers. The generators may also be driven by gas or steam turbines. In the following, two examples of integrated electric drive will be shown: the first example is a cruise ship with diesel electric drive, and the second is a cruise ship with a COGES drive. COGES stands for *combined gas and steam turbine, integrated electric drive system*. Both examples have been taken from Significant Ships of 2000 [RINA, 2001].

P&O Cruises' Aurora, a 6450 dwt cruise ship, has a diesel-electric power plant. Four medium-speed diesel engines, developing 14700 kilowatts at 514 rpm, connected to alternators provide primary electric power that serve the auxiliary systems and two electric motors that are directly coupled to two FP propellers. The EFD would be quite similar to the EFD in Figure 5.12, provided four main engines feed the net and two branches of propulsion are included. Figure 5.13 shows a diagram of the installation. For safety reasons the machinery has been located in separate engine rooms. The switchboards and cabling have been left out.

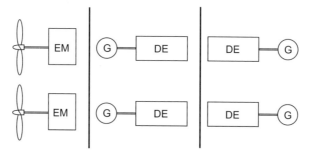

Figure 5.13   Diagram of the power plant of cruise ship Aurora.

The second example is a cruise ship of Celebrity Cruises Inc USA. The Millennium is a 8500 dwt cruise liner with COGES drive. In this concept, two gas turbine-driven alternators and a steam turbine-driven alternator provide the electric energy for the electric propulsion motors and for all other systems on board. The propulsion motors are integrated with the propeller in an azimuthing pod. The steam turbine draws its steam from the waste-heat boilers that are fitted in the exhaust lines from the gas turbines. This makes the EFD of this system more complex than the one shown in Figure 5.12. The EFD of this COGES drive also includes the energy conversion from energy source to heat, thus considering the heat that would otherwise be lost in the exhaust gases of the gas turbines, see Figure 5.14.

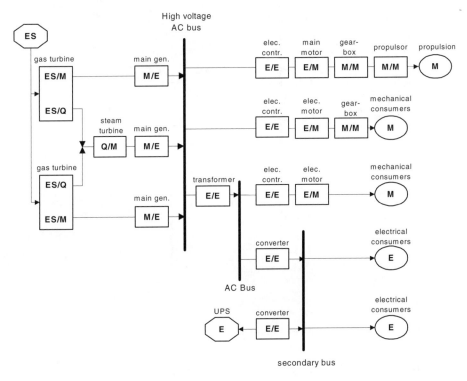

Figure 5.14   The EFD of a COGES drive.

5.3.2 *Electric drive of submarines*

The electric drive of a submarine is perhaps the oldest example of the fully integrated concept. At or near the surface (snorting), diesel generator sets provide electric energy for the primary net. In submarines, this is a DC net from which energy is stored in batteries. The electric conversion before the main switchboard (DC bus) consists of rectifiers which convert the AC-power generated by the main generators to DC-power.

The energy storage in the batteries makes submerged operation possible without the diesel engines running, albeit for a limited time. The propulsion and the large mechanical consumers (for example air compressors and ballast pumps) are powered with energy from the primary net. The primary net also feeds the secondary AC net by means of converters. The EFD is shown in Figure 5.15.

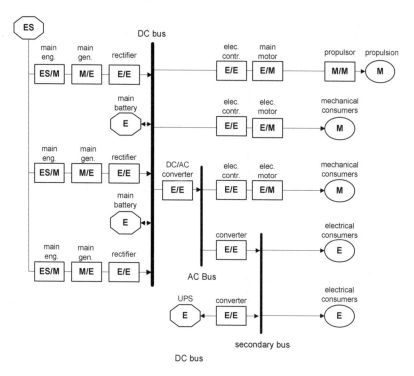

Figure 5.15   The EFD of a DC electric-drive for submarines.

5.3.3   *Hybrid drive*

A hybrid drive is a combination of mechanical and electric drives. Figure 5.16 shows the EFD of a hybrid drive. The propulsion power is delivered by a mechanical drive and by a DC electric drive. The auxiliary systems are served from a secondary AC net.

An example of a hybrid drive is CODLAG: Combined diesel-electric and gas turbine drive. The diagram of such a power plant is shown in Figure 5.17. Mechanical propulsion power is developed by two gas turbines, each through a gearbox connected to FP propeller. Additionally electric motors, fed by diesel generator sets, are delivering propulsion power. The diagram also shows how the machinery may be located in separate engine rooms to ensure a high degree of redundancy.

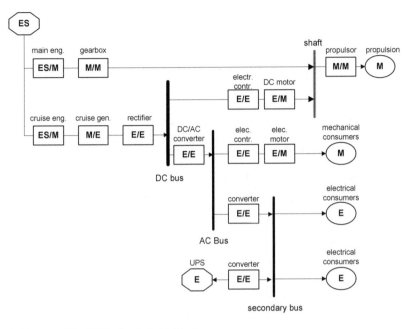

Figure 5.16 The EFD of a hybrid drive.

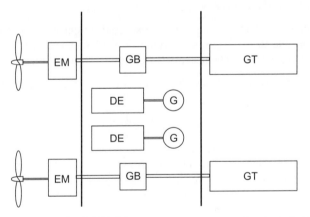

Figure 5.17 Diagram of a CODLAG concept as an example of a hybrid drive.

5.4 Redundancy

Redundancy plays an important role in the design of machinery plants. Redundancy may ensure safety, but also availability of the system as a whole to fulfil a mission. Especially for the navy it is important that a ship is able to fulfil its mission after battle damage. For the merchant marine, on the other hand, economic and environmental damage are important drivers for redundancy as well. Redundancy of a system can be achieved in several ways:

▪ Full-backup redundancy of a component or system: the goal is to achieve full availability of a function, i.e. no loss of performance, after failure of a component or system.

   Example: lubricating oil pumps on a diesel engine are an example of full-backup redundancy: one is required to do the job, but two are installed. Since only one will be running the other is referred to as the *cold spare*.

▪ Two or more components to fulfil one function: the components may be identical, but not necessarily. After failure of one component the function is still available, though performance may have degraded. The performance may have degraded on two levels:

   – degradation of full capacity to a lower level.

   Example: On a submarine, three diesel generator sets charge the batteries. After failure of one of them, it is acceptable that the submarine will snort for a longer period of time in order to charge the batteries to the desired level.

   – degradation of capacity under extreme conditions only.

   Example: Two sea water cooling pumps have been installed, but two pumps are only required under extreme conditions such as high sea water temperature and high power. Under normal operation one pump is sufficient, so the system has a certain level of redundancy.

▪ Two or more equivalent systems that operate on different working principles to fulfil one function: due to the different working principles of the systems, degradation of performance usually has to be accepted after failure of one of them.

   Example: Generation of 24 volts DC with a converter backed up by batteries. This is referred to a *hot spare*.

The examples of redundancy as mentioned above are referred to as functional redundancy. In practice, redundancy will often also include *spatial* redundancy. To achieve spatial redundancy, the redundant units are installed in separate compartments, which are preferably located as far from each other as practically possible. In case of damage from an external cause, like fire or flooding of a compartment, two redundant units in separate spaces are less likely to fail at the same time, thus increasing availability of a function.

One of the grounds on which a multiple shaft or multiple engine concept may be chosen is the desired level of functional redundancy, as discussed in section 5.2.4. To fully benefit from the functional redundancy, the prime movers are often located in separate engine rooms; see for examples Figure 5.7, Figure 5.9 and Figure 5.11. Other examples are the fire fighting pumps which will be divided between several watertight compartments over the length of the ship.

In order to determine the desired level of redundancy, it is important to be fully aware of the functions of a system and of its importance to the task of the ship. Redundancy is by definition expensive and requires space and weight. It is probably one of the larger cost drivers of a ship for which high levels of redundancy are required.

5.5 Engine room layout

The arrangement of machinery in machinery spaces is strongly affected by the selection and specification of the machinery and by the overall ship design. As such, the marine engineer should work closely together with the naval architect as the overall ship designer. In this section, some criteria will be given with regard to number and location of machinery spaces and the arrangement of equipment in those spaces.

5.5.1 The number of machinery spaces

The number of machinery spaces mainly depends on the complexity and the extent of the machinery plant, the overall ship design and the required or desired level of separation of machinery. Identical machinery might need to be located in separate spaces to provide redundancy, other equipment may be separated to isolate fire or other casualties.

The ship's hull normally is divided in a number of watertight compartments. If the space required by machinery exceeds the space available in one watertight hull compartment, additional machinery space will be provided in (part of) another compartment. Thus more than one machinery space may be required.

Redundancy and other safety considerations may also lead to separate machinery spaces. For instance, the use of two propulsion machinery spaces may ensure that even in case of a serious hull damage, resulting in one of the machinery spaces flooded or otherwise unavailable, part of the propulsion power may still be delivered. Similar considerations may lead to two generator rooms, two chiller rooms, two switchboard rooms, and others.

Machinery may also be located in separate spaces in order to control damage by fire or explosion from adjacent machinery, or in order to contain dirt, noise or heat. Also, the classification societies, national authorities and international organisations may require machinery to be located in separate spaces. Examples are the emergency generator room (including the emergency generator set and associated transforming gear) and the steering gear room that have to be separate from the main machinery space.

For a simple machinery system of a small cargo vessel, the number of spaces will be limited. For example:

- a main machinery space, in which propulsion engine, gearbox transmission, diesel generators and auxiliaries are located,

- a steering gear room, which is always located above rudder,

- a workshop, in which overhaul and maintenance tasks can be carried out,

- a control and/or main switchboard room.

For a more extensive machinery plant, for instance of a cruise vessel or a frigate, more machinery spaces may be required. For example:

- one or two propulsion engine rooms, containing propulsion diesel engines or gas turbines, gearbox transmissions and the auxiliary systems for that machinery (cooling, fuel oil, lubricating oil and ventilation systems),

- one or two diesel generator rooms for the electric power supply,

- one or two main switchboard rooms,

- one or two chiller rooms containing the refrigeration machinery necessary for the air conditioning systems and the cargo and stores refrigeration,

- a separator room for the centrifugal separators and auxiliaries needed for fuel and lubricating oil cleaning,

- pump rooms for the fire fighting equipment,

- machinery control room,

- workshops and spare parts storage rooms.

Many of the examples used to describe the different power plant concepts contained several machinery spaces: refer to Figure 5.7, Figure 5.9, Figure 5.11, Figure 5.13 and Figure 5.17.

5.5.2   *The location of machinery spaces*

The location of the machinery spaces also depends strongly on the complexity and the extent of the plant and the overall ship design. For a simple machinery plant of a small cargo vessel or a large tanker the main machinery space is usually located in the aftermost hull compartment. In this arrangement the transmission system is short and compact, auxiliary systems are compact and the machinery space does not interfere with cargo spaces.

The shape of the aftship, and consequently the width available for gear transmissions and propulsion engines may not be suitable for multiple-engine or multiple-shaft configurations.

Multiple-engine and multiple-shaft configurations with a mechanical transmission require that the propulsion machinery spaces are low in the hull in order to connect the drive to the propeller, and usually that the spaces are wider than the aftermost compartment. Consequently, the propulsion machinery spaces are usually located more forward than the aftermost compartment; for instance at one third or half the ship's length from the aft.

In case of electrical transmission only the location of the electric motors for propulsion is dictated by the location of the propulsor. The prime movers and generators may be located at any convenient place in the ship: sometimes low in the ship in order to create distance between the major sources of noise and the spaces where noise ought to be kept at a minimum (for instance passenger cabins), other times they are located high in the structure enabling easy access for maintenance by replacement.

In case identical equipment is located in separate spaces, for instance two or more diesel generator rooms are provided, the spaces will be distributed over the ship length. This ensures high redundancy in case of hull damage (flooding) or fire. Another advantage is that that it puts electrical power supply close to the consumers. The location of the main switchboards is associated with the location of the generators as the un-protected cables between generator and switchboard should be as short as practical.

5.5.3 The dimensions of machinery spaces

The dimensions of machinery spaces are dictated by the volume of the machinery in the space (and clearances necessary for maintenance and overhaul), and the overall ship design. In some cases, the ship design is a definite constraint of the space available for machinery.

The length of an engine room is one hull compartment. The length of a hull compartment that houses the engine room is in the first place determined by damage stability criteria and to a certain extent by the length of the machinery that needs to be located in the space. The length of the main engine is often a leading factor.

The total width of the hull compartment that houses the machinery spaces may be used for machinery spaces. Some spaces, such as main engine rooms, may occupy the full width, whereas other spaces, such as diesel generator rooms, chiller rooms and pump rooms, may occupy only part of the width.

On large containerships, the main engine room does not require the total hull width because the large two-stroke, low-speed (propulsion) diesel engine has a considerable length, but its width is limited. Consequently, the machinery space housing the engine will be relatively long, creating sufficient room for other machinery without using the full width of the hull. Containers or tanks may be located next to the engine room.

The height of the machinery spaces is also determined by the dimensions of the machinery. The propulsion machinery space often uses the full height of the hull, i.e. from bottom to main deck, and also part of the superstructure for casings to house ventilation and exhaust systems. A low-speed, two-stroke diesel engine almost always requires the full height of the hull. But also medium- or high-speed diesel engines and gas turbines will frequently require the full height.

On the other hand, the overall design of a Ro-Ro ferry may limit the height of the machinery spaces, because it requires a car deck above the machinery spaces. Consequently, the ship layout dictates the use of a smaller (also in height) medium-speed diesel engine for propulsion instead of a low-speed diesel engine that may be too high for the available space. Also in other ship types the main machinery spaces may be one or more decks lower than the full height. In frigates for example, the propulsion machinery spaces are one deck lower and the diesel generator and chiller rooms are two decks lower than the height.

5.5.4   *The arrangement of equipment*

The arrangement of the equipment in a machinery space follows a limited number of rather straightforward considerations:

- A mechanical drive propulsion plant is located in such a way that it can be connected to the propulsors.

- Auxiliary equipment is located in the direct vicinity of the main equipment it has to support. This reduces piping and cabling. If possible, cooling-water pumps and coolers are located near the interface connections of a diesel engine. The lubricating oil pumps, coolers, filters and separators are located directly adjacent to the main gearbox transmission system. Sometimes, it makes sense to combine this equipment on service units, which can be assembled and tested in a shore-based workshop and installed on board as a complete unit. Examples of these service units are: a lubricating service unit for a gearing system and a fuel oil separator unit including centrifugal separators, heaters, filters and control equipment.

- Some equipment needs to be located low in machinery spaces. Sea cooling water pumps are preferably of the centrifugal non self-priming type. They need a location below the waterline of the ship. Fuel and lubricating oil transfer pumps also need a low location in order to enable good suction behaviour from the storage tanks, which are located low in the ship. Similar considerations apply to bilge pumps.

- Some equipment needs to be located high in the machinery spaces. For example a cooling water expansion tank has to maintain a static pressure in the cooling water system of the diesel engine. In order to succeed it is located high in the machinery space and sometimes in the casings. The same considerations apply to the lubrication tank of the stern tube. The tank needs a high location in order to maintain a lubricating-oil pressure in the stern tube that is higher than the ambient pressure of the seawater. Fans and ducting ventilation systems are located high in the engine room or in casings because the required air is taken in through filters in the superstructures. Exhaust gas boilers, using the waste heat in the exhaust gases or diesel engines or gas turbines are located high in casings because the exhaust gases are led to the funnel.

- Much equipment does not have strict location requirements. This applies to chillers, hydraulic equipment, air compressors, boilers, air vessels, switchboards. They are located at places which are convenient from a total ship layout point of view. Considerations may be location of weight and centre of gravity, and vicinity of consumers (connections).

- In addition, sufficient space should be available for access, control, monitoring and maintenance of machinery and electrical equipment. It is necessary that all local controls and instruments (both mechanical and electrical) have a good accessibility. Electrical panels, acoustic enclosures, filter systems should be located such that they can be opened or removed and daily maintenance can be done. For overhaul, it is necessary that heavy pieces of machinery can be dismantled, hoisted and transported through the machinery spaces to workshops outside the ship. This requires, for instance, hoisting gear above the diesel engine to dismantle the cylinder heads, pistons, piston rods and connecting rods. If a ship is powered by a gas turbine, it may be required that the gas generator can be removed easily and quickly to be replaced by a spare unit. This requires a removal route, on which as little other equipment as possible needs to be removed.

Figure 5.18 and Figure 5.19 show the engine room of a large container vessel: P&O Nedlloyd's Africa. The ship has a diesel-direct drive with a shaft generator.

5.6 Exercises

Exercise 1

Describe the considerations that might have led to the choice of the propulsion and electric power plant of a large container vessel described below.
The propulsion plant consists of a low-speed, two-stroke diesel engine driving a FP propeller and a shaft alternator directly. The capacity of the shaft alternator meets the demand during sea service. The electric power supply plant further consists of two diesel-generator sets and a harbour/emergency generator. The plant provides power to the hotel systems, machinery auxiliaries, the bow thruster and 20% of the containers, which are reefer containers.

Exercise 2

Determine a suitable propulsion and electric power plant for a frigate, and describe the considerations that have lead to that plant.
The frigate has a full displacement of 4200 tonnes. The maximum speed should be over 30 knots for which approximately 40 MW is required, The cruise speed, at which a satisfactorily low fuel consumption is required, is 20 knots. This requires approximately 10 MW propulsion power. During sea operation, the electric power demand may vary between 600 and 1400 kW. In port, the power demand will be approximately 400 kW.

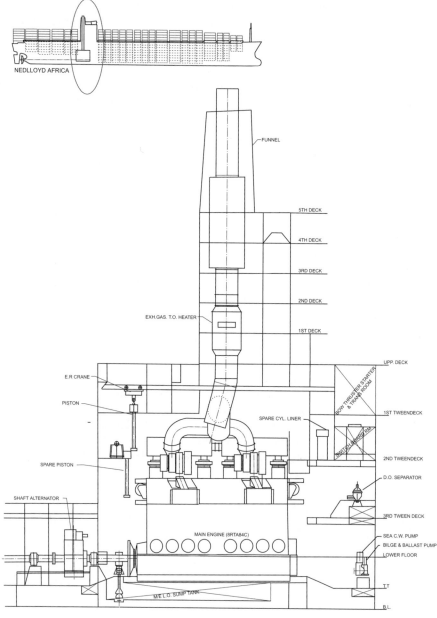

Figure 5.18   General arrangement of the engine room: diesel-direct drive with shaft
generator.

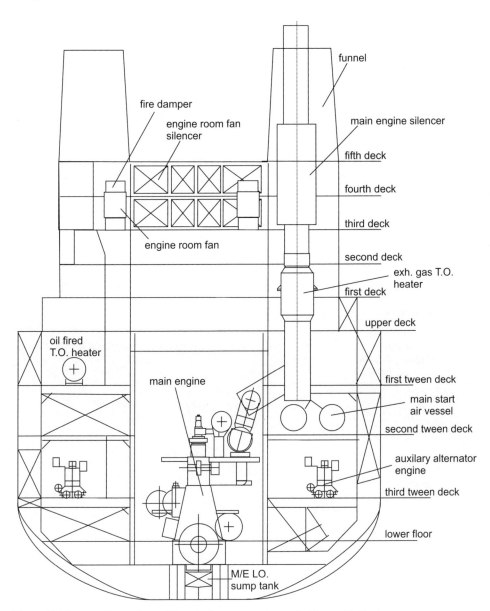

fire damper

engine room fan
silencer

engine room fan

funnel

main engine silencer

fifth deck

fourth deck

third deck

second deck

exh. gas T.O.
heater

first deck

upper deck

oil fired
T.O. heater

main engine

first tween deck

main start
air vessel

second tween deck

auxilary alternator
engine

third tween deck

lower floor

M/E LO.
sump tank

Figure 5.19   Rear view of the engine room shown in Figure 5.18.

5.7   References and further reading

Jost, 1996

V. Jost (MTU): *"Propulsion plants for naval and civilian ships: possible similarities and necessary differencs"*, INEC 96: 3rd International Naval Engineering Conference, Den Helder, April 1996

Naval Architect, May 1987

"North Sea Ferries enters the jumbo era", Naval Architect, May 1987

Nurmi, 1998

Jari Nurmi (Deltamarin), *"Are gas turbines an option for LNG tanker propulsion"*, The Naval Architect, February 1998.

Watson, 1998

David Watson: *"Practical Ship Design"*, Elsevier Science Ltd, UK 1998

RINA, 1999 / RINA, 2000 / RINA, 2001

Ship descriptions mainly taken from *Significant Ships of 1998, 1999 and 2000*: Three Publications of The Royal Institution of Naval Architects, published in the UK in 1999, 2000 and 2001 respectively.

Chapter 6

An Overview of Main Machinery

6.0 Learning goals

After studying this chapter, the student should be able to:

- *Describe the main characteristics of the diesel engine, the gas turbine, the steam turbine plant, the Fixed Pitch (FP) and Controllable Pitch (CP) propeller and the waterjet.*

- *Describe some of the properties of the fuels combusted in the prime movers.*

- *Describe the functions of couplings, clutches and gearboxes.*

- *Describe the main characteristics of electric motors and generators, switchboards and power electronics.*

6.1 Introduction

In Chapter 3 the main components of the ship power plant were introduced. To integrate these components in systems, basic knowledge of their main characteristics is required. This chapter will introduce the main characteristics of the most common types of prime movers (mechanical energy generation), propulsors, transmission components and electric machines.

6.2 Prime movers

The term *prime mover* covers all machines that convert primary energy (i.e. energy source) to mechanical energy for use in propulsion or electric energy supply systems. The ones discussed here, i.e. the diesel engine, the gas turbine and the steam turbine plant, are combustion engines. They convert chemical energy in fossil fuels into thermal energy by means of combustion. This energy is in turn converted into mechanical energy.

Based on their characteristics, prime movers can be divided into groups. Firstly, they can be divided into prime movers with internal combustion and those with external combustion. In prime movers with internal combustion, combustion takes place within the working fluid, as is the case for petrol engines, diesel engines, and gas turbines. External combustion takes places outside the working fluid. Steam turbine plants and Stirling engines have external combustion. For the steam turbine, the working fluid is steam and the fuel is combusted with air in a boiler, which is separate from the turbine. The working fluid of a Stirling engine may be air, helium or other fluids. Prime movers can also be divided into reciprocating engines and rotating machines; petrol, diesel and Stirling engines are reciprocating or piston engines, whereas gas and steam turbines are rotating machines.

The choice of a prime mover not only depends on the system in which it will function, but also on the performance characteristics of the prime mover itself. Examples of important performance parameters are power density, fuel and air consumption, and fuel economy.

6.2.1   *The diesel engine*

The diesel engine is a reciprocating internal combustion engine. Diesel engines are used to drive cars, trains, ships and other marine structures, electric generators, pumps, compressors etc. Obviously, in this text the focus will be on marine applications of the diesel engine. The diesel engine is still the most frequently used prime mover in the merchant marine. Powers range between 1 MW for the smallest high speed engines to 80 MW for the biggest low-speed engines. Today its main advantages over other prime movers, are that the diesel engine;

- is relatively insensitive to fuel quality,
- has high reliability,
- has high maintainability due to simple technology,
- has high efficiency,
- has low costs, in terms of initial and operational costs.

The disadvantages of the diesel engine are its pollutant emissions, particularly smoke and particles and, when compared to the gas turbine, its low power density.

In this section the most important features of the diesel engine, such as construction, working principle and performance are introduced. For a more detailed discussion of the diesel engine refer to *Chapter 7 Diesel Engine*.

Construction

With regard to construction, two different types of diesel engines can be distinguished: crosshead engines and trunk piston engines. Figure 6.1 shows the different constructions and the most important parts of the diesel engine. The engines shown are in-line engines, i.e. all cylinders are positioned on one line. Trunk piston engines are also built with two lines of cylinders in a V-configuration, i.e. V-engines.

The engine shown in Figure 6.1-A is a *crosshead engine*. In a crosshead engine the conversion of the reciprocating motion of the piston into the rotating motion of the output shaft is achieved through a piston rod, a connecting rod and a crosshead construction, which is mounted separately from the piston to counteract the side forces. Figure 6.1-B shows a *trunk piston engine*. In this engine, the conversion of the reciprocating motion in a rotating motion is also achieved through a connecting rod. However, the piston skirt is used to counteract the side forces caused by the connecting rod, as a result the piston must be larger than that used in a crosshead engine. Although the piston is larger, the main advantage of a trunk piston engine is its compact size; in particular its height is significantly lower than that of the crosshead engine.

On the other hand, the crosshead engine has some advantages over the trunk piston engine:

- Due to the crosshead construction there is less cylinder-piston wear, so the engine has a longer lifespan.
- Due to the separation between crankcase and combustion chamber, the driving gear is protected from harmful fuel constituents, enabling the use of poorer quality fuels.
- Due to the separate combustion chamber, the engine can use cheaper lubricating oil.

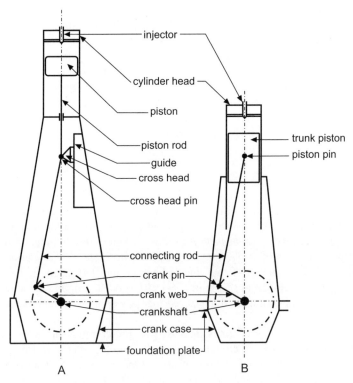

Figure 6.1   Main parts of a diesel engine A) *Crosshead engine* and B) *Trunk piston engine*.

Working principle

The process of energy conversion in a diesel engine is examined briefly. The energy conversion is a cycle of four processes: air inlet, compression, expansion, and exhaust. Combustion mainly takes place during expansion. Consider a cylinder with a piston connected to a crankshaft as is depicted in Figure 6.1. Air enters the combustion chamber above the piston and while the piston moves upwards the charge of air is compressed. When the fuel is injected, it is ignited by the high temperature of the compressed air. As combustion takes place, the gas pressures in the cylinder force the piston down. The reciprocating motion of the piston is transferred to the rotating motion of the crankshaft by a system of rods and pins.

The main difference between the diesel engine and the petrol engine, both being reciprocating internal combustion engines, is the ignition process. In a diesel engine fuel is injected into a charge of compressed air, and the mixture ignites due to the high temperature of that compressed air. This is called compression ignition or CI. In a petrol engine, on the other hand, fuel and air are mixed before entering the cylinder, and aided by a spark the mixture is ignited. A petrol engine is therefore referred to as a spark ignition (SI) engine.

The diesel cycle of processes can be made to occur in four strokes of the piston (two revolutions of the crankshaft) or in two strokes of the piston (one revolution of the crankshaft). The two types of cycles, 2-stroke and 4-stroke cycles, will be examined in detail in *Chapter 7 Diesel Engines*. Four-stroke engines are usually trunk piston engines, whereas two stroke-engines are usually crosshead engines nowadays.

The output of the rotating crankshaft is mechanical energy in the form of a torque M_B (Nm) at an angular velocity ω_e (1/s) or an engine's rotational speed n_e in revolutions per second. The power delivered by an engine is therefore:

$$P_B = M_B \cdot \omega_e = M_B \cdot 2\pi \cdot n_e \qquad\qquad \text{ref. (3.38)}$$

Turbocharging

Today, the principle of turbocharging, see Figure 6.2, is invariably used on marine diesel engines. Turbocharged diesel engines, as opposed to naturally aspirating engines, have a system that pre-compresses combustion air before it enters the cylinder. This is done in order to bring more mass of oxygen into the cylinder to increase the amount of fuel that can be combusted. The amount of fuel injected and combusted determines the amount of mechanical energy developed in the engine. So, if turbocharged, an engine delivers more power out of the same volume, thus increasing power density and decreasing space needed per kilowatt.

The density of the charge of air is increased by pre-compressing it in a compressor, and by cooling it. The charge air compressor is located in the inlet, and driven by a turbine that is located in the hot gas stream of the cylinder exhaust. The combination of compressor and turbine is called the turbocharger. The turbocharger is in fact a small waste-heat driven gas turbine. The charge air is compressed to a pressure that is two to four (or even more) times the ambient pressure. To further increase density the air is cooled, as far as possible, to ambient temperature. Onboard ships this is normally done with cooling water.

More advanced systems of turbocharging will be discussed in *Chapter 7 Diesel Engines*.

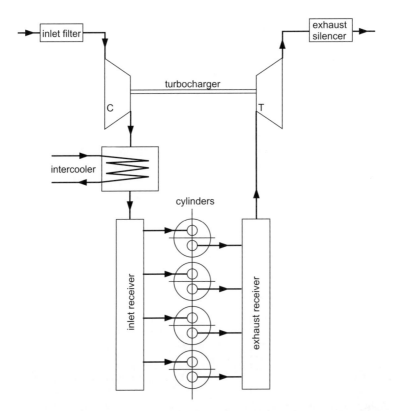

Figure 6.2   Principle diagram of exhaust-driven turbocharging of a diesel engine, including inter-cooling of the charge air. (C=compressor and T=turbine).

Performance

The efficiency of a diesel engine is much better than the efficiency of a steam plant or a gas turbine; this is true at the design point and even more so at part load. The fundamental cause for the high efficiency of diesel engines is the intermittent character of the combustion, which allows high peak temperatures in the cylinder without causing an extreme continuous thermal loading of the surrounding materials. A major disadvantage is that the harmful nitrogen oxides (NO_x) easily form at high temperatures.

As for any other machine involved in energy conversion, the power–speed characteristics, the power density and the fuel economy are important issues for a diesel engine. Other characteristics are maximum obtainable power, air consumption, emissions and costs. Table 6.1 gives an overview of the range of values for different performance parameters. As shown in the table, diesel engines can, broadly speaking, be divided into three categories based on engine speed: low-speed, medium-speed and high-speed diesel engines. Please note that the limits of the categories are not absolute: they must be seen as an indication to mark the categories.

Application

The diesel engine is much older than the gas turbine and in the days of steam found its application in ships where the required power was modest. This of course was before the advent of turbocharging. Since 1950, the development of turbocharging has resulted in a power increase in the order of two to three for a given cylinder volume. As a result, it is now possible to power even the largest ships with diesel engines.

The large, low-speed, 2-stroke diesel engines that can only be installed in relatively big ships may have an output of 30 to 80 MW, a figure that is still growing, particularly for containerships. On the other end, small 2-stroke engines with outputs down to 8 MW are also available. For smaller vessels however, the medium-speed 4-stroke diesel engines are popular. The power of these engines is lower: currently, the Wärtsilä 64 (with a bore of 640 mm and a stroke of 900 mm in-line and 700 mm in V) develops a maximum power of about 18 MW with a 9-cylinder in-line engine and 35 MW with an 18-cylinder V-engine. The power density of a medium-speed engine is higher than the power density of a low-speed engine; this results in lower weight and volume for a required power. For small and fast ships, such as fast ferries, fast patrol boats and frigates, the high-speed 4-stroke diesel engine offers a compact solution up to 7 or 8 MW per engine.

SPECIFIC DATA	DIESEL ENGINES		
	Low-speed	*Medium-speed*	*High-speed*
Process	2-stroke	4-stroke	4-stroke
Construction	Crosshead	Trunk piston	Trunk piston
Output power range [kW]	80000–8000	35000–500	9000–500
Output speed range [rpm]	80–300	300–1000	1000–3500
Fuel type	mostly HFO	HFO or MDF	MDF
Spec. Fuel Cons. [g/kWh]	160–180	170–210	200–220
Spec. Air Cons. [kg/kWh]	9–7	9–6	7.5–5.5
Spec NO$_x$ Emission [g/kWh]	22–14	18–10	13–7
Specific Mass [kg/kW]	60–17	20–5	6–2.3
Specific volume [dm^3/kW]	55–12	28–4	8–2.8
Specific Cost [Euro/kW]	420–400	Line: 330–220 V: 280–170	V: 240–180

Table 6.1   Performance parameters of diesel engines (State of the art 2001).

6.2.2   *The gas turbine*

Unlike the diesel engine, the gas turbine consists of rotating components only, so it can be categorised as a rotating machine. In marine applications, gas turbines are currently used in a range of 4 to 30 MW. They are mainly used in propulsion systems and sometimes in electric power generation plants. Figure 6.3 shows a gas turbine for marine applications.

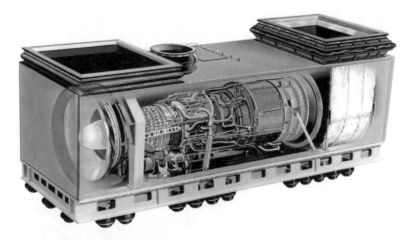

Figure 6.3   A gas turbine module for marine applications: General Electric LM 2500 (Courtesy of GE Marine Engines).

In the beginning of the seventies the gas turbine superseded the steam installation as the propulsion power for naval ships, mainly due to its better efficiency. When compared to the steam installation at that time, other advantages that paved the way for the gas turbine, were:

- *Fast starting-up time*: a gas turbine starts within a minute and can almost directly be loaded. This must be compared with the (many) hours required to heat up the boilers of a steam installation.

- *Modular construction*: the gas turbine essentially consists of a box-like unit having exchangeable sub-units suitable for repair by replacement. This is quite different from the complicated steam plants with all its equipment connected by piping.

- *Easily automated*: since the advent of gas turbines, propulsion can be directly controlled from the bridge.

- *High reliability and maintainability*: the gas turbine is less prone to leakages. Also, the boiler, which has always been a vulnerable and maintenance-critical item in a steam plant, has been omitted.

Nowadays the diesel engine is the most common prime mover for merchant vessels, so it is useful to compare the gas turbine to the diesel engine. When compared to the diesel engine, the gas turbine has a high power density, so it is a light compact piece of machinery. This major advantage for vessels where space and weight are precious, has to be weighed against the following disadvantages:

▪   It has a low efficiency and a high fuel consumption .

▪   It needs a fuel of higher quality.

▪   It is more difficult to repair in situ because it has been designed for repair by replacement.

The breakthrough of gas turbines in the naval field and their application in frigates of many navies around the world has made them "proven at sea". The application in merchant ships, particularly in the larger fast ferries and recently in large cruise liners, builds upon the experience gained by the navies in the last thirty years.

Working principle

The gas turbine as a system consists of an intake duct, a compressor, a combustion chamber, a turbine, and an exhaust duct. Figure 6.4 shows these components in a 3-D cut away drawing of a core engine, i.e. the bare engine without frame, enclosure etc.

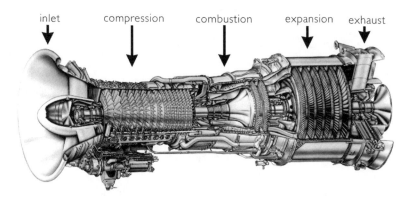

Figure 6.4   3-D cut-away drawing of the core engine of a gas turbine for marine
application: General Electric LM 2500 (Courtesy of GE Marine Engines).

The energy conversion process in a basic (single-shaft) gas turbine is a simple cycle: air inlet, compression, combustion, expansion and exhaust. In the rotating compressor, air is compressed, in one or two compressor sections, from atmospheric pressure to the combustion pressure, which is in the order of 10 to 30 bar. Fuel is injected in the combustion chamber and, after combustion at almost constant pressure, the hot gas expands to atmospheric pressure in a turbine. The turbine delivers power to drive the compressor and a load. The plant as a whole delivers power when the power required by the compressor is less than the power delivered by the turbine. The output speed is high; between 3000 and 7000 rpm, so if a gas turbine is used to drive a propeller, a reduction gearbox is required.

The temperature after combustion is high; for a state-of-the-art gas turbine up to 1500 degrees Kelvin. In order to keep the temperature within acceptable limits the gas turbine uses a large amount of excess air when compared to the steam plant and to the diesel engine. Therefore, the intake and exhaust ducts are of considerable size and require large openings in the main deck of a ship. Moreover, the intake ducts will need silencers which often are located high in the ship. The intake air also has to be clean and the salt concentration in particular must be low: it was the development of special air filter systems that made the use of gas turbines at sea possible at all.

Types

In basic applications the turbine that drives the compressor is also connected to the load: the gas turbine is of the *single-shaft type* as shown by Figure 6.5. In that case, the load may not force the shaft speed to become too low since the compressor would no longer be able to deliver pressure anymore. Single-shaft gas turbines are used for generator drive in which case the shaft speed is kept constant.

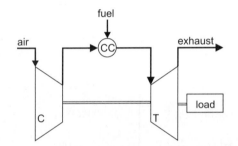

Figure 6.5   Diagram of a single-shaft simple cycle gas turbine consisting of a compressor (C), a combustion chamber (CC) and a turbine (T).

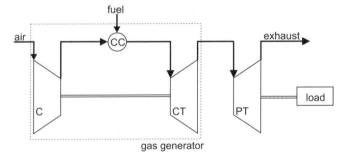

Figure 6.6   Diagram of a twin-shaft simple cycle gas turbine consisting of a *single-spool gas generator* (compressor [C], combustion chamber [CC] and compressor turbine [CT]), and a separate *power turbine (PT)*.

For direct mechanical drive of a propeller shaft, a gas turbine invariably has a separate turbine for the load: the power turbine. With a separate power turbine, the load can follow the *propeller law*. The compressor, the corresponding compressor turbine and the combustion chamber form a separate unit: the gas generator. Figure 6.6 shows a single-spool gas generator and a power turbine. In a twin-spool gas generator, two compressors would each drive their own turbine through a concentric shaft.

If the gas generator is derived from an engine used in the aircraft industry the engine is an *aero-derived gas turbine*, which of course is light and often high-tech. The process of adding a power turbine and adapting the burners from kerosene to diesel fuels is called *marinising* the gas turbine. A marinised gas turbine with its core-engine mounted on a frame and provided with an enclosure is a modular, box-like unit: the gas turbine module.

The bigger gas turbines that are directly designed for stationary applications are called *industrial gas turbines* or *heavy duty gas turbines*. Apart from generally being bigger (up to and over 100 MW), these are relatively heavy machines not designed for aeronautical purposes. In the past, heavy duty gas turbines used to be technologically more conservative (lower maximum temperatures) when compared to aero-derived gas turbines, but this difference has disappeared in modern engines.

SPECIFIC DATA	*GAS TURBINES* Aero-derived	
Process	Simple cycle	Advanced cycle
Construction	2-shaft	2-shaft
Output power range [kW]	26000–6000	24000
Output speed range [rpm]	3600–7000	3600
Fuel type	MDF	MDF
Spec. Fuel Cons. [g/kWh]	240–280	200
Spec. Air Cons. [kg/kWh]	10–15	10.5
Spec NO_x Emission [g/kWh]	2–5	3
Specific Mass [kg/kW]	1.0–1.4	1.8
Specific volume [dm^3/kW]	2.5–4.5	4.1
Specific Cost [Euro/kW]	180–280	470

Table 6.2   Performance parameters of aero-derived marine gas turbines (State of the art 2001).

Performance

The efficiency of the simple cycle, as described above, is generally better than that of a steam plant, but it is inferior when compared to the modern turbocharged diesel engine. Table 6.2 shows several performance parameters.

One of the measures to improve the performance of a simple cycle is *internal waste heat utilisation*. The heat in the exhaust gases can be used to heat the compressed air in a heat exchanger see Figure 6.7, thus diminishing the heat that needs to be supplied by the fuel in the combustion chamber. It will be clear that this form of waste heat utilisation has the potential to save fuel.

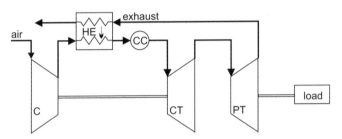

Figure 6.7   Diagram of a twin-shaft gas turbine with a heat exchanger (HE) in which the exhaust gases heat the compressed air that enters the combustion chamber.

Other measures such as multiple compressors, intercooling, multiple combustion chambers and variable geometry blades in the turbine and/or compressor will be discussed in *Chapter 8 Gas Turbines*, where complex cycle gas turbines will be treated.

6.2.3   The steam turbine plant

The steam turbine has lost ground in the propulsion power applications because it has low power density, lower fuel economy than diesel engines and high initial costs. However, a steam turbine plant can burn most fuels in its boilers or use a nuclear reaction as a heat source.

Currently, a steam turbine plant may be used in naval vessels and LNG carriers. The application in LNG carriers has been discussed in *Chapter 5 Power Plant Concepts*. In this section, the focus is on the fossil-fired steam turbine plant, and some attention will be paid to the nuclear power plant.

Sometimes a steam turbine is used in combination with a gas turbine: this combined power generation is sometimes referred to as COGEN, but also as COGAS (combined gas and steam turbine plant). A gas turbine produces exhaust gases, which contain a large amount of thermal energy. This energy can be used to generate steam for a steam turbine. This increases the overall efficiency of the power plant, but it also increases initial costs.

Construction

The steam turbine plant consists of:

- boiler(s) in which steam is generated by burning fuel,

- turbine(s) in which steam expands delivering power to an output shaft; they may be connected to an alternator for electric power generation (turbo generators), or to a gearbox for propulsion,

- a sea water-cooled condenser in which steam condenses to water that can re-enter the power cycle,

- a pump which feeds water into the boiler.

Figure 6.8 shows the components of a steam turbine plant mentioned above.

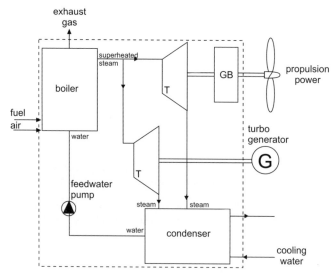

Figure 6.8   Diagram of a basic fossil-fuelled steam turbine plant.

The boilers are large and vulnerable. In large installations the boilers are water tube units. The walls of these boilers consist of tubes in which the water is vaporised. The boiler also contains oil-burners, so it requires inlet and exhaust ducts for the air and exhaust gases.

The pressure is an important parameter for the boiler design with respect to strength and also with respect to efficiency. The temperature of the boiling water is linked to the pressure. Marine boilers have a pressure of about 40 bar, which corresponds to a vapour temperature of 250°C, and in case of superheating the temperatures are up to 450°C. Even then, the temperatures are thermodynamically low, so efficiencies of marine steam turbine plants are low; 28 to 32 %. Land-based installations, on the other hand, have higher pressures and consequently higher temperatures, so they can have higher efficiencies; up to 43 % in non-combined power generation.

The expansion may take place in several stages: a high, a medium and a low pressure turbine, each connected to the gearbox. Also, a separate turbine for astern sailing may be provided and, on naval ships, a cruise turbine could be found to provide economical power at moderate speeds. The end pressure of the expansion process is the pressure in the condenser. The condenser (vacuum) pressure is an important design and operational parameter.

Figure 6.9 shows the schematic layout of a steam turbine plant which includes an economiser, a reheater and a superheater.

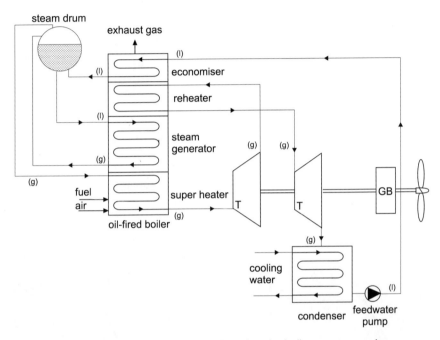

Figure 6.9   Schematic layout of a steam turbine plant including an economiser, a reheater and a superheater in the boiler (l=liquid and g=gas, i.e. steam).

Working principle

There are four processes: feeding water, steam generation, expansion and condensation. The turbine delivers work W_T as a result of the expansion. Heat Q_{in} is added in order to generate steam when fuel is burned. In case of superheating additional heat is added in a second stage. The only work added to the cycle is W_P which is required by the feedwater pump. In the condenser the steam is cooled to condense to water; the heat transferred from the steam to the water and ultimately to the environment is Q_{out}. Figure 6.11 shows the steam cycle of an ideal Rankine cycle in a T–s diagram. The numbers correspond to the processes as indicated in Figure 6.10.

The relations valid for the processes are given next. Heat transfer into the system, in the boiler, has been defined by equation (2.10): it is the enthalpy change between input and exit flow of the working fluid, which at input is water and at exit is steam:

$$\dot{Q}_{in} = \dot{m} \cdot (h_3 - h_{1'})$$

(6.1)

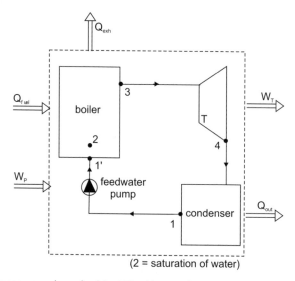

Figure 6.10   Process numbers for ideal Rankine cycle.

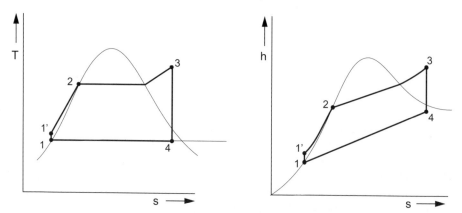

Figure 6.11   Ideal steam turbine plant process: also referred to as the Rankine cycle.

Figure 6.11 shows that heat is added in two stages: first the water is heated to saturation (point 2) and then it is evaporated and superheated (point 3).

Power delivered by a turbine, refer to equation (2.9), is the change of enthalpy in the input and exit flow of steam.

$$\dot{W}_T = \dot{m} \cdot (h_3 - h_4) \tag{6.2}$$

In the condenser, the heat is rejected from the system. Again refer to equation (2.10). In equation (6.3) the input flow is steam and the exit flow is water:

$$\dot{Q}_{out} = \dot{m} \cdot (h_4 - h_1) \tag{6.3}$$

The power added to the pump to feed water from the condenser to the boiler can be defined by:

$$\dot{W}_P = \dot{m} \cdot (h_{1'} - h_1) \tag{6.4}$$

Refer to equation (2.25) where it has been shown that, in the ideal reversible case, this is equal to:

$$\dot{W} = \dot{V} \cdot \Delta p = \frac{\dot{m}}{\rho} \cdot (p_{1'} - p_1) \tag{6.5}$$

With these equations for work and heat flows, the thermodynamic efficiency of a Rankine cycle can be defined as:

$$\eta_{th} = \frac{\dot{W}_{cycle}}{\dot{Q}_{in}} = \frac{\dot{W}_T - \dot{W}_P}{\dot{Q}_{in}} = \frac{(h_3 - h_4) - (h_{1'} - h_1)}{(h_3 - h_{1'})} \tag{6.6}$$

It should be noted that the boiler efficiency (i.e. $(Q_{fuel} - Q_{exh})/Q_{fuel}$) has not been included in this equation.

Steam turbines will not be dealt with in more detail. The interested readers should consult other textbooks to learn more about propulsion or electric power generation with steam turbines.

Nuclear reactor

A steam plant may also be powered by a nuclear reactor instead of by an oil-fired boiler. In merchant shipping, it turned out that nuclear propulsion was not commercially feasible. However, many naval vessels, mainly submarines but also aircraft carriers, are equipped with a nuclear installation. For submarines the main military advantage is that the nuclear reactor does not need air as does a boiler or a diesel engine, so they can stay below sea level for longer periods of time.

In a nuclear installation, see Figure 6.12, the reactor adds heat to the primary water circuit. The primary circuit is radioactive. The water/steam system as found in conventional steam turbine plants is found here as the secondary water circuit. The secondary circuit obtains heat from the primary circuit in a heat exchanger. Temperatures in the secondary system are lower than the temperatures in a conventional steam system, so the thermodynamic efficiency of this plant is even lower.

The nuclear installation described here is also referred to as pressurised water-cooled reactor (PWR), because the primary system is pressurised to prevent the water from vaporising. Vapour would deteriorate the heat transfer.

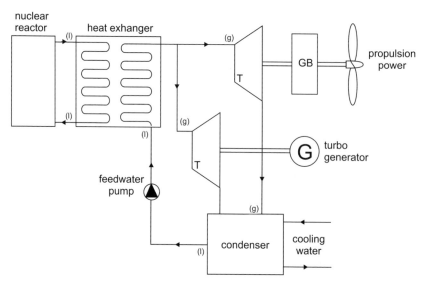

Figure 6.12   Diagram of a basic steam turbine plant powered by a nuclear reactor
(l=liquid, g=gas [i.e. steam]).

6.2.4   Other prime movers

The fuel cell

Although, the fuel cell is not a generator of mechanical power it may be a future alternative for prime movers like diesel engines and gas turbines. The fuel cell may become attractive as it converts chemical energy directly into electric energy without combustion engines and generators. Whether the fuel cell becomes a real alternative for diesel engines and gas turbines depends on its ability to work on (cheap) common marine fuels.

The physical principle of the fuel cell has already been mentioned when the energy conversion of chemical energy to electric energy was introduced. The ideal efficiency of this conversion is equal to the ratio of the change in Gibbs energy and enthalpy of formation (in practice the heating value):

$$\eta_{\text{chemical}} = \frac{\Delta G}{\Delta H} = 1 - \frac{T \cdot \Delta S}{\Delta H} \tag{6.7}$$

A fuel cell consists of two electrodes with an electrolyte in the middle. A fuel, in the most basic cell hydrogen, is continuously fed to one electrode (the anode) and oxygen to the other (the cathode). Chemical reactions at the electrodes form ions that will pass through the electrolyte, and electrons create a current that can be utilised to energise electric users before the electrons are returned to the cathode. Figure 6.13 gives the working principle of a Solid Polymer Fuel Cell (SPFC). Influenced by an anode catalyst the hydrogen atom splits in a proton (a hydrogen ion) and an electron. The protons pass through the electrolyte and at the cathode they form water with the oxygen and the electrons.

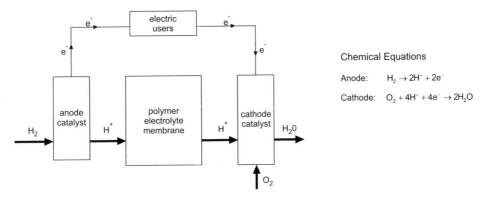

Chemical Equations

Anode: $H_2 \rightarrow 2H^+ + 2e^-$

Cathode: $O_2 + 4H^+ + 4e^- \rightarrow 2H_2O$

Figure 6.13   Working principle of a (SPFC) fuel cell.

The advantages of a fuel cell are numerous: high efficiency, clean emissions (water) and silent operation. The latter is especially advantageous for naval applications, in particular for submarines.

Several types of fuel cells are in use or in development. They are usually referred to by their electrolyte. For low power applications the following cells are noteworthy:

- Alkaline Fuel Cell (AFC): This type has been used in NASA space missions.

- Phosphoric Acid Fuel Cell (PAFC): This cell is commercially available today, but has a modest efficiency.

- Solid Polymer Fuel Cell (SPFC): Also called Polymer Electrolyte Fuel cell (PEFC) or Proton Exchange Membrane Fuel Cell (PEMFC).

The AFC, PAFC and SPFC use hydrogen and oxygen as reactants, but if the latter two include a fuel reformer in the system, the cells can obtain hydrogen from liquid hydrocarbon fuels (which are easier to handle). Fuel cells that do not need a fuel reformer because they can use a hydrocarbon as fuel directly, are:

- Direct Methanol Fuel Cell (DMFC).

For large scale land-based applications, the following are under development:

- Molten Carbonate Fuel Cell (MCFC).

- Solid Oxide Fuel Cell (SOFC).

Both have been successfully demonstrated. The latter has been proposed for marine installations, provided that it is modified to use light fuels and a reformer.

The Stirling engine

Although the Stirling engine was invented before the Diesel engine, it never became as popular. A Stirling engine also is a reciprocating, or piston engine but it does not use internal combustion. The difference with other reciprocating engines is that it has two kinds of piston: a working piston and a displacer, which move out-of-phase. Due to the complex motion of the pistons, the working fluid can flow from one space to another.

The working fluid is a confined mass of gas (air or helium for example) that is repeatedly expanded and compressed. If the temperature during expansion (working piston) is higher than the temperature during compression (displacing piston), the heat energy absorbed from an external heat source is higher than the heat energy rejected to the environment during compression. Theoretically, the difference can be delivered as mechanical work. Internal heat rejection and absorption take place in the regenerator: heat rejected after expansion is absorbed by the gas after compression.

The working principle of the Stirling engine is illustrated by Figure 6.14 and Figure 6.15 shows the theoretical cycle.

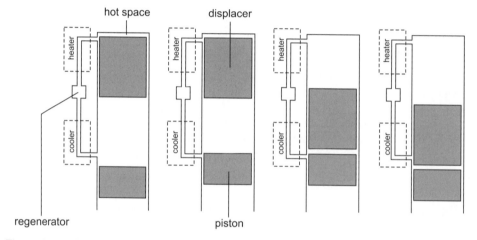

Figure 6.14   Working principle of a free piston or Stirling engine.

If the external heat is delivered by combustion, the external combustion is continuous so the temperatures are limited as for gas turbines. Thermodynamically, however, the cycle is efficient, equal to that of a Diesel engine and better than that of a gas turbine. Compared to the Diesel engine the Stirling engine is quiet because the combustion is continuous and external and therefore the heat addition to the fluid is non-explosive. This is one of the reasons why it has been used by the Swedish navy in a submarine. Also, the Stirling engine can use any form of heat, provided that the temperature is high enough: external combustion of fossil fuels, solar or nuclear sources, etc. So, with the increasing importance of reducing the impact of fossil fuels on global warming, the Stirling engine may offer an alternative.

Stirling engines are currently available in the low power range, up to 100 kW per cylinder, and therefore cannot compete with the diesel engine and the gas turbine at the present time.

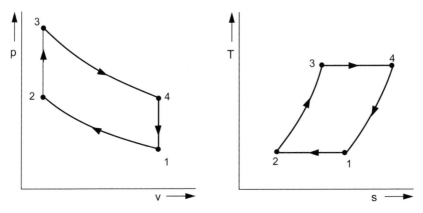

Figure 6.15   Theoretical thermodynamic processes in a Stirling engine.

6.3   Marine fuels

The fuels used in marine combustion engines and oil-fired boilers are fossil fuels. A fossil fuel is a mixture of many hydrocarbons, i.e. structures of carbon (C) with hydrogen (H) attached to it. Besides carbon and hydrogen, fossil fuels may contain some sulphur (S), nitrogen (N), oxygen (O), vanadium (V), sodium (Na) etc. The properties of fossil fuels are mainly determined by their chemical structure: the carbon structures (i.e. straight, branched or cyclic structures) and the chemical bonds, i.e. saturated (single bonds) or non-saturated (double or even triple bonds). These properties fix the ratio of carbon atoms to hydrogen atoms: the so-called C/H ratio, which is important for many properties such as density, viscosity, stoichiometric ratio and heating value. They also determine the chemical stability, or more precisely, their inclination to react with oxygen.

The distillate and residual fuels that are used within the marine industry are the products of a sophisticated refinery process which crude oils undergo. The chemical structure and the refinery process of the crude oil will not be discussed in this book. In this section the most common fuel types and the main characteristics are briefly discussed.

6.3.1   Fuel types

Fuels are referred to by different names, which are sometimes confusing and do not adhere to well defined specifications. For many years the British Standard Specifications (national standard) were used when buying fuels. Also, CIMAC (Conseils International des Machines à Combustion) has been publishing recommendations regarding fuel requirements for marine and stationary diesel engines since 1982. See for example the recommendations in [CIMAC, 1990].

Products	ISO
Distillate products	

–   Gaseous fuels
      methane
      propane
      butane
      (the latter two make LPG)	

–   Light fuels (road transport and aviation)
      gasoline (or petrol)
      kerosene
      gas oil (GO), bunker gas oil, marine gas oil	

–   Diesel fuels
      Marine Gas Oil (MGO)
      Light Diesel Fuel Oil (LDF or LDO)
      Marine Diesel Fuel Oil (MDF or MDO)
      Blended Marine Diesel Fuel Oil (BMDF)
           (light distillate oil blended with up to 20% residual oil)
	DMX
	DMA
	DMB
	DMC

– Lubricating oil	
Residual products	
– Intermediate fuel oils (IFO) Also referred to as Light Marine Fuel Oil or Thin Fuel Oil (TFO) (residual oil blended with up to 40% distillate oil).	RMA to RMH
– Heavy Fuel Oil (HFO) Also referred to as Marine Fuel Oil (MFO), Bunker Fuel Oil (BFO) or Bunker C.	RMH to RML

Table 6.3   Marine fuels and their ISO designation.

In 1987, International Standard ISO 8217 [ISO 8217, 1987] was issued concerning marine fuels and has since replaced the national standards. Table 6.3 is an overview of products with their ISO-designation. The ISO standard uses the DM (Distillate Marine) and RM (Residual Marine) type designation. Additionally, the standard specifies for every fuel type the density at 15°C, the kinematic viscosity at 100°C, the flash point, the pour point, the carbon residue and the ash, water, sulphur, vanadium and aluminium content. In practice, however, the heavy fuels are still often designated by their viscosity number at 50°C: for instance RMG 35 is equivalent to IFO 380.

6.3.2 Fuel properties

Density

The density of fuel oils is normally less then that of water, although for heavy fuel the difference may be very small. It is an important parameter for quantity calculations for transport and storage, and for the selection of the method of purification. According to the ISO standard the density should be determined at a reference temperature of 15°C. In practice, it is measured at storage temperature and corrected back to the reference temperature. Practical upper and lower limits for fuels used in the marine sector are:

$$840 \le \rho_f^{15} \le 1010 \ kg/m^3$$

Viscosity

The viscosity of a fuel is a measure of resistance of the fuel to flow at a quoted temperature. The viscosity used to be given in Redwood, Saybolt and Engler units at degrees Fahrenheit (100°F) but these units are now obsolete. With metrification it became kinematic viscosity in centistokes (cSt = 10^{-6} m^2/s). Viscosity decreases with increasing temperature. For distillate fuels the reference temperature is 40°C and for residuals 50°C. According to the ISO-standard the kinematic viscosity of heavy fuels should be specified in cSt at 100°C.

The most common type of heavy fuel oil in commercial shipping used to be known as Bunker C with 3500 Redwood seconds at 100°F; then its notation became HFO with 380 cSt at 50°C and now it is RMG with 35 cSt at 100°C and classified as an IFO, albeit at the heavy end.

The viscosity depends on the type of oil. In general, a heavier fuel oil (higher density) has a higher viscosity. However, viscosity also depends on chemical structure. If two fuels with the same C/H ratio are compared, the one with a high percentage of long chain-like carbon structures (alkanes or paraffins) has a higher viscosity than the one with a high percentage of cyclic molecules (aromatics). Practical upper and lower limits for marine fuels are for instance:

$$\upsilon_f^{50} = 700 \ cSt \ \text{at 50 °C, for HFO with} \ \rho_f^{15} = 1010 \ kg/m^3$$

$$\upsilon_f^{40} = 1.5 \ cSt \ \text{at 40 °C, for LDO with} \ \rho_f^{15} = 840 \ kg/m^3$$

Viscosity determines whether the fuel can be transferred (often heating is required for pumping), or whether it can be separated in a centrifuge and also the temperature range that is required for satisfactory injection and combustion. Viscosity values for several duties are:

- $\quad v_f \leq 500 \ cSt \qquad$ for pumping,

- $\quad v_f \leq 40 \ cSt \qquad$ for separating in a centrifuge,

- $\quad v_f \leq 15 \ cSt \qquad$ for fuel injection and atomising.

In practice this means that heavy fuel oils must be heated to 50–80 °C or even higher before centrifuging and to 100–150 °C before fuel injection. Also, the fuel injection lines of HFO diesel engines must be heated right up to the injectors, otherwise no ignition will occur, and fuel lines will be blocked during idle time.

Heating value

The heating value, loosely defined as the amount of heat that is released during combustion of one kilogram of that fuel, depends on the chemical structure of a fuel. As a fuel is a mixture of many hydrocarbons and other elements, the precise mixture of which is normally not known, the heating value needs to be measured. Contents of other elements such as water, sulphur and ash have an adverse effect on the heating value. Assumed that after combustion the water is present as vapour, the condensation heat is not included and the value is referred to as the lower heating value.

The general trend of the heating value is that it decreases with increasing density. When expressed as heat released per volume the heating value increases at increasing density, because the decrease in heating value (kJ/kg) is much less than the increase of density associated with it. The consequence is that given a certain tank capacity the energy stored on board a ship is greater for heavy fuels despite their lower heating value. Provided that the ship can carry the extra weight and assuming that the efficiency of the engine is not lowered too much, the range of the vessel is increased when using heavier fuel.

Examples of lower heating values are:

- gasoline   44000 kJ/kg.
- MDF   42000 kJ/kg.
- HFO   40500 kJ/kg.

Ignition properties

The problem of defining ignition properties is that one has to specify a *combined* feature: i.e. ignition depends on properties related to the fuel and on the characteristics of the engine in which it is used. One of the older methods, pioneered by Broeze in the thirties [Broeze, 1960] is the Cetane number. The ignition properties of the fuel under consideration are compared with a blend of:

- Cetane (CT) which has very good ignition properties.
- Heptamethylnonane (HMN) which has a very low ignition quality (this used to be α-methyl-naphtalene).

The mix that resembles the actual fuel in a standardised test engine defines the Cetane number:

$$CN = \% \ CT + 0.15 \cdot \% \ HMN$$

Consequently, cetane has a Cetane number of hundred and lower values indicate worse ignition quality. Good ignition is still assured for values in the range of 40 to 60. The Cetane Index (CI), which is calculated from the density and the mid-boiling point (temperature at which 50% of the fuel is evaporated), is a calculated Cetane Number. They are used to indicate the ignition properties of distillate fuels.

For the ignition quality of residual fuels two empirical measures were developed: the calculated ignition index (CII) and the Calculated Carbon Aromaticity Index (CCAI). The equations of both indices use the density and viscosity parameters of the fuel. The CII gives values in the same range as the CI for distillate fuels, and the CCAI gives values in the range of 760–870. After some trial and error the following (CCAI) was proposed [Zeelenberg, 1983]:

$$CCAI = (\rho_f^{15} - 81) - 141 \cdot \log \log(\upsilon_f^{50} + 0.85)$$

The CCAI number is scaled such that at a viscosity of 1 cSt, the CCAI equals the density. For higher viscosities the CCAI decreases, indicating better ignition performance.

The correlation between CCAI and effective ignition quality is, in practice, still weak. Therefore, combustion test vessels are available, that enable onboard testing of ignition delay of (heavy) fuel oils.

Other properties

Apart from the main properties that were discussed in the previous sections the following properties frequently will be found in fuel specifications:

- Carbon residue.

  This is a measure of the tendency to form carbon deposits in the cylinder, particularly near the exhaust valve. It is the amount of carbon that remains after heating a fuel in a Ramsbottom or Conradson test apparatus. The carbon residue for distillate fuels is low, for example 0.25% on a mass basis, but for residual fuels it can amount to 22%.

- Ash content.

  The ash content is the amount of inorganic materials such as metals and metal oxides (nickel, vanadium, iron, sodium). It can amount to 0.2% for heavy fuels.

- Aluminium content

  The aluminium content is a remnant from the catalysts added during the cracking process (refinery) and thus a measure of the number of "catfines" i.e. small particles (few micron) that can cause abrasive wear. The limit is 30 mg/kg.

- Vanadium content

  Vanadium will form vanadium pentoxide V_2O_5, which is highly corrosive and below 675 °C (melting point) can form deposits in the cylinder and on the exhaust valves (high temperature corrosion).

- Cloud point

  The temperature at which paraffin (wax) crystals will begin to form. This is not wanted, particularly during storage.

- Cold filter plugging point (CFPP)

  The paraffin crystals can obstruct the flow through filters and narrow flow areas. Therefore, another criterion is the cold filter plugging point: the CFPP is the temperature below which it is not possible to pump the fuel through a 45 micron filter.

- Pour point

  The temperature at which so many paraffin crystals are formed that the fuel is hardly liquid is the pour point. Together with viscosity, it is a measure for pumping.

- Flash point

  The temperature at which it is possible to ignite the fuel vapour above a fuel with a small lighter is the flash point. For safety reasons, the flashpoint of fuel stored on board ships must be higher than 60°C.

- Brome number

  A measure for the mixing capability and storage stability of the fuel.

- Sulphur content

  The sulphur content is highly dependent on the source of the crude oil. Sulphur lowers the heating value and after combustion forms sulphur oxides, which are a major exhaust emission pollutant because they can, with water, form sulphuric acid. The sulphur content of heavy residuals fuels is normally around 3 % but may be as high as 5 %. The IMO has agreed on a limit value of 4.5 %. For the lighter distillate fuels, European legislation requires that the sulphur content may not exceed 0.2%.

  At low temperature, H_2SO_4 may be formed in the exhaust gases. This is highly corrosive and damages the exhaust ducting. The exhaust gases may therefore not reach a temperature lower than 120°C.

- Water content

  If water fuel emulsions are proposed as a measure for exhaust emission reduction (NOx), the water in the mixture should be distilled. Any foul water, for instance from the storage tanks, must be avoided in a diesel engine. Particularly the sodium of slightly salt water will, in combination with vanadium, result in high temperature corrosion of the hot parts in the cylinder and exhaust. Moreover, when buying fuel one pays for the fuel not for the water.

6.3.3   *Fuel treatment*

Before the fuel is burnt in a diesel engine, a gas turbine or a boiler, the fuel needs to be treated after bunkering. Although fuel treatment is an auxiliary system that will not be treated in this book, it will be discussed briefly.

Bunker tanks for storage of heavy fuels oils on board ships must be heated since otherwise pumping from those tanks to the settling tank is not possible. A temperature of 5 °C above the pour point is usually sufficient. In general, the temperature will be kept at about 35°C.

The settling tank is the first step in the fuel cleaning process. Water and sediments can be segregated by gravity. The tank must be sufficiently high and preferably tapered to the bottom. The water and sediments can be drained off at the bottom of the tank. For modern heavy fuels the settling tank must be heated to temperatures of 50 to 100°C, to increase the rate of separation.

After settling, fuel treatment of distillate fuels may only consist of a filter if virtually no water is present. If water is expected a centrifuge and a filter will be fitted to remove any water that is still present. In case of more stringent requirements, as for a gas turbine plant, a centrifuge and a coalescer filter might have to be installed.

For residual fuels the treatment will be more extensive. If the residual fuel is burnt in a boiler, the fuel will go through cold and hot filters after the settling tank. If the residual fuel is burnt in an engine, the treatment is more complex: in addition to the settling tank and filters, centrifuges will be installed to separate particles (clarifier) and water (purifier) from the fuel.

6.4 Transmission components

The transmission system is located between the prime mover(s) and the propulsor(s). Its main function is to convert or transmit mechanical energy. The transmission system transmits (1) the torque generated by the prime mover(s) to the propulsor(s), and (2) the thrust generated by the propulsor(s) to the hull.

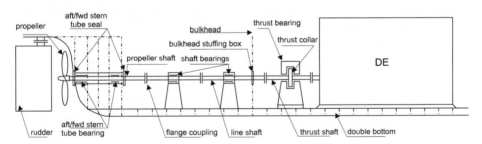

Figure 6.16   Transmission components in a direct drive (single screw).

Figure 6.16 shows an example of a transmission system layout for a single-screw diesel-direct installation. In the example the following components can be distinguished:

- One or multiple *line shafts* transmit the torque generated by the engine, and they transmit thrust if located behind the thrust bearing. The shaft sections are connected to each other with flange couplings.

- The *thrust bearing* and the *thrust shaft* (with *thrust collar*) transmit the thrust, generated by the propeller, to the hull. The thrust bearing may be independent of the engine, but mostly is integrated in the engine.

- The *shaft bearings* support the weight of the shafts.
- The *propeller shaft* connects the shafting system inside the ship with the propeller.
- The *stern tube* guides the propeller shaft through the hull. In the stern tube, the shaft is supported by one or two oil-lubricated bearings: the aft and forward bearing. These bearings carry the shaft and propeller weight, and also the transverse hydrodynamic load acting on the propeller.
- The *forward stern tube seal* assures that the lubrication oil stays within the stern tube.
- The *aft stern tube seal* has two functions: to keep the lubrication oil in and to keep sea water out.
- Where the shaft line passes through a bulkhead, a *bulkhead stuffing box* assures that the bulkhead stays watertight.

In more complex power plant configurations such as in geared drive (single- and multiple propeller configurations) with one or more prime mover, some additional components may be encountered. See Figure 6.17 for an example of a twin-screw ship with two diesel engines per propeller.

- The *(reduction) gearbox* is installed in order to reduce the speed of the engine to the speed required for efficient operation of the propeller. Reduction can be achieved in one or two steps: in one step for medium- and high-speed diesel engines (1:2 to 1:6) and in two steps for gas turbines and high-speed diesel engines (1:10 to 1:35). The thrust bearing is usually integrated with the gearbox or installed close to the gearbox.
- A *clutch* is used to connect or disconnect the engines to the shaft line. It is often included in the gearbox, but sometimes it is integrated with an elastic coupling.
- The *elastic coupling* has two functions: (1) it improves the torsional behaviour of the installation, and (2) it accommodates inaccuracies of shaft alignment and movements of the engine relative to the gearbox.
- The *stern tube bearing* may be water-lubricated instead of oil-lubricated. In that case, only one stern tube seal will be necessary to prevent sea water from entering the ship.
- The propeller shaft is situated behind the ship in the water. It is supported by the *strut* and *water-lubricated strut bearing* just before the propeller. Due to its shape this strut is often referred to as an A-bracket. The shaft is usually protected against corrosion by a glass- or synthetic-fibre coating.
- A *muff coupling* connects the propeller shaft and the stern tube shaft. This coupling does not require flanges at the end of each shaft, so it enables removal of the shafts through the strut bearing or the stern tube. Also, a muff coupling is slender, so it minimises flow disturbances around the shaft, i.e. it minimises added resistance.

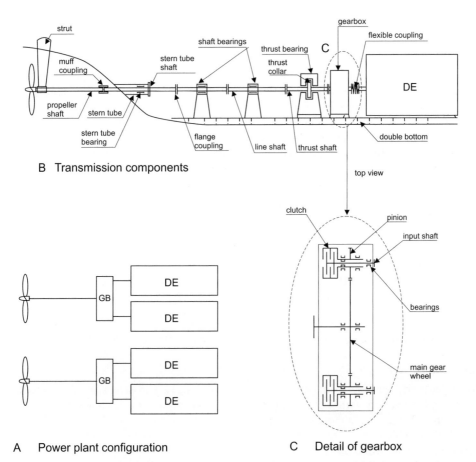

B Transmission components

A   Power plant configuration   C   Detail of gearbox

Figure 6.17   Transmission components of a twin-screw geared drive with two diesel engines per propeller shaft.

6.4.1 Shafting components

Propeller shafts

In general shafts are made of forged (mild) steel. Sometimes high tensile steel, or alloys such as stainless steel are used. Firstly, the shaft and attached flanges are produced in a forging process at a diameter and length that are slightly larger than required. Secondly, the forging piece will be accurately machined in a lathe. Table 6.4 gives an overview of the composition of shafts and some properties of the shaft material.

Most often shafts are solid, but they may also be hollow for example when light shafts are required in passenger vessels or naval vessels or when controllable pitch propellers are used.

Approximate composition	*Material properties*	
	Tensile strength σ_t	400 – 800 MPa
0.2 – 0.5 % C	Yield stress σ_y	200 – 700 MPa
0.4 – 0.9 % Mn	Bending stress σ_b	180 – 400 MPa
< 0.05 % S and P	Elongation ε	app. 20 %
0.1 – 0.45 % Si	Modulus of elasticity E	≈ 205 GPa
	Shear modulus of elasticity G	≈ 83 GPa

Table 6.4   Approximate composition and mechanical properties of a shaft.

Shaft connections

Most shafts are connected to each other by means of flanges. The flanges are forged to the shafts and connected with tight fitting bolts. Muff couplings, as discussed before, and removable flanges are alternatives. Whether connections are established with flanges, bolts or other couplings, it is very important to ensure smooth transitions from one component to the other. Sharp edges should be avoided because shafts are heavily loaded and sharp edges would cause stress concentration that may lead to damage.

FP propellers are fitted to the shaft line with a conical connection. In rare cases, the connection is secured with a key. Due to inevitable stress concentrations around a keyway and the danger of hair cracks, a 'key-less' connection is preferred. A CP propeller is attached to the shaft line by a flange and bolts.

Shaft bearings

Shaft bearings support the shafts. In general sleeve bearings are used. In sleeve bearings the shaft is supported in a lubricating film in a bearing that is usually lined with white metal (babbit). The oil is added to the bearing through a ring that is mounted on the shaft, and distributed by the rotation of the shaft. The bearing capacity of these bearings lies in the range of 0.3 to 0.5 N/mm^2 on the projected bearing surface (length times diameter of the bearing). The length–diameter ratio of sleeve bearing lies in the range of 0.8 to 1. An example of a (self-aligning) sleeve bearing is given in Figure 6.18.

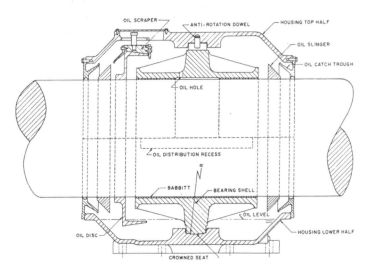

Figure 6.18   Example of a self-aligning sleeve bearing. [Harrington, 1992]

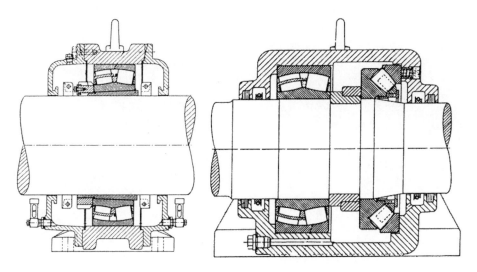

Figure 6.19   Roller bearing in a line shaft bearing (left) and in a thrust bearing (right).

The roller bearing, an example of which is given in Figure 6.19, may be used as an alternative for the sleeve bearing. It is sometimes applied in shaft and thrust bearings. In relation to the sleeve bearing it has the following advantages:

- it is smaller (lower weight),
- friction losses are less,
- there is no clearance,
- it is well-suited for low shaft speeds.

However, the disadvantages need to be considered as well: a roller bearing is more sensitive to dirt and impulse loads, and it offers hardly any to no damping for vibrations in the shaft. Also it is less reliable and has higher maintenance costs. Additionally, roller bearings are applicable for shaft diameters up to 600 mm, whereas sleeve bearings can be made for any shaft diameter.

Thrust bearing

The thrust bearing converts the mechanical energy in the rotating shaft into translating mechanical energy to propel the ship. The thrust bearing has to transfer thrust to the hull while sailing both forward and astern.

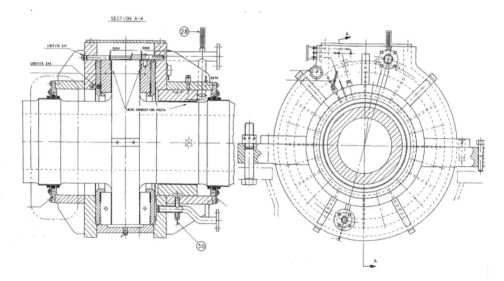

Figure 6.20   An example of a Michell type thrust bearing (Courtesy of Schelde Gears).

In a Michell thrust bearing (Figure 6.20), the thrust is transferred through the thrust collar on the thrust shaft to tilting pads that are supported by an oil film. The bearing capacity of a Michell type thrust bearing lies in the range of 2 to 3.5 N/mm^2 on the pads. The thrust collar and tilting pads are located in the thrust block that needs to be rigidly secured to the ship structure to minimise deformation of the structure, which might lead to non-uniform loading of the pads. As mentioned before the thrust block may be separate but usually is integrated in the gearbox or the diesel engine.

Stern tube and stern tube bearings

In general, two types of stern tube can be distinguished:

- stern tube with oil-lubricated bearings.
- stern tube with water-lubricated bearings.

Water-lubricated bearings are only rarely applied in merchant vessels. In naval vessels however, the stern tube bearings and the A-bracket bearing are sometimes water-lubricated. In that case, the shaft is fitted with a bronze sleeve for protection against corrosion by the sea water. The bearings will consist of a bronze bearing bush on which the bearing material, rubber or synthetic material, will be mounted. The acceptable mean surface pressure is 100 to 300 kPa and the length–diameter ratio will lie between 1 and 4. In case of water-lubricated bearings, the stern tube only needs a forward stern tube seal to prevent flooding of the ship.

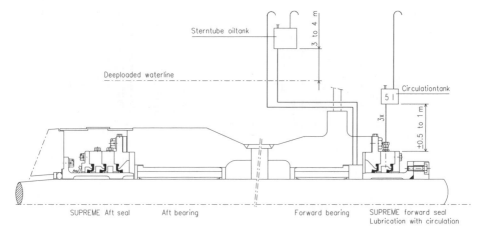

Figure 6.21   Oil-lubricated stern tube bearings and seals (Type SUPREME –Courtesy of IHC Lagersmit).

In case of oil-lubricated stern tube bearings, for example Figure 6.21, the shaft does not need to be protected against corrosion because the stern tube is filled with oil from a tank. This tank will be located three to five metres above the waterline and ensures a slight overpressure relative to the sea water pressure. The bearing bush is often of cast iron and the inner surface of the bush is centrifugally cast with white metal. Common values for length–diameter ratios of oil-lubricated aft bearings are in the range of 1.5 to 2.5. Larger ratios are usually not effective as most of the weight, the propeller, is behind the bearing resulting in high surface pressures aft and low, or no, surface pressure at the front part of the bearing. The forward bearing may have a smaller length–diameter ratio in the range of 0.8 to 1.5 because it has to carry less weight. Acceptable mean surface pressures for these bearings are 250 to 500 kPa.

The stern tube will require two stern tube seals: the aft seal and the forward seal. The aft seal shown in Figure 6.22 (left) includes three lip seals: two water repellent lip seals to keep the water out, and one oil-repellent lip seal to keep the oil in. The forward seal also shown in Figure 6.22 (right) has two lip seals, both to keep the oil in the stern tube.

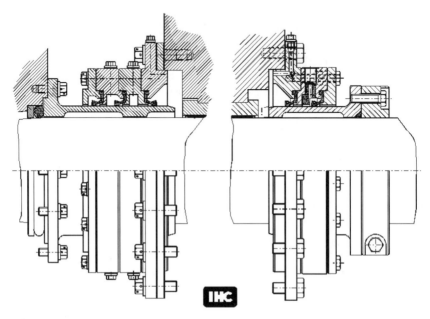

Figure 6.22   Standard SUPREME aft (left) and forward (right) seal (Courtesy of IHC Lagersmit).

6.4.2   *Couplings and clutches*

Flexible coupling

To reduce vibration in a system to an acceptable level, flexible couplings need to be fitted. In a geared drive, these couplings are fitted between engine and gearbox to allow some misalignment and to control the torque variations within the system. An elastic coupling introduces a low stiffness, thus reducing the natural frequencies of the system. Also, they may have good damping quality thus reducing the amplitude of the torsional vibrations. An example of a flexible coupling with rubber elements is the Vulkan Rato S coupling, see Figure 6.23. The torsionally flexible rubber coupling compensates radial, axial and angular shaft displacements of the connected machinery. In the figure the most important parts can be distinguished: the torsionally flexible rubber parts, the membrane permitting axial displacement and the connection parts.

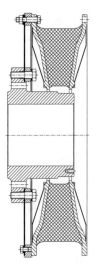

Figure 6.23   A standard RATO-S couplings with rubber elements and a membrane
(Courtesy of Vulkan Benelux).

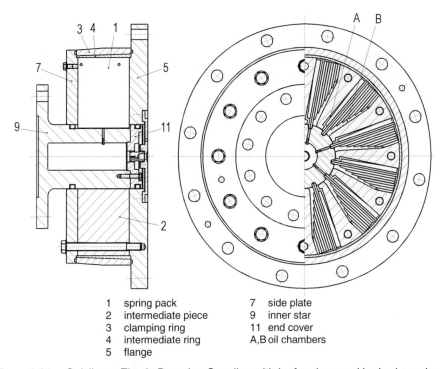

1	spring pack	7	side plate
2	intermediate piece	9	inner star
3	clamping ring	11	end cover
4	intermediate ring	A,B	oil chambers
5	flange		

Figure 6.24   Geislinger Elastic Damping Coupling with leaf springs and hydrodynamic
damping by oil displacement. (Courtesy of Geislinger).

Rubber elements are not the only solution to effectively damp torsional vibrations. Instead of rubber elements a coupling may also use elastic leaf springs combined with oil displacement damping (i.e. hydrodynamic damping). This is used in the Geislinger Elastic Damping Coupling shown in Figure 6.24. The springs themselves have a stiffness, and the oil, while moving from one oil chamber to the other, is subjected to resistance, which retards the movement of the outer part relative to the inner part of the coupling.

Low-speed engines have a rigid foundation, but it is common practice to mount medium- and high-speed engines resiliently. Vibration-absorbing mounts, usually of rubber material, reduce the transmission of structure-borne noise originating from the engine to the hull. If resilient mounting is applied, the elastic coupling should be able to absorb the displacements of the engine that result from this configuration. The engine will be moving in reaction to the engine torque and the ship's motions. To accommodate the engine motions the above-mentioned couplings are often not sufficient, so special arrangements need to be made, for example:

- two elastic couplings in series with an intermediate shaft, see Figure 6.26.

- a coupling with flexible elements in series with an elastic coupling, see Figure 6.25.

With these solutions radial displacements up to fifty millimetres may be absorbed.

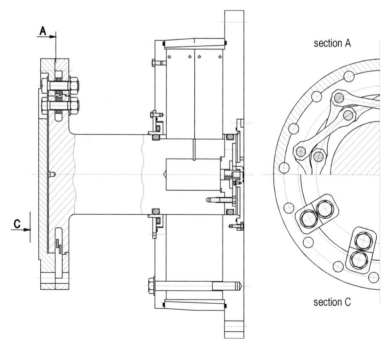

Figure 6.25   Geislinger Flexible Link in series with a leaf spring elastic coupling: the flexible links are shown in section A (Courtesy of Geislinger).

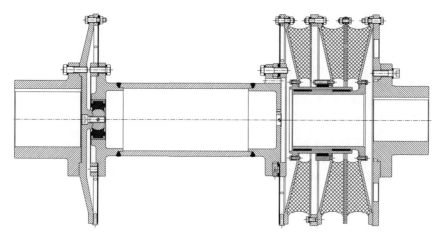

Figure 6.26   Highly flexible RATO-S coupling with 2-row element for articulated drive
shafts (Courtesy of Vulkan Benelux).

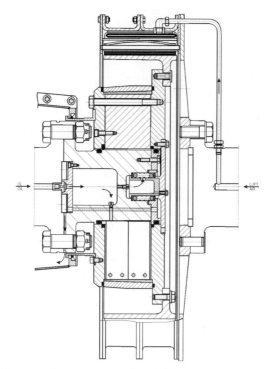

Figure 6.27   Combination of an elastic coupling (with leaf springs) and an air-actuated
Eaton-Airflex clutch (Courtesy of Geislinger).

Clutches

If a ship is equipped with one shaft line and two or more engines, the need arises to connect and disconnect engines to the shaft line in order to sail with one or more engines. This is the task of a clutch. They are either pneumatically (air) or hydraulically (oil) actuated. Figure 6.27 shows an air-actuated clutch integrated with an elastic coupling. The connection between input and output shaft is established by compressed air forcing the inner ring of the drum to move into contact with the drive.

In a plate-type clutch the input shaft has a hub with steel pressure plates at its extreme end. When the input shaft has to be connected to the drive, the pressure plates and the clutch plates that are positioned between the pressure plates are moved into contact. The clutch plates are connected to the clutch spider and the pinion. As the input shaft rotates so does the pinion which drives the output gear wheel. Figure 6.28 shows a diagram of a multiple disc clutch in a gearbox. (See also Figure 6.31 in section 6.4.3 Gearboxes).

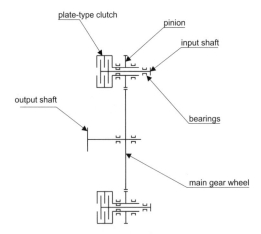

Figure 6.28   Diagram of a plate-type clutch integrated in a gearbox.

In configurations with a steam or gas turbine a self-shifting-synchronous (SSS) clutch will often be used. This is a clutch, with teeth, which engages automatically when input and output speeds are synchronised.

Hydraulic or fluid couplings combine the clutch function and the vibration attenuation function of a flexible coupling. In a hydraulic coupling the input shaft delivers kinetic energy to oil, and the oil will transfer the kinetic energy to the output shaft. The clutch operates smoothly and no wear will take place between the shafts.

6.4.3   Gearboxes

Basically, marine gearboxes consist of meshing teeth on pinions and wheels, which transfer power from a drive shaft (primary) to a driven shaft (secondary) and reduce speed:

$$i = \frac{n_{\text{primary}}}{n_{\text{secondary}}} \tag{6.8}$$

In a propulsion plant:

$$i = \frac{n_e}{n_p} \qquad \text{ref. (3.40)}$$

As a result of the speed reduction the torque at the low-speed end (M_S) has increased:

$$M_S = \eta_{GB} \cdot i \cdot M_B \tag{6.9}$$

A basic problem in the design of gearing systems is achieving a uniform distribution of the forces along the face width of the tooth. If the load is concentrated on a shorter length of the tooth than intended, pitting of the tooth may be the result. For a uniform distribution of forces it is important to avoid misalignments (within the gearbox, gearbox relative to engine, bearings, etc.). Another effect is gear hammer, which causes noise and damage and should therefore always be avoided. The gear may hammer if the load on the teeth changes direction either from the propeller side, as a result of the propeller hitting ice, or from the engine side due to torque variations.

The power loss of a gearbox is 1 to 2 % for single step reduction gearboxes, and 3 to 5 % for more complex gearboxes. As gearboxes transfer high powers, the heat generated in the gearbox due to friction may nevertheless be considerable. The gears are cooled and lubricated by oil.

Most gearing systems contain wheels and pinion where the teeth form part of a helix on the periphery: helical gearing. By placing the teeth at an angle, several teeth are in contact at any time.

In this section, examples of simple parallel gearboxes, a more complex locked train gearbox and an epicyclic gearbox will be discussed.

Parallel gearing

Parallel configurations consist of pinions and wheels with teeth on the periphery. Single and double stage reduction systems are used. In single gears, the diesel engine drives a pinion with a small number of teeth. This pinion drives the main wheel that is directly coupled to the propeller shaft. The double reduction systems are more usual for turbine drives. In a double gear, the prime mover would drive the primary pinion, which drives the primary wheel. The primary wheel is connected by a shaft to the secondary pinion, which drives the main wheel.

Figure 6.29 shows a single input, single output gear and Figure 6.30 shows a double input, single output gear. The drive of these gearboxes is by one or two diesel engines via a flexible coupling or by electric motor drive. The bearings and teeth are lubricated and cooled by oil. A Michell thrust bearing is an integral part of the gear. The gear wheels are made of alloy steel and the housing of cast-iron (other gearboxes may have a welded construction). An important design parameter for the double input gear is the minimum distance between two engines.

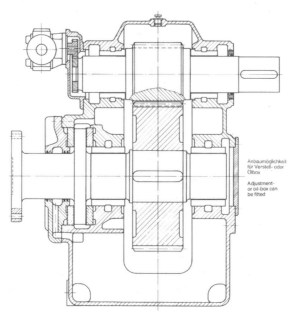

Anbaumöglichkeit
für Verstell- oder
Ölbox

Adjustment-
or oil-box can
be fitted

Figure 6.29   Single input, single output gear. (Courtesy of Renk Tacke).

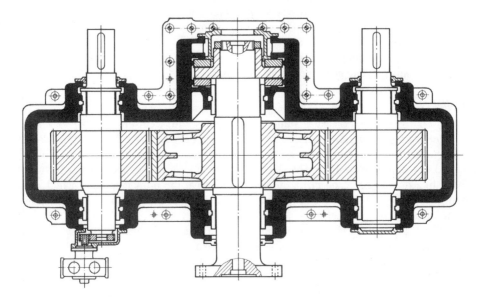

Figure 6.30   Double input, single output gear. (Courtesy of Renk Tacke).

Figure 6.31 shows a special type of the double gear. The type has a quill shaft with a PTO for the drive of, for instance, a generator. The PTO in this example is connected to the primary (input) side of the gearbox, i.e. the engine side. The combination of multiple disc couplings and quill shafts makes it possible to use the engine to drive only the PTO shaft or only the propeller shaft or both shafts.

A quill shaft consists of a hollow shaft through which another shaft is led. In the example the input shaft, connected to the driving engine, is led through a hollow shaft with a pinion. A clutch coupling is provided on the free end of the inner shaft and the hollow shaft. With the clutch it is possible to connect and disconnect the driving engine and the shaft line.

Marine gears are often of the double helical type which means they have two sets of helical teeth in opposite direction on the same wheel or pinion. A single set would produce a resulting axial force; the double set balances out the axial force.

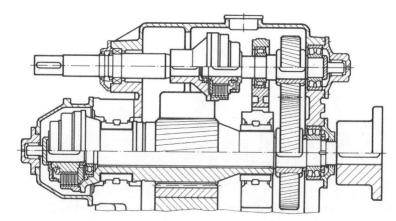

Figure 6.31   Double input, single output and PTO: shown are one of the input shafts and the PTO shaft. (Courtesy of Renk Tacke).

Locked train gearing

Figure 6.32 shows the schematic layout of a gear transmission system for a CODOG propulsion plant of a frigate. It shows the input line for the diesel engine, which drives a pinion with double helical teeth through two clutches. The diesel engine is provided with a single stage reduction: the diesel input pinion is directly in contact with the output main gear wheel. The reduction ratio is 8.6.

The two clutches are installed in series. The first is a fluid coupling, which is used to engage the diesel drive smoothly by gradually filling the fluid coupling with oil. The fluid coupling also ensures an almost complete separation of torque fluctuations of the diesel engine from the gear transmission. It has a very good torsional vibration reduction capability. The second clutch is a self-shifting-synchronous (SSS) clutch, which has meshing teeth. This type of clutch ensures that the input is engaged at the moment of synchronous input and output shaft speeds. As long as the input speed is below the synchronous output speed, this type of clutch is disengaged.

The gas turbine input line is also provided with an SSS-clutch, with the same function as the diesel engine SSS-clutch. The gas turbine needs a higher reduction ratio of 17.1 and is consequently provided with two reduction stages. Because of the high torque to be transmitted, the gas turbine power is split over two parallel gear trains. The gas turbine input pinion meshes with two intermediate gear wheels, which should transmit 50% of the torque each. The intermediate gear wheels are connected by intermediate shafts to two secondary pinions, which mesh with the main gear wheel. In order to achieve a good distribution of torque over the two parallel gear branches, the gears should be accurately adjusted relatively to each other. This type of gear transmission is called a *locked train*.

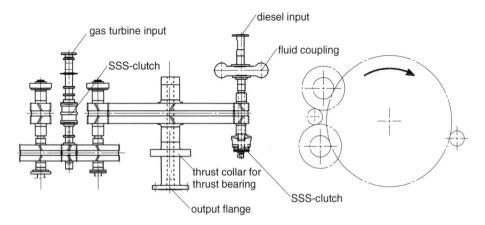

Figure 6.32   Schematic layout of the gear transmission system (starboard side) of a
                CODOG propulsion plant (Courtesy of Schelde Gears).

Besides the diesel engine and gas turbine transmissions this gearbox also includes a Michell type thrust bearing, a turning gear and a locking device. The turning gear can be used to rotate the transmission and the output shaft when the engines are stopped. The locking device can be used to lock the complete system if the shaft is not available, for instance due to damage, so that single-shaft operation on the other shaft is possible. Figure 6.33 shows the view of the input side of the transmission system.

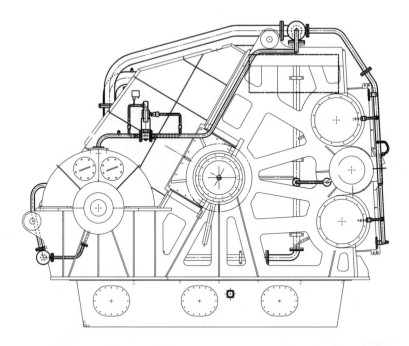

Figure 6.33   View on the input side of a CODOG transmission system (Courtesy of Schelde Gears).

Epicyclic gearing

In an epicyclic system, one or more wheels travel around the outside or inside of another wheel whose axis is fixed. They are referred to as planetary, solar and star gears. Figure 6.34 is an example of a planetary gearbox as made by Renk Tacke.

Note that the input and output shafts are in-line. The wheel on the principal axis is called the sun wheel. The wheels whose axis revolves around the principal axis are the planet wheels. The internal teeth-gear that meshes with the planet is called the annulus. The different arrangements of fixed arms and the sizing of sun and planet wheels provide a variety of different reduction ratios.

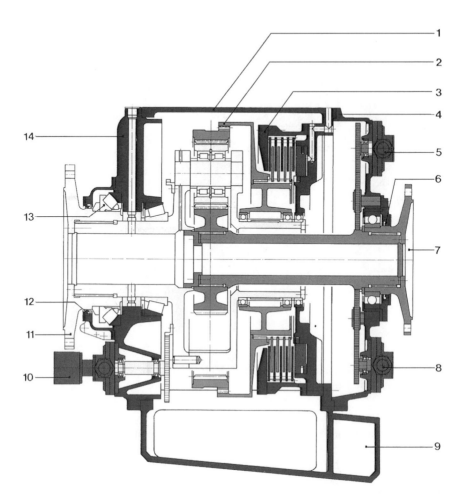

1.	Gear unit housing	6.	Profiled seal, contactless, spark-proof	11.	Output shaft with planet carrier
2.	Annulus, disconnectable	7.	Drive shaft with sun pinion	12.	Profiled seal, contactless, spark-proof
3.	Multi-disc brake, idling	8.	Primary oil pump	13.	Propeller thrust bearing
4.	End cover input side	9.	Oil tank	14.	End cover output side
5.	Primary oil pump	10.	Secondary oil pump (trailing pump)		

Figure 6.34   Planetary gear: Type PLS (Courtesy of Renk Tacke).

6.5 Electrical components

Electric motors, generators and power electronic converters are used as components in an electric drive and in the electric power plant.

6.5.1 Electric motors

For the drive of auxiliary machinery, such as pumps, compressors, winches, capstans and hoisting gear almost always electric motors will be used. The electric motor converts electrical energy, supplied by the electric power plant, to mechanical energy.

In an electric drive an electric motor drives directly or through a gearbox the propulsor. The principles of operation of electric motors are described in Chapter 9. The most frequently used type of electric motor is the AC-motor. An AC-motor is powered by an alternating current supply. For motor powers more than 500 W almost always a three-phase AC power supply is used. For small powers a single phase AC supply may be used.

The "work horse" on board ships to drive auxiliary machinery (although this type is also used in electric propulsion drive), is the asynchronous motor. This AC-type motor is also called an induction motor. The term "asynchronous" refers to the fact that the rotational speed of an asynchronous motor is always somewhat lower than the synchronous speed, which matches with the AC-frequency. The synchronous speed of a motor is:

$$n_s = 2 \ f/p \tag{6.10}$$

where
$$n_s \quad = \quad \text{synchronous (rotational) speed } [s^{-1}]$$
$$f \quad = \quad \text{the frequency of the AC-supply } [Hz]$$
$$p \quad = \quad \text{the number of poles of the electric motor } [-]$$

This leads to synchronous speeds of 3000, 1500, 1000, 750, 600 rpm for a 50 Hz supply and to 3600, 1800, 1200, 900, 720 rpm for a 60 Hz supply, with respectively 2, 4, 6, 8, 10 poles.

The actual asynchronous rotational speed depends on the load of the asynchronous motor and will be in the order of 2900, 1450, 950, 710, 570 rpm for a 50 Hz supply and 3500, 1740, 1150, 860, 680 rpm for a 60 Hz supply.

The term "induction" refers to the fact that the current flowing in the rotor conductors or windings are induced by the rotating magnetic field, created by the stator windings. The most simple type of induction motor, which is also the most frequently used, is the cage rotor motor. This motor has a very simple construction, is very reliable, requires almost no maintenance, and does not use slip rings or commutator brushes. The main characteristics of this motor type are shown in Figure 6.35, showing developed motor torque and absorbed current as function of motor speed.

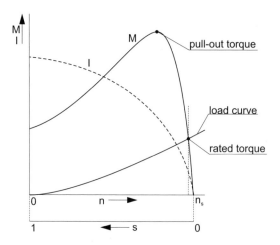

Figure 6.35   Torque-speed curve of an induction motor.

As well as the cage rotor motor, a second type of induction asynchronous motor is the wound rotor type. A wound rotor motor has the advantage over a cage rotor motor in that it offers a simple way of speed control and starting current control. (see Chapter 9). Its disadvantage is that it uses slip rings, which increase the maintenance load. Figure 6.36 shows the torque and absorbed current characteristics of a wound rotor motor, with different rotor resistances switched in series with the rotor windings.

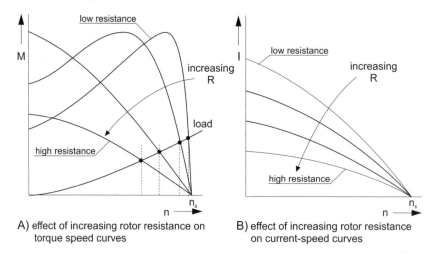

A) effect of increasing rotor resistance on   B) effect of increasing rotor resistance
   torque speed curves   on current-speed curves

Figure 6.36   Torque-speed curves for different rotor resistances.

The synchronous AC-motor is less popular than the asynchronous motor. The synchronous motor, however, has a high efficiency and is frequently used as the propulsion motor in an electric drive. The disadvantage of the synchronous motor is that it uses sliprings to power the rotor windings with a DC-supply. As the name of the motor implies, the rotational speed of the motor matches the frequency of the AC-supply and runs synchronously. The synchronous motor has a very simple drive characteristic, it supplies only torque at synchronous speed. In case the load torque exceeds the pull-out torque (maximum allowable torque), synchronisation will be lost and no torque will be transferred at all.

DC-electric motors are powered by a direct current power supply and are nowadays not frequently used. They require commutator brushes, through which the full motor current flows. This limits their power output; they also require more maintenance than AC-motors. An important feature of DC-motors is that their output speed can be controlled very effectively. Because power electronic converters offer good speed control of both motor types, the application of DC-motors is restricted to submarines and offshore applications.

6.5.2 *Generators*

A generator converts mechanical energy to electrical energy. The operation is based on Faraday's principle (see Chapter 2) and is further explained in Chapter 9. Generators on board ships are nowadays always of the 3-phase AC-type. DC generators are not used because of the disadvantage mentioned above. In case DC-power is needed, AC generators will be used in combination with rectifiers. An AC generator is the same machine as a synchronous electric motor. It uses rotor field windings, powered by a direct current, which induce an AC output voltage on the stator armature windings. The number of poles of the generator is depending on the driving machine.

Turbogenerators may run at 3000 or 3600 rpm resulting in 50 or 60 Hz power supplies with two pole generators. With diesel engines as the driving machinery, the number of poles varies between 4 and 10. The corresponding engine speeds vary between 1800 rpm for 60 Hz 4-pole generators and 600 rpm for 50 Hz 10-pole generators.

The capacity of generators is not expressed in real power terms: kW, but in the apparent power kVA (the product of current and rated voltage; see section 2.3.4), because the armature windings of the generator are not dimensioned by the real or active power, but by the apparent power (i.e. the actual current flowing in the machine (the measure for copper (resistance) losses and heat generated in the armature windings) and rated voltage (isolation class). On the other hand the real or active power (the product of active current and rated voltage) determines the required capacity output of the driving machine.

6.5.3 *Converters*

Converters are used to adapt the voltage and/or the frequency of an electric power supply to the need of a secondary power supply or the need of an electric drive system.

Transformers are used to adapt the voltage of an electric AC supply. They are almost always used to adapt the voltage of the main power supply to the voltage of a secondary power supply, e.g to generate 115 V, 60 Hz single phase AC out of 440 V, 60 Hz three phase AC, but also the creation of 24 V DC out of 400 V, 50 Hz three phase AC requires a transformer in combination with a rectifier.

Transformers are also used in power supply systems which use a medium or high voltage (3-15 kV) for an electric drive to the standardised low voltage (400V, 50 Hz or 440 V, 60 Hz) systems for hotel and auxiliary consumers.

Rectifiers are used to generate DC power out of an AC supply. Uncontrolled rectifiers use diodes and they generate a DC output voltage which is fully determined by the voltage of the AC supply. A single phase rectifier bridge is used to rectify a single phase supply to DC. Three phase rectifier bridges rectify three phase AC to DC. The latter have an output voltage that is much closer to the desired output DC voltage than a single phase bridge.

Controlled rectifiers use thyristors as active components. They are capable of generating a DC output voltage between zero and a maximum value, depending on the voltage of the AC. Controlled rectifiers are used in synchro-converters.

For speed control of electric motors a range of different power electronic converters are used:

-   choppers (Figure 6.37) are used to power the main armatures or field windings of a DC motor, in order to obtain efficient speed control of a DC motor. A chopper supplies chunks of a DC power source to a DC motor. It uses transistors or GTO thyristors as active components. The ratio of the 'on time' of the transistor (or thyristor) to the total time determines the effective voltage supplied to the electric motor and consequently the motor speed.

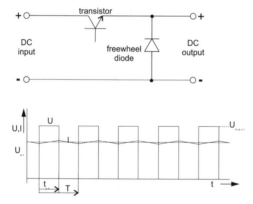

Figure 6.37   Circuit of a chopper and its voltage and current output.

-   synchro-converters (Figure 6.38) are used to power and control the speed of synchronous motors. A synchro-converter has a dual conversion process: it converts three phase AC with a constant voltage and frequency to a DC with a varying voltage and then again to a three phase AC with varying voltage and varying frequency, as required by the motor to run at the desired speed. Synchro-converters are AC-DC-AC converters and are said to have a DC-link. They have ordinary thyristors and can be used only in combination with a synchronous motor. They cannot be used to drive an induction asynchronous motor. The combination of synchro-converter and synchronous motor enables full four-quadrant operation.

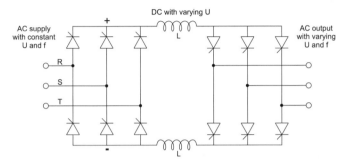

Figure 6.38   Synchro-converter consisting of a controlled rectifier a current source DC link and a thyristor inverter.

- pulse width modulation (PWM) converters (Figure 6.39) are used to power and control the speed of asynchronous induction motors. As with the synchro-converter, the pwm converter has a dual conversion process (AC-DC-AC) and uses a DC link. The DC link, however, may have an uncontrolled voltage, using an uncontrolled rectifier, in which case the voltage is fully determined by the AC supply voltage. The pwm inverter, which converts the DC power to AC, controls both the voltage and frequency of the output AC. To enable this inversion process it uses transistors or GTO thyristors as active components. The pwm converter is not suitable for regenerative braking and therefore operation is only possible in the first and third quadrants. In principle, it can be used in combination with a synchronous motor, but this is never done because this combination has no advantages over the synchro-converter in combination with a synchronous motor.

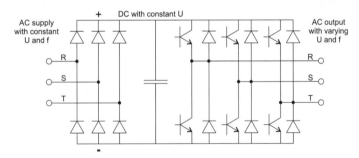

Figure 6.39   PWM converter consisting of an uncontrolled (diode) rectifier, a voltage source DC link and a PWM inverter (using transistors or GTO thyristors).

- cyclo-converters (Figure 6.40) are used to power and control the speed of synchronous motors. They can also be used for asynchronous induction motors. A cyclo-converter is a single stage (AC-AC) converter and converts AC with a constant frequency directly to an AC with a varying frequency, as required for the desired motor speed. Cyclo-converters use ordinary thyristors and enable full four-quadrant operation.

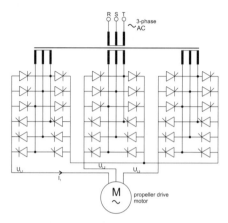

Figure 6.40   Motor drive supplying each motor winding with a 12-pulse cyclo-converter.

The principles of operation of the different types of converters are discussed in Chapter 9.

6.6   Propulsors

6.6.1   Introduction

The screw propeller is the most common propulsor, but there are other types that will also be addressed in this chapter, such as the waterjet and the Voith Schneider.

A propeller generates thrust by means of lift on the blades that rotate at an angle of attack relative to a flow. The geometry of the propeller, in particular the blades, is very important in light of efficiency and cavitation. A propeller will be custom-made to suit the ship and its propulsion engine. Propeller, ship and engine need to be matched to fit all operational conditions in a satisfying manner. This is the subject of Chapter 11. In the current section, the general geometry of a propeller will be introduced, as well as the different types of propeller. Figure 6.41 shows a sketch of a fixed pitch propeller that will be used to introduce the terminology.

The propeller consists of blades and a hub or boss. The connection between hub and blades is the fillet area or the blade root. If a ship is viewed from aft, the side of the propeller blades facing aft is the face or the pressure side of the propeller, whereas the side facing the ship is the back or the suction side. A propeller is said to be right-handed if viewed from aft the propeller rotates clockwise during sailing ahead. So, the propeller shown is a right-handed propeller. The edge of the blade facing the flow of the water when rotating is the leading edge. The flow leaves the blade at the trailing edge.

The propeller pitch P is the distance that a propeller theoretically (i.e. without slip) advances during one revolution. See Figure 6.42. The pitch angle varies with increasing radius. For calculation purposes, a nominal pitch is defined. The nominal pitch is the pitch at 0.7 of the radius. When speaking of the pitch of the propeller it is this value that is referred to.

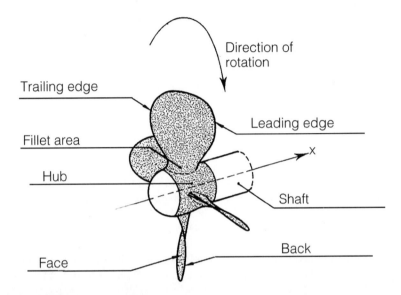

Figure 6.41   Sketch of a propeller.

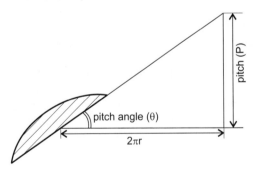

Figure 6.42   Definition of pitch and pitch angle of a propeller.

Two other properties of the propeller blade are rake and skew. If the blades do not stand perpendicular to the shaft centre line in the propeller plane, but lean backward or forward the propeller is said to have rake. Rake is the distance between the blade and the propeller plane at a certain angle. A backward rake, increasing the tip clearance when fitted behind a ship, is a positive rake. A propeller is skewed when the tip of the blades is shifted in relation to the blade reference line. For a detailed description of the propeller geometry, reference is made to [Kuiper, 1994].

The most commonly used propulsors are the fixed pitch propeller, the controllable pitch propeller and the waterjet. Propellers may be equipped with a duct.

Fixed pitch propeller

The pitch of the fixed pitch propeller (FP propeller), although not constant along the radius of the blades, is fixed in any point, since the blades are rigidly attached to the hub. The amount of thrust developed by a propeller is controlled by the rotational speed of the propeller. Stopping and reversing the ship require special measures: it must be possible to change the direction of rotation of the propeller in either the gearbox or the driving machinery.

Controllable pitch propeller

A controllable pitch propeller (CP propeller) consists of a hub with the blades mounted on separately, so that they can rotate, thus changing their pitch. The shaft is hollow and contains a control system, mainly hydraulic, that can adjust the pitch angle of the blades. Adjusting the position of the blades changes the angle of attack in the flow, thus changing the thrust without changing the rotational speed. This has major advantages with respect to manoeuvrability of the ship, as is discussed in more detail in section 6.6.2 (reversing, low speed capability).

On the other hand, the disadvantages are a larger hub, a hollow shaft, a control system and the restrictions to the blade design because the blades have to pass each other when reversing direction. A CP propeller has a slightly lower efficiency, is more complicated and expensive, and is more prone to cavitation than a FP propeller.

Ducted or shrouded propeller

The propeller, either a fixed pitch or a controllable pitch propeller, may be placed in a duct. A duct is a ring surrounding the propeller with a cross section that has a wing-like profile. It can offer protection to the propeller blades and also contributes to the thrust generated by the propeller, particularly at low loads. The profile contributes to the thrust by shaping its cross section in such a way that the water flow is accelerated through the duct. The additional friction between the flow and the duct, however, causes a slightly lower overall efficiency compared to an open propeller. On the other hand, the same amount of thrust can be generated from a propeller with a smaller diameter, making it a very suitable solution for small draught vessels.

Waterjet

Another propulsor that will be discussed in more detail is the waterjet. In concept, it is a ducted propeller where the duct has been prolonged and integrated in the vessel structure. The water is thrust out of the stern through a nozzle. The water is accelerated by an axial or mixed flow pump (basically a propeller) and thrust out of the stern through a nozzle.

6.6.2   The controllable pitch propeller

A common type of propeller is the controllable pitch propeller (CP propeller). The advantages and disadvantages of a CP propeller become clear when it is compared with a FP propeller. CP propellers are used instead of FP propellers for one of the following reasons:

- *To improve manoeuvrability of the ship.*
  - If a CP propeller is installed, the ship speed can continuously be controlled down to zero by reducing the propeller pitch to zero. If a FP propeller is installed, it is hardly possible to reduce the shaft speed until the ship speed is zero, because this causes problems with the lubrication of the shaft bearings at low speeds. If, for example, the prime mover is a diesel engine, the minimum shaft speed is determined by the idling speed of the engine, which is in the range of 25 to 35 % of the maximum engine speed. Consequently, the minimum propeller speed is about 30 % of the maximum propeller speed and also the minimum continuous ship speed is about 30 % of the maximum ship speed. For some applications this may lead to unacceptable situations: if the minimum speed is too high, manoeuvring at low speeds would have to be done by starting and stopping the propulsion plant instead of controlling engine speed. A CP propeller would increase the low-speed manoeuvrability.
  - With a CP propeller, astern thrust, i.e. reversed ship speed, can be delivered by changing the pitch of the propeller. So, the gearbox and the driving gear do not have to be reversible because the direction of rotation of the propeller does not have to be reversed. Also, reversing the direction of rotation of the shaft is, in many cases, only possible when the ship speed is considerably lower than the maximum ship speed. With a CP propeller, these restrictions are largely reduced and the ship will be able to reverse its speed or come to a stop in a shorter period of time, thus increasing the manoeuvrability.

- *To adapt the load characteristic to the drive characteristic.*

  In certain ship power systems, the load as experienced by the driving machinery varies significantly. An example of such a system with a varying load is a tugboat. For a tugboat, the thrust to be delivered in free sailing condition is much lower than the thrust to be delivered in a towing condition. Another example is a dredging ship where the load increases considerably when the ship is dredging. During dredging the ship resistance increases, and sometimes also the dredging pump will have to be driven by the propulsion engine.

  It may not be possible to match these varying loads adequately to the drive characteristic of the driving machinery if a FP propeller is used. With a CP propeller, on the other hand, the load characteristic as experienced by the driving machinery can be adapted, through pitch control, so full power can be utilised.

- *To generate constant-frequency electric power with a shaft generator.*

  A shaft alternator generates electric power with a frequency that is proportional to the engine speed. If the engine speed is variable, the frequency of the electric power will also vary. In most cases, electric power of constant frequency is desired. If a CP propeller is fitted, ship speed can be controlled by controlling the propeller pitch instead of the propeller speed. The propeller speed can be kept constant over a wide range of ship speeds, so it is possible to generate electric power with a constant frequency. However, it may be economically unfavourable to control the ship speed by pitch control alone over the whole speed range of the ship. If the maximum propeller speed is maintained at lower ship speeds, the propeller efficiency will decrease significantly, thus destroying part of the gain of the shaft generator.

- *To improve propulsive efficiency.*

  It is often said that propulsive efficiency improves by applying a CP propeller; some caution needs to be taken though. On the one hand, a CP propeller, in principle, could optimise the propulsive efficiency over the whole speed range of the ship. On the other hand, however, the efficiency of a CP propeller in the design point is lower than that of a FP propeller with equal pitch and diameter, mainly because of the larger hub diameter of the CP propeller. Also, the efficiency of a given blade whose pitch has changed is less than the efficiency of a propeller that has been designed for that pitch. So, unless the load characteristics of the ship are varying strongly, it may not be expected that a CP propeller improves the propulsive efficiency.

Construction of controllable pitch propellers

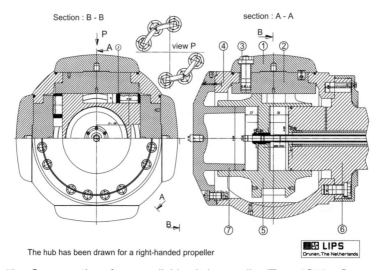

The hub has been drawn for a right-handed propeller

LIPS Drunen, The Netherlands

Figure 6.43   Cross-section of a controllable pitch propeller (Type 4C13 – Courtesy of Wärtsilä Propulsion Netherlands).

Figure 6.43 shows how the propeller blades are attached to the hub and the controlling mechanism of the blades for a Lips CP propeller with a C-type hub. The propeller blade (1) is connected to the crank ring (2) by means of bolts (3) through the propeller root and the crank ring thus enclosing a part of the hub body (4). All hydrodynamic forces on the blade are transmitted to the hub through the bearing between this system of flanges and the hub. The moving cylinder (5) is sealed off at the front by the propeller shaft (6), and at the rear by a cylinder, which is part of the hub cap (7). To rotate the blades, there is a three, four, or five-sided crosshead, depending on the number of propeller blades, on the outside of the cylinder (5). At each side of this crosshead there is a so-called Scotch-yoke that is connected to the crank ring by means of an alignment pin, thus transforming the longitudinal motion of the cylinder into a rotating movement of the propeller blade.

The system controlling the pitch consists of a servo valve, hydraulic piston and a mechanical linking system. The most common configurations have the hydraulic piston incorporated in the propeller hub. The servo valve is located inboard. The hydraulic oil necessary for the control of the pitch is supplied to the hub through piping in the hollow propeller shaft. The oil is supplied to these pipes either through the oil distribution assembly at the front of the gearbox, or through the oil distribution assembly somewhere in the shaft line, see Figure 6.44. The latter will be selected in cases of very long shafting, or if no gearbox is installed. Instead of being incorporated in the hub, the hydraulic piston can also be situated inboard. In that case, the motion of the piston is transmitted to the propeller blades through a long mechanical link in the hollow propeller shaft. This configuration, however, is not very common for high power installations.

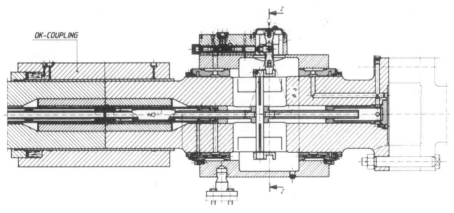

Figure 6.44   Oil distribution assembly of a CP propeller. (Courtesy of Wärtsilä Propulsion Netherlands).

6.6.3   The waterjet

In the foregoing chapters, it was assumed that a screw type propeller is used to propel a ship. However, for high-speed craft the waterjet is often an attractive, light and efficient solution. A waterjet mainly consists of a water inlet channel, a pump that accelerates the water and a nozzle. In an ideal waterjet, the thrust developed is equal to the change in velocity over the pump times the mass flow:

$$T = \dot{m} \cdot (v_{out} - v_{in}) = \dot{m} \cdot \Delta v \qquad (6.11)$$

The water inlet is located in the bottom of the ship and the outlet nozzle in the ship's stern, either just under or just above water level. Behind the nozzle, in the stream of water at the outlet, a steering and reversing bucket is mounted, which is controlled by hydraulic rams.

Figure 6.45 shows the cross section of a Lips waterjet. The main components are indicated. Waterjets can be used in a wide power range: currently from 300 kW for small units to 25 000 kW for large unit. Larger units of 50 000 kW are being developed. Up to powers of 1000 kW at 1800 to 2500 rpm, waterjets can be direct-driven units, thus eliminating the gearbox and making the unit lighter.

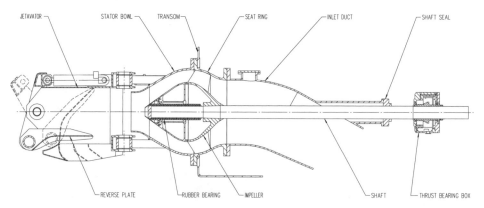

Figure 6.45   A typical cross section of a direct drive waterjet unit (Courtesy of Wärtsilä Propulsion Netherlands).

Advantages of the waterjet are:

- no underwater appendages, so very suitable for ships with draught restrictions and no added resistance.

- average overall efficiency for modern waterjet driven vessel: 65 to 70 % (maximum achievable overall efficiency is currently 74 %).

- low weight.

- low underwater noise.

- no reverse gear required.

- no long and complex transmission line.

Operational characteristics

Manufacturers of waterjets usually supply diagrams in which effective thrust T and required torque M_D are shown as functions of ship speed and impeller speed. The diagrams apply to a certain application of a waterjet in combination with a certain hull and location of the jet relative to the hull: the diagrams take into account the interaction between the waterjet and the hull. Such diagrams are shown in Figure 6.46.

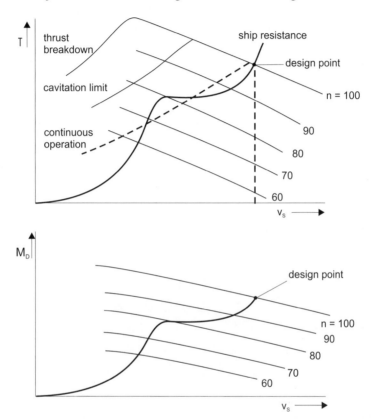

Figure 6.46   Operational characteristics of a waterjet including the ship resistance curve of a fast ship.

Effective thrust is the thrust which can be compared with the ship's resistance *R*. The thrust diagram includes limitation lines for continuous operation, cavitation and thrust breakdown. Additionally, it shows a ship resistance curve for a high speed ship and the operational point of the waterjet. Continuous operation is allowed below the continuous operation limit. In the zone between continuous operation and cavitation, intermittent operation for acceleration is allowed.

The combination of a waterjet and a prime mover will be dealt with in Chapter 10.

6.6.4   Other propulsors

Besides the FP propeller, the CP propeller and the waterjet other propulsors may be found. In this section, some are mentioned briefly.

Pump jet and counter-rotating propellers

The pump jet and the counter-rotating propeller are two methods of propulsion that are hardly ever used in commercial vessels. They are, however, used in naval applications: pump jets on submarines and counter-rotating propellers on torpedoes.

Counter-rotating propeller arrangements consist of two propellers behind each other driven by a coaxial shaft system. Both propellers can have different diameters and blade numbers but their direction of rotation is opposite, hence *counter-rotating*. The second propeller is installed with the intention to win back a major part of the kinetic energy in the wake caused by the first propeller, thus increasing efficiency. An additional advantage is that noise and vibrations are reduced, because for a given propeller diameter the thrust is distributed over almost twice the propeller blade area, which is favourable for the radiated noise

A pump jet is actually a ducted propeller with a large number of blades: more than 7. It is located in a duct that decelerates the water flow, see Figure 6.47. The rotation of the wake is eliminated by means of guide vanes placed in front of or behind the propeller. The radiated noise is reduced through a large blade area, and thus low propeller loading, and the occurrence of tip vortexes, is avoided. Their low noise emission makes these propellers very suitable for submarines.

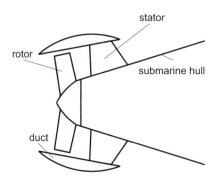

Figure 6.47   Diagram of a pump jet in a decelerating duct on a submarine.

Azimuth thrusters

An azimuth thruster is a propeller that can rotate through 360 degrees in the horizontal plane, thus allowing the thrust to be generated in any desired direction. It therefore eliminates the use of rudders to direct the thrust. Azimuth thrusters offer ships enhanced manoeuvrability. Large ships equipped with azimuth thrusters often do not need a tug during manoeuvring. Thrusters are also used for dynamic positioning in the offshore industry. They are either powered through a mechanical Z- or L-drive or by an electric motor built into the so-called pod (podded drive). If podded, space within the hull otherwise taken by propulsion motors and shaft lines may be used for other purposes. Figure 6.48 shows a thruster with a ducted CP propeller driven through a Z-drive.

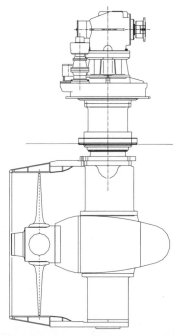

Figure 6.48   Steerable thruster in Z-configuration; the propeller is a ducted CP propeller
(Courtesy of Wärtsilä Propulsion Netherlands).

Figure 6.49 shows the structure of an azimuthing podded thruster. Small types are available in a range from 400 kW up to 5.0 MW. Larger types are available up to 38 MW.

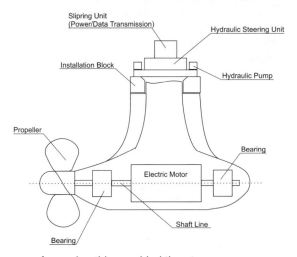

Figure 6.49   Diagram of an azimuthing podded thruster.

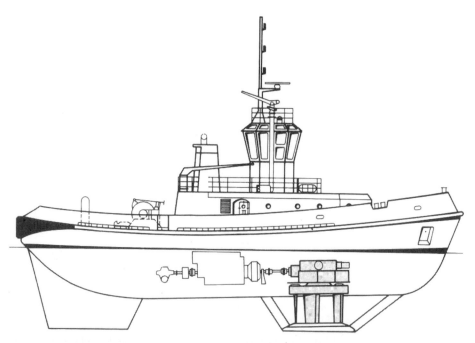

Figure 6.50   A tug with Voith-Schneider propeller (Courtesy of Voith-Schneider).

Voith-Schneider propeller

A Voith-Schneider propeller consists of a number of vertically placed foils underneath the ship. A Voith-Schneider propeller offers a ship excellent manoeuvrability and low noise and vibration. Voith-Schneiders are found in ships in which accurate propulsion (and stopping) and steering are the main functions, such as tugs, mine hunters, ferries and floating cranes. An example of the application of a Voith-Schneider is the tug in Figure 6.50. The propeller blades rotate along a circle and around their own vertical axis in such a manner that thrust is generated.

Each of the blades generate thrust as they flow through the water. The pitch angle of the blades and the speed of rotation can be controlled to change the thrust. Through displacement of the steering centre, thrust can be produced in any direction.

Whale tail

The whale tail is, like the old paddle wheel, an example of a propulsor working in discrete strokes based on the impulse principle. It consists of two wheels with a number of horizontal foils in between. The propulsor is mounted over a large part of the width of the aftbody of the ship.

It is basically the horizontal version of a Voith-Schneider propeller. However, the span of the blades of a whale tail may be larger, leading to a lower thrust loading per unit area. Also the path of the blades through the water is different (trochoid versus cycloid) and the angles of the blades of a whale tail are continuously adjusted by a servomotor.

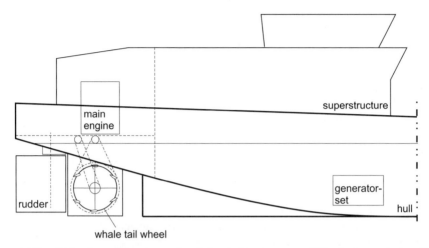

Figure 6.51 Side view of the stern of an inland shipping vessel fitted with a whale tail wheel that is mounted over about 80% of the width of the ship. Two or three rudders may be necessary.

In a whale tail propeller, a relatively large amount of water is set in motion at low speed. This offers the potential for high efficiency. As a result of the low water-velocities, cavitation is less likely to occur. Additionally, noise and vibration on board caused by the propulsor have low levels because the pressure pulse at the hull above the propulsor are low.

The drive of a whale tail is technically challenging. Where the drive of the Voith-Schneider is inside the hull at the top of the blades, the horizontal version has to be driven at two sides and it is submerged in water. This introduces advanced bearings and a more complex construction than the Voith-Schneider.

A whale tail wheel may be an interesting alternative for inland shipping vessels (Figure 6.51) where the thrust loading coefficient of a propeller would be high and the diameter of the propeller is limited by draught restrictions. To obtain higher efficiency, lower thrust loading is desirable. Thrust loading decreases with increasing propulsor area. Tests at MARIN have shown that the efficiency of whale tail propulsion is better than the efficiency of conventional propeller propulsion.

6.7   References and further reading

Broeze, 1960

J.J Broeze: *"Combustion in piston engines"*, De Technische Uitgeverij H.Stam, 1960.

CIMAC, 1990

"Recommendations regarding fuel requirements for diesel engines", 3rd edition, CIMAC 1990.

Cowley, 1994

Dr J Cowley: *"The Running and Maintenance of Marine Machinery"*, The Institute of Marine Engineers, UK 1994.

Harrington, 1992

R. L. Harrington: *"Marine Engineering"*, The Society of Naval Architects and Marine Engineers, USA 1992.

ISO 8217, 1987

"Petroleum Products Fuel (Class F)–specifications for marine fuels", ISO, 1987.

Kuiper, 1994

G. Kuiper: *"Resistance and Propulsion of Ships"*, Delft University of Technology, 1994.

Taylor, 1990

D. A. Taylor: *"Introduction to Marine Engineering"*, Second edition, Butterworth and Heinemann Ltd, USA 1990 (reprinted 2001).

Zeelenberg, 1983

A.P. Zeelenberg, H.J. Fijn van Draat, H.L. Barker: *"The ignition performance of fuel oils in Marine Diesel engines"*, CIMAC Paris 1983.

Chapter 7

Diesel Engines

7.0   Learning goals

After studying this chapter, the student should be able to:

-   *Describe the working principles of the 2-stroke and 4-stroke diesel engine and sketch the associated indicator (p–V) diagram.*

-   *Define and apply the thermodynamic concepts power, work, heat, mean effective pressure and efficiency.*

-   *Define compression ratio, stroke–bore ratio, specific fuel consumption, air–fuel ratio, air excess ratio and mean piston speed.*

-   *Explain the purpose and working principle of turbocharging and distinguish the different types.*

-   *Explain the limits of the operating envelope of a diesel engine.*

-   *Explain methods to broaden the operating envelope.*

-   *Explain the limits to power and power density.*

-   *Explain the influence of design parameters to the performance of an engine by using air–standard cycles.*

-   *Apply Seiliger cycle, also called dual cycle, to calculate engine performance.*

7.1   Introduction

In this chapter, the diesel engine is studied in more detail. Before studying this chapter, the student must be familiar with the basic thermodynamic principles that were dealt with in Chapter 2 and the introduction of the diesel engine in Chapter 6.

The working principle of the diesel engine and parameters that quantify the output of the engine, such as mean effective pressure and indicated work, will be described. The output of energy will be weighed against the input of energy in section 7.4 *Performance*. An important performance parameter is the effective efficiency, which relates the work output to the fuel-related heat input. Effective efficiency includes the effects of heat loss, incomplete combustion of the fuel and mechanical losses. Other important performance parameters are fuel consumption, air consumption, air–fuel ratio and air excess ratio.

To increase the power output, most engines are equipped with a turbocharger, so the working principles of turbocharging and the effect on operation will be studied in detail.

These considerations are used to compare the operating envelope of naturally aspirating engines with the envelope of a turbocharged engine.

Power density is an important parameter to express the output of an engine related to its size or weight, which are important for a marine engineer. The effect of parameters like engine speed, mean piston speed and mean effective pressure on the power density is studied in section 7.7 *Power density*.

For accurate calculations, the need arises for an analytical description of the complex cylinder processes. In this chapter, it will be shown that the Seiliger cycle, also referred to as the air-standard dual cycle, is a suitable tool. Using basic thermodynamic principles, the processes in the cylinder can be described, and parameters like efficiency and mean effective pressure can be found.

The aim of the chapter is to give the student a deep understanding of the characteristics of an engine in order to integrate the engine in marine systems, not to design the engine. However, the marine engineer should realise that some design parameters, such as peak pressure, mean piston speed and air excess ratio introduce restrictions on characteristics that are important for the operational side of the engine such as power or power density.

7.2   Working principle

Diesel engines transform chemical energy stored in fuels into mechanical energy at the output shaft. This conversion process takes place in two steps: first, chemical energy is converted into thermal energy by means of a combustion reaction of the fuel, with the working medium, air and second, the thermal energy is converted into mechanical energy.

The basic diesel cycle consists of air inlet, compression, combustion and expansion, and exhaust. These processes can be achieved in two strokes of the piston or in four strokes, i.e. in a 2-stroke cycle or in a 4-stroke cycle. Before discussing the different cycles, focus is on the cylinder geometry.

7.2.1   Cylinder geometry

A stroke is defined as the distance travelled by the piston between the extreme top position and the extreme bottom position: top dead centre (TDC) and bottom dead centre (BDC). The inside diameter of the cylinder is the bore D_B [m]. The stroke–bore ratio λ_S [-] is the ratio of stroke length L_S [m] to bore diameter. The cylinder volume that corresponds with the stroke is the swept volume V_S [m³], and equals the product of bore area and stroke length. The volume above the piston at BDC is the maximum cylinder volume V_{BDC}, whereas the volume above the piston at TDC is the clearance or compression volume V_{TDC}. The ratio of V_{BDC} to V_{TDC} is the geometric compression ratio ε [-].

$$\lambda_S = \frac{L_S}{D_B} \tag{7.1}$$

$$V_S = A_B \cdot L_S = \frac{\pi}{4} \cdot D_B^2 \cdot L_S \tag{7.2}$$

$$\varepsilon = \frac{V_{BDC}}{V_{TDC}} \qquad (7.3)$$

7.2.2 The 4-stroke cycle

Figure 7.1 depicts the basic cycle of a 4-stroke diesel engine.

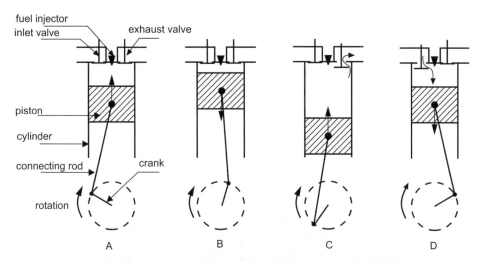

Figure 7.1   Working principle of a 4-stroke diesel engine: A) Compression, B) combustion and expansion, C) exhaust, and D) air inlet.

A. *Compression stroke:*

The piston moves upward from BDC to TDC. Inlet and exhaust valves are closed and the combustion air is compressed. The compression of air causes an increase in temperature. Fuel is injected several crank degrees before TDC, and ignited by the high temperature of the compressed charge. At the end of the compression stroke combustion has started.

B. *Power stroke:*

The combustion is continued over a considerable crank angle after TDC, while the combustion gases expand and perform work on the piston forcing it down from TDC to BDC. Towards the end of the stroke the exhaust valve opens, thereby releasing the gas into the exhaust manifold. During the outflow the high cylinder pressure and the exhaust pressure are equalized; this is called the blow down.

C. *Exhaust stroke:*

The piston moves from BDC to TDC. The exhaust valve is open and the rest of the combustion gases are forced out of the cylinder by the upward stroke of the piston. The gases that remain in the clearance volume may be dispelled by a scavenging process; in that case the inlet valve must be opened early whereas the exhaust valve must be closed late, so that both are open at the same time (valve overlap). Scavenging also requires that the pressure in the inlet air manifold is higher than the pressure in the exhaustmanifold.

D   *Intake stroke (charging):*

The piston moves downward from TDC to BDC. The inlet valve is open, and the exhaust valve closed, while the cylinder fills with a charge of fresh air and will be ready for the compression stroke.

A complete cycle takes four strokes, or two crank revolutions. Only one of these strokes is a power stroke (B). In other words, one power stroke takes place every 4 strokes of the piston, or every two crankshaft revolutions.

7.2.3   The 2-stroke cycle

The cycle of processes can also be completed in two piston strokes. The main difference with the 4-stroke cycle is that charging and exhaust take place without the piston enforcing the process. Figure 7.2 shows the basic cycle of a 2-stroke diesel engine.

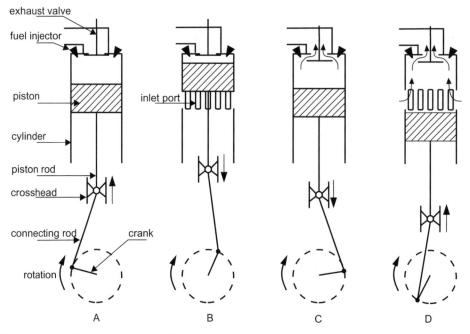

Figure 7.2   Working principle of a 2-stroke diesel engine: A) Compression, B) combustion and expansion, C) exhaust, and D) air inlet.

A. *Compression stroke:*

The inlet ports and exhaust valve are closed and a volume of air is trapped in the cylinder. The piston moves upward to TDC thus compressing this combustion air and causing a temperature rise that is sufficient to ignite the fuel that has been injected several degrees before TDC. At the end of the compression stroke combustion has started.

B. *Power stroke:*

Combustion is continued. The combustion gases expand and perform work on the piston forcing it down from TDC to BDC. Towards the end of the expansion the exhaust valve opens.

C. *Exhaust:*

The combustion gases blow down to manifold pressure. By the time the inlet ports are open, the cylinder pressure will have reached a pressure lower than that of the scavenging air, so scavenging starts.

D. *Scavenging:*

Scavenging, which started in C while the piston moved downward, is completed while the piston moves upward. Both the inlet ports and exhaust valves are open: fresh air (scavenging air) enters the cylinder forcing the exhaust gases out. See also Figure 7.3. In order to scavenge the cylinder it is necessary to pre-compress the scavenging air with a scavenging air compressor or with the compressor of the turbocharging system.

Processes B and C take place in one stroke, A and D in another, thus describing a two-stroke cycle. One power stroke occurs every two strokes, or every revolution of the crankshaft.

The process described here is valid for a 2-stroke diesel engine with *uni-flow scavenging*. This type of engine has inlet ports low in the cylinder wall and an exhaust valve in the cylinder head. This is by far the most common type of 2-stroke diesel engine nowadays. Another kind of scavenging that was common until the 1980s is loop scavenging. For this kind of scavenging the engine has inlet as well as exhaust ports in the cylinder wall causing the flow to *loop*. See Figure 7.3.

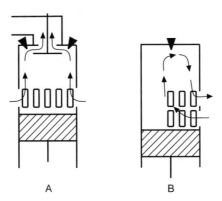

A   B

Figure 7.3   Scavenging in a 2-stroke diesel engine: A) *Uni-flow scavenging* and B) *Loop scavenging.*

7.3   The indicator diagram

The indicator diagram shows the relation between volume and pressure in a cylinder. It can be obtained from a cylinder with a sensor that measures gas pressure during the cycle. (The pressure sensor used to be a mechanical device called a pressure indicator, hence *indicator diagram*). The area in the diagram represents the work developed within the engine cylinder; the indicated work. Other concepts, such as effective work, mechanical efficiency, mean indicated pressure and mean effective pressure, can also be derived from the indicator diagram.

7.3.1   The indicator (p–V) diagram.

A diesel cylinder process can be depicted in a diagram plotting the indicated pressure versus volume, i.e. the indicator diagram. Figure 7.4 shows the pressure in the cylinder as a function of cylinder volume: A) applies to 4-stroke engines and B) applies to 2-stroke engines. Table 7.1 describes the processes that can be distinguished in the diagram.

Process	Description
1–2	The air in the cylinder is compressed by the upward moving piston.
2–3	Combustion of the injected fuel takes place at almost constant volume (pressure increases).
3–4	Combustion continues at almost constant pressure (volume increases).
4–5	Expansion of the combustion gases until the exhaust valves or ports are opened before BDC.
5–6	The combustion gases blow down to exhaust-manifold pressure before the piston reaches BDC.
6–7	The combustion gases are forced out of the cylinder. In a 4-stroke engine, this is done by the piston. In a 2-stroke engine, the inlet ports are open and combustion gases exit by scavenging.
7–8	Through the opened inlet valve (4-stroke cycle) the cylinder is charged with air. In a 4-stroke engine, the piston moves down.
8–1	In a 4-stroke diesel engine, the inlet valve is often closed after BDC whereby some charge air may be lost, but compression work is diminished (Miller timing). In a 2-stroke engine process 8–1 is available for scavenging.

Table 7.1   Description of processes in indicator diagram.

Note that the processes 1–2, 2–3, 3–4, 4–5 and 8–1 are roughly the same for both cycles. The indicator diagram of a 4-stroke cycle clearly distinguishes processes 6–7 and 7–8 because the piston makes an extra stroke to expel gas and to take in air.

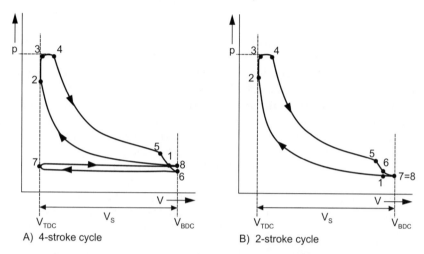

A) 4-stroke cycle   B) 2-stroke cycle

Figure 7.4   Cycle process of a diesel engine in indicator diagrams: A) *4-stroke cycle* and B) *2-stroke cycle*.

7.3.2   *Indicated work*

The indicated work W_i in Joule per cycle is the sum of delivered expansion work and exerted compression work. During expansion, when the piston moves from top dead centre to bottom dead centre, the process delivers work to the piston. The work delivered to the piston during the complete expansion stroke is defined by equation (7.4) (When it is assumed that the process is reversible, which is approximately true).

$$W_{exp} = \int_{V_{TDC}}^{V_{BDC}} p_{exp} \cdot dV \qquad (7.4)$$

Where p_{exp} [Pa] is the pressure during expansion. This is the area under the expansion line in the p–V diagram (Figure 7.4). During compression, when the piston moves upward from bottom dead centre to top dead centre, work is exerted on the process. The work exerted on the process to compress the charge air, is found from:

$$W_{comp} = \int_{V_{BDC}}^{V_{TDC}} p_{comp} \cdot dV \qquad (7.5)$$

Where p_{comp} [Pa] is the pressure during compression. The compression work is represented in the p–V diagram by the area underneath the compression line. The total delivered work for a 2-stroke cycle, the indicated work W_i, equals the sum of expansion and compression work:

$$W_i = W_{exp} + W_{comp} = \oint_{cycle} p \cdot dV \qquad (7.6)$$

Note that the expansion work, which is delivered to the piston, is positive whereas the compression work, which is delivered to the process, is negative. This could be considered a matter of convention, but it also logically follows from the definitions of expansion and compression work: $dV > 0$ in equation (7.4) and $dV < 0$ in equation (7.5).

For a 4-stroke diesel engine, the area enclosed by the lines of processes 6–7 (exhaust) and 7–8 (charging) also represents work. The net work of this area (the pump losses) is negative for naturally aspirating engines, but it is positive in most cases of turbocharged engines, where the pressure during air inlet is higher than the pressure during exhaust. This net work is normally not included in the indicated work but will be dealt with separately in the mechanical efficiency, which will be introduced shortly. Note that the cycle delivers work when the indicator diagram depicts the cycle of processes in clockwise direction and the cycle requires work when the direction of the cycle is counter clockwise.

7.3.3   Mean indicated pressure

Mathematically it is possible to define a mean value of pressure as the pressure integral over volume divided by the total displaced volume over that pressure trace. Note that this would be a pure mathematical definition of mean pressure. A 2-stroke and 4-stroke engine would use two and four times the swept volume respectively:

$$\overline{p} \stackrel{def}{=} \frac{\displaystyle\oint_{cycle} p \cdot dV}{2 \cdot k \cdot V_S} \qquad (7.7)$$

where

$$k = 1 \ \textit{for 2-stroke engines}$$
$$k = 2 \ \textit{for 4-stroke engines}$$

The disadvantage of this definition is that the mean pressure of a 4-stroke engine is almost half of that of a 2-stroke engine, so the two cannot be compared. Therefore, just one cylinder swept volume is normally used as reference volume for a diesel engine. The numerator of equation (7.7) is the indicated work of equation (7.6), so equation (7.7) changes to

$$p_{mi} \stackrel{def}{=} \frac{W_i}{V_S} \qquad (7.8)$$

where index m stands for *mean* and index i denotes *indicated* (i.e. as measured with a pressure indicator on the cylinder)[1]. The swept volume is by definition the nominal volume of one cylinder as the piston is displaced during the expansion stroke. The implication of equation (7.8) is that the mean indicated pressure p_{mi}, if present during the expansion stroke, would produce the same work as the real intermittent pressure during the whole 2- or 4-stroke cycle.

It is common practice to state mean indicated pressure in *bar* instead of Pascal *Pa*; $1 \text{ bar} = 10^5 \text{ Pa}$. Numerical values for maximum mean indicated pressure are 6 to 7.5 bar for naturally aspirating engines and 20 to 33 bar for modern turbocharged 4-stroke engines.

7.3.4 Mean effective pressure

Mean indicated pressure is a measure for the work exerted on the piston, i.e. the indicated work. For practical purposes the work delivered at the output flange of the engine (per cycle per cylinder), i.e. the effective work, needs to be known:

$$W_e \overset{def}{=} \frac{1}{i} \int_0^{2\pi k} M_{Flange} \cdot d\alpha \qquad (7.9)$$

where,

M_{Flange} = *torque delivered at the output flange*

α = *crank angle*

i = *number of cylinders*

Between the indicated work and the effective work there are mechanical losses such as friction between the piston and the wall, friction in bearings and pump losses (i.e. the energy associated with the air intake and gas exhaust). The losses also include the mechanical drive of the cylinder valves and the power take off for the lubricating oil pump, the cooling water pumps and the fuel pumps. These considerable losses are put into the mechanical efficiency:

$$\eta_m \overset{def}{=} \frac{W_e}{W_i} \qquad (7.10)$$

The mechanical efficiency of a diesel engine in full load condition is approximately 90 %. In other words, ten percent of the indicated work is lost. Note that for naturally aspirating engines η_m may be as low as 80 %, but the higher the turbocharging pressure the higher is the η_m (up to 95 % for large 2-stroke engines).

---

[1] Other symbols for mean indicated pressure or indicated mean effective pressure often found in literature are "MIP" or "imep".

In analogy with the mean indicated pressure, the mean effective pressure p_{me} is defined[2]:

$$p_{me} \overset{\text{def}}{=} \frac{W_e}{V_s} \tag{7.11}$$

Obviously, mechanical efficiency is also the ratio of mean effective pressure p_{me} to mean indicated pressure p_{mi}.

$$\eta_m = \frac{W_e}{W_i} = \frac{p_{me}}{p_{mi}} \tag{7.12}$$

Typical values for the mean effective pressure of modern engines lie between 15 and 30 bar. They are obtained by using charge pressures between 2.5 and 5 bar. Mean effective pressure is often used to indicate the power density of an engine: roughly speaking p_{me} is the work output of an engine (W_e) related to its size (swept volume V_s).

7.4   Performance

Until now, the output of an engine has been considered as indicated work, and mechanical efficiency has been introduced to determine effective work. However, not all energy entering the diesel process in the form of fuel is converted to indicated work. The losses and related efficiencies that are encountered by the conversion of fuel energy to work output are discussed in this section.

7.4.1   *Efficiency*

The overall, or effective, efficiency of an engine is work output divided by heat input:

$$\eta_e \overset{\text{def}}{=} \frac{W_e}{Q_f} \tag{7.13}$$

And in analogy, the indicated efficiency η_i can be defined as the ratio of indicated work and Q_f:

$$\eta_i \overset{\text{def}}{=} \frac{W_i}{Q_f} \tag{7.14}$$

Note that the following relationship exists between η_e and η_i:

$$\eta_e = \eta_m \cdot \eta_i \tag{7.15}$$

---

[2] Sometimes 'bmep' is used which stands for "brake mean effective pressure". Also 'MEP' can be encountered meaning "Mean Effective Pressure".

In equations (7.13) and (7.14), the input of the cycle is the energy in the fuel. This heat input Q_f is assumed to be equal to fuel injected per cycle m_f times the lower heating value (h^L in J/kg) of the fuel:

$$Q_f \cong m_f \cdot h^L \tag{7.16}$$

In this relation, the lower heating value is a property of the injected fuel indicating the enthalpy of combustion. Two heating values are distinguished: the higher heating value (h^H) and the lower heating value (h^L). The higher heating value is obtained when all the water formed by combustion of the hydrocarbon fuel is liquid, whereas the lower heating value is obtained when all water is vapour. The difference between these values is the energy required to vaporise the liquid. Because condensation is avoided in a diesel engine, the lower heating value will be used.

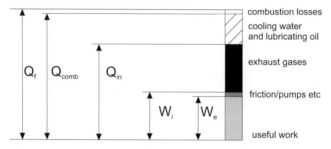

Figure 7.5   Energy losses in a diesel engine.

Not all input heat goes into the thermodynamic work cycle: see Figure 7.5. Firstly, combustion may be incomplete. This is expressed by the combustion efficiency η_{comb}: the ratio of combustion heat to heat input.

$$\eta_{comb} \overset{def}{=} \frac{Q_{comb}}{Q_f} \tag{7.17}$$

Secondly, a significant amount of the combustion heat is lost: it is carried away through the cylinder liner and the cylinder head into the jacket cooling water and through the piston crown to the cooling oil. The heat input efficiency η_q indicates the percentage of the combustion heat Q_{comb} that is actually put into the cycle process.

$$\eta_q \overset{def}{=} \frac{Q_{in}}{Q_{comb}} \tag{7.18}$$

Where Q_{in} is the heat that really is put into the cycle process. It can be written as:

$$Q_{in} = \eta_{comb} \cdot \eta_q \cdot Q_f \tag{7.19}$$

In this expression, the combustion efficiency η_{comb} is almost 100 % but the heat input efficiency η_q can be 80 to 90%, i.e. a heat loss of 10 to 20 % during combustion.

The heat loss during compression and the last part of expansion (when combustion has ended) is not included in the definition of η_q. The effects of these heat losses must be included in the indicator work for the processes. To describe the thermodynamic losses a thermodynamic efficiency η_{td} may be defined as:

$$\eta_{td} \overset{def}{=} \frac{W_i}{Q_{in}} \qquad (7.20)$$

The thermodynamic efficiency η_{td} is completely determined by the shape of the cycle in the thermodynamic diagrams, i.e. the p–V and the T–S diagrams. In the same way that work can be represented as an area in a p–V diagram, the heat input can be represented with good accuracy as an area in the T–S diagram, even though the combustion process is (highly) irreversible[3]. So, the input heat Q_{in} as defined above is equal to an area in the temperature–entropy diagram:

$$Q_{in} = \int_{combustion} T \cdot dS \qquad \text{ref. (2.17)}$$

Equation (2.17) may be used if the process may be regarded as internally reversible: this implies that heat transfer takes place from a large number of bodies with an infinitesimal small temperature difference. The thermodynamic efficiency can then be written as:

$$\eta_{td} \overset{def}{=} \frac{W_i}{Q_{in}} = \frac{\oint_{cycle} p \cdot dV}{\int_{combustion} T \cdot dS} \qquad \text{ref. (7.20)}$$

After the partial efficiencies have been defined, namely mechanical, heat loss, combustion and thermodynamic efficiency, the effective efficiency η_e can be written as:

$$\eta_e = \eta_m \cdot \eta_i = \eta_m \cdot \eta_{comb} \cdot \eta_q \cdot \eta_{td} \qquad (7.21)$$

In conclusion, the thermodynamic efficiency of a diesel engine can be determined from p–V and T–S diagrams. The effective efficiency, however, is greatly influenced by the mechanical and heat losses. These losses are smaller for large low- speed engines when compared with smaller, high-speed engines. This trend can be observed in Figure 7.6, where effective engine efficiency is plotted against engine design speed.

---

[3] See also Chapter 2 for a review of basic thermodynamic principles.

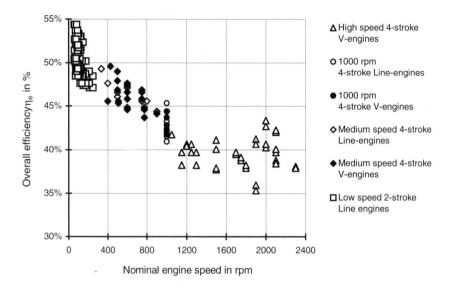

Figure 7.6   Trend of effective efficiency of diesel engines as function of nominal engine speed.

7.4.2   *Power and torque*

The power developed by one cylinder is defined as the work delivered by the process during a time unit, i.e. a second. So, power can be calculated if the number of crankshaft revolutions, i.e. engine speed n_e, is known.

Consider a 2-stroke engine with engine speed n_e in revolutions per second. There are as many crankshaft revolutions as there are power strokes of the cylinder, consequently the indicated power P_i [W/cylinder] equals:

$$P_i = W_i \cdot n_e \qquad (7.22)$$

For a 4-stroke cycle, the number of power strokes is half the number of crankshaft revolutions; in other words, one power stroke in every four strokes. Therefore, work per unit time per cylinder is:

$$P_i = W_i \cdot \frac{n_e}{2} \qquad (7.23)$$

In general terms, the number of revolutions of the crankshaft per complete working cycle is defined by the constant k, which has already been mentioned in equation (7.7):

$$k = 1 \ \textit{for 2-stroke engines}$$
$$k = 2 \ \textit{for 4-stroke engines}$$

If i is the number of cylinders of the engine, the indicated power of the engine can be found by:

$$P_i \overset{\text{def}}{=} W_i \cdot \frac{n_e \cdot i}{k} = p_{mi} \cdot V_S \cdot \frac{n_e \cdot i}{k} \tag{7.24}$$

In this expression a factor called the engine firing frequency can be distinguished, see equation (7.25). This factor is used to determine overall engine properties from cylinder cycle properties.

$$f = \frac{n_e \cdot i}{k} \tag{7.25}$$

Here it has been used to determine the indicated power of the engine from the indicated work per cycle per cylinder (W_i).

The effective power, more commonly referred to as brake power P_B, is the output power which is related to the effective work in the same way as indicated power is related to indicated work:

$$P_B \overset{\text{def}}{=} W_e \cdot \frac{n_e \cdot i}{k} = p_{me} \cdot V_S \cdot \frac{n_e \cdot i}{k} \tag{7.26}$$

The mean effective pressure p_{me} is the most commonly used parameter for expressing the engine load. When the variables in equation (7.26) are rearranged, p_{me} can be solved:

$$p_{me} = k \cdot \frac{P_B}{i \cdot n_e \cdot V_S} \qquad \text{ref. (7.26)}$$

From this expression, it will be clear that mean effective pressure can be looked at as a specific power. In general, the mean effective pressure of a piston engine is a specific power related to volume flow $\dot{V}$ through the engine (contrary to specific power of a gas turbine, which relates power to mass flow):

$$\dot{V} = V_S \cdot \frac{i \cdot n_e}{k} \tag{7.27}$$

When another definition of brake power is used, namely

$$P_B \overset{\text{def}}{=} M_B \cdot 2\pi \cdot n_e \tag{7.28}$$

mean effective pressure can also be written as:

$$p_{me} = 2\pi \cdot k \cdot \frac{M_B}{i \cdot V_S} \tag{7.29}$$

Equation (7.29) shows that mean effective pressure equals the torque scaled with total swept volume. By combining Equations (7.11) and (7.29), the delivered effective work per cylinder cycle can be written as:

$$W_e = p_{me} \cdot V_S = \frac{2\pi \cdot k}{i} \cdot M_B = \frac{1}{i} \int_0^{2\pi k} M_{Flange} \cdot d\alpha \tag{7.30}$$

Note that brake torque is the average torque of the engine, i.e. of all cylinders, whereas effective work corresponds to only one cylinder.

7.4.3 Fuel consumption

Fuel economy is important, not only because of the direct operational cost consequences for a diesel plant operator, but also in view of the ultimate scarcity of fossil fuel and the direct link with the emission of pollutants. Efficiency has already been introduced as a measure of fuel economy: efficiency relates effective work output W_e to the amount of fuel injected per cycle m_f[kg], see equation (7.13) and (7.16):

$$\eta_e = \frac{W_e}{Q_f} = \frac{W_e}{m_f \cdot h^L} \tag{7.31}$$

Another measure for fuel economy is specific fuel consumption *sfc*. The specific fuel consumption is by definition the fuel consumption of the engine related to brake power.

$$sfc = \frac{\dot{m}_f}{P_B} \tag{7.32}$$

With equation (7.31), specific fuel consumption can also be rewritten as:

$$sfc = \frac{\dot{m}_f}{P_B} = \frac{m_f}{W_e} = \frac{1}{\eta_e \cdot h^L} \tag{7.33}$$

Pay attention to the units of the variables involved. When SI units are used, i.e. $\dot{m}_f$ in kg/s, P_B in W and h^L in J/kg, then *sfc* is in kg/Ws. It is, however, more common to express specific fuel consumption in g/kWh, P_B in kW and h^L in kJ/kg. Equation (7.33) then requires a multiplier of 1000 [g/kg]·3600 [s/h] to be added in the definition:

$$sfc = \frac{3600000 \cdot \dot{m}_f}{P_B} = \frac{3600000}{\eta_e \cdot h^L} \text{ [g/kWh]} \qquad \text{ref. (7.33)}$$

The specific fuel consumption is a characteristic of an engine that is often used in specifications. By using equation (7.33), a range of values can be determined. The nominal lower heating value h^L of marine diesel oil (MDO) is approximately 42,700 kJ/kg (this is the value for which manufacturers specify the *sfc* of their engines according to ISO). The range of effective efficiency is $\eta_e \cong 0.38$–0.52, so the specific fuel consumption will have a value in the range of *sfc* $\cong 220$-160 g/kWh. For heavy fuel oil (HFO), the value can be as low as 40,500 kJ/kg. When used in a low-speed engine with $\eta_e = 0.52$, this would give *sfc* = 170 g/kWh.

7.4.4   Air consumption

Combustion requires oxygen. The oxygen is contained in the combustion air that is trapped in the cylinder. The amount of air required to burn the fuel adequately (i.e. with a high combustion efficiency) is normally related to the amount of fuel; this ratio is called the air–fuel ratio, which is formally defined as:

$$\text{afr} \stackrel{\text{def}}{=} \frac{m_{ca}}{m_f} \tag{7.34}$$

By using basic chemistry, the minimum required, so called stoichiometric, amount of air can be determined when the composition of the air is defined and the composition of the fuel is known; this then leads to the definition of the stoichiometric air–fuel ratio:

$$\sigma \stackrel{\text{def}}{=} \frac{m_{ca,min}}{m_f} \tag{7.35}$$

Assume 1 kg of marine diesel oil of the following composition: 85% C, 13% H, 1% S and 1% other components. Also, assume complete combustion. Then, the process equations of combustion of carbon, hydrogen and sulphur are:

$C + O_2 \Rightarrow CO_2$
$2H_2 + O_2 \Rightarrow 2H_2O$
$S + O_2 \Rightarrow SO_2$

Molecular weights M in kilograms per mol are:

$M(H_2)=2$
$M(C)=12$
$M(O_2)=32$
$M(S)=32$

The oxygen required for combustion of 1 kilogram diesel oil is:

$$\left(0.85 \cdot \frac{32}{12} + 0.13 \cdot \frac{16}{2} + 0.01 \cdot \frac{32}{32}\right) \text{kg O}_2 = 3.32 \text{ kg O}_2$$

Because one kilogram of air contains approximately 0.23 kilogram O_2, the theoretically required kilograms of air can be determined per kilogram diesel oil. This is the stoichiometric air–fuel ratio σ:

$$\sigma = 3.32 \text{ kg O}_2 \cdot \frac{1}{0.23} \cong 14.5 \text{ kg air/kg diesel oil}$$

The ratio of the actual amount of combustion air to the minimum amount of combustion air is by definition the air excess ratio λ:

$$\lambda \stackrel{def}{=} \frac{m_{ca}}{m_{ca,min}} \tag{7.36}$$

The actual amount of combustion air m_{ca} is bigger than the theoretical $m_{ca\,min}$:

1) to improve combustion,

2) to cool the combustion chamber to keep temperatures within limits.

The air–fuel ratio where visible smoke (black smoke) can be observed coming out of the exhaust due to incomplete combustion is called the smoke limit. As a margin to the smoke limit the air excess ratio can be written as the ratio between practical and theoretical air–fuel ratio:

$$\lambda = \frac{afr}{\sigma} \tag{7.37}$$

This air excess ratio relates only to combustion air. In general, it lies between 1.8 and 2.2 depending on the fuel quality: light distillate fuels allow a lower air excess ratio than heavy fuel oils.

The total airflow into the engine is greater for turbocharged engines, particularly for 2-stroke engines, due to the scavenging flow through the engine. The total air excess ratio, i.e. including the air for scavenging, is by definition:

$$\lambda_{tot} \stackrel{def}{=} \frac{\dot{m}_{air,in}}{\dot{m}_{ca,min}} \tag{7.38}$$

Then the total air–fuel ratio is:

$$afr_{tot} = \frac{\dot{m}_{air,in}}{\dot{m}_f} = \lambda_{tot} \cdot \frac{\dot{m}_{ca,min}}{\dot{m}_f} = \lambda_{tot} \cdot \sigma \tag{7.39}$$

Where σ is defined according to equation (7.35)

The total air excess ratio has a value between 1.8 for a 4-stroke engine using a light distillate fuel and without valve overlap, and 2.8 for a 2-stroke using heavy fuel oil and with an ample scavenging period. If σ has a value of about 14.5, the total air–fuel ratio lies in the range of 26 to 40 kg air/kg fuel. It is useful to relate air consumption to power output rather than to fuel input, thus defining specific air consumption in [kg/Ws] as:

$$sac \stackrel{def}{=} \frac{\dot{m}_{air,in}}{P_B} = \frac{\dot{m}_{air,in}}{\dot{m}_f} \frac{\dot{m}_f}{P_B} = afr_{tot} \cdot sfc \tag{7.40}$$

The specific air consumption lies between 5 kg/kWh for high-speed engines and 8 kg/kWh for low-speed engines.

7.4.5   Cylinder liner wear

In a section on performance, something must be said about wear and about reliability, availability and maintenance aspects of the diesel engine in general. Intuitively one tends to think that there must be a trade off between high performance and low wear rates.

In particular, wear of the cylinder liner, i.e. the (sometimes abrasive) slow erosion, seems to be linked to high load and/or speed of the engine. As an indicator for "load", the mean effective pressure seems appropriate. For "speed" of the engine, the piston speed is more important for liner wear than the rotational speed. Introduce the mean piston speed, considering that the piston travels twice the stroke length during one revolution:

$$c_m \overset{\text{def}}{=} \frac{distance}{time} = \frac{2 \cdot L_S}{1/n_e} \rightarrow c_m = 2 \cdot n_e \cdot L_S \tag{7.41}$$

The mean piston speed shows only slight variations for different types of engines: approximately 8 m/s for low-speed engines and approximately 9 to 12 m/s for medium and high-speed engines. The mean piston speed squared is also proportional to the inertial forces in the driving gear.

Wear is an extensive variable in the sense that maintenance costs related to wear are higher for larger engines than for small ones. It seems logical to assume that engine wear is proportional to the number of cylinders and the bore diameter. Therefore, the wear index of an engine can be introduced as:

$$Wear\ index = i \cdot D_B \cdot p_{me} \cdot c_m \tag{7.42}$$

The product of mean effective pressure and mean piston speed is called the technology parameter and is seen as an important quantity that represents the technology of the engine.

$$Technology\ parameter = p_{me} \cdot c_m \tag{7.43}$$

High values of both factors within the technology parameter (for instance 30 bar and 12 m/s) can be found in the high tech high-speed engines. Medium-speed engines (with 20 to 25 bar and 10 m/s) are more conservative as they are designed with more emphasis on reliability and continuous operation. The sturdy and reliable low-speed diesel engines (with 18 bar and 8 m/s) seem even more conservative in this respect. Figure 7.7 shows the trend of the technology parameter. The technology parameter will also prove to be related to power density in section 7.7.2.

Cylinder liner wear is one of the most important criteria for the allowed time between overhaul of large diesel engines. Liner wear used to be of the order of 0.1 mm per 1000 running hours. Improved piston ring design, better quality lubrication oils and the adoption of an anti-polishing ring have brought this figure down to a value of 0.01 to 0.02 mm/1000 hrs. The anti-polishing ring is a ring near the top of the cylinder. It calibrates the top diameter of the cylinder (above the piston rings) by scraping off the carbon deposits on the piston. These deposits, if thick enough to make contact between the piston top land and the cylinder liner, could result in "bore polishing" which would lead to increased liner wear. Apart from the beneficial effect on liner wear, the anti-polishing ring also decreases lubrication oil consumption. Figure 7.8 shows the anti-polishing ring and the wear rate of the cylinder liner if the engine is equipped with the rings.

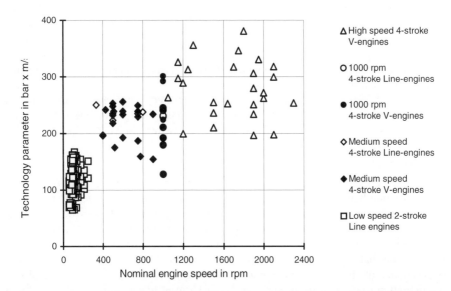

Figure 7.7   Trend of the technology parameter as a function of nominal engine speed.

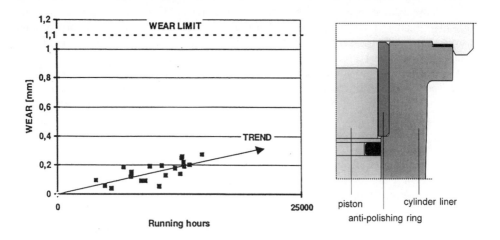

Figure 7.8   Wear rate of Wärtsilä 46 cylinder liner with anti-polishing ring [Kytölä, 1998].

Of course, cylinder liner wear is only one item within the larger field of diesel engine maintainability issues. Other examples are the risk of liner cracking, which is dependent on liner temperature (distribution) and thus on the thermal load of the engine. Also directly related with engine load, but this time mechanical load, is the wear of the main and crank bearings. The mean piston speed is also an indicator for the mechanical dynamics of the engine (i.e. accelerations and decelerations of the reciprocating parts) and in particular the construction of the crank–rod mechanism. It therefore is sometimes assumed that not only liner wear, but also maintenance costs in general are proportional to the wear index as defined.

There are other areas, such as fuel injection equipment (pump and injector) and the turbocharger (to be discussed in section 7.5) that, from a maintenance point of view are important cost drivers. These items seem only loosely connected with the wear index as defined.

7.4.6   Emissions

The emissions found in the exhaust gases are directly linked to the combustion of fossil fuels. On the one hand, there are *non-pollutant* emissions, such as water (H_2O) formed from combustion (or already present at the intake), oxygen (O_2) left over because of the air excess and nitrogen (N_2) which for the greater part is not involved in the combustion and comes out as it went in.

On the other hand, there are *pollutant* emissions. Pollutant emission may be *gaseous*, such as sulphur oxide (SO_x), which is one of the causes of acid rain. Carbon dioxide (CO_2), though not pollutant in the sense of being harmful to the human body, reinforces the greenhouse effect of the earth's atmosphere and therefore is thought to influence climatic change. Even worse and really pollutant, however, are the nitrogen oxides (NO_x), which cause acid rain and ozone depletion, and the *particles*, such as soot (C) and particulate matter (PM), which have a harmful effect on the human respiratory system. Nowadays minimising these pollutant emissions is seen as a factor of prime importance, equal to good engine performance.

Emission of carbon dioxide (CO_2) is inherent to combustion of fossil fuels but can be minimised by minimising fuel consumption. The emission of sulphur oxides (SO_x) is also inherent to combustion if sulphur is a fuel constituent, which not necessarily is the case. Heavy fuel oil (HFO) may contain up to 4.5% S. The light distillate fuels that (after blending) originate from the top stream of the oil refinery process contain much less sulphur: normally 0.2 to 0.5%.

Other pollutant emissions like unburned hydrocarbons (UHC or HC, sometimes VOC, for Volatile Organic Components), carbon monoxide (CO), soot (C) and particulate matter (PM) are a result of incomplete combustion and can be minimised by careful design, mainly of the fuel injection system. Particulates are also fuel related since in particular Heavy Fuel Oil contains a certain amount of incombustible matter, which, if not trapped, will end up in the exhaust.

Nitrogen oxides: NO, NO_2 and to a lesser extent N_2O, are normally known as NO_x. NO is formed at high temperatures and later on (for the greater part outside the engine) it is converted to NO_2. Forming of nitrogen oxides is related to combustion in the sense that oxygen is needed and high temperatures are required (both are present locally during diesel engine combustion). It can be minimised by a set of proper measures. Forming of NO_x is fuel related (and seemingly unavoidable) insofar as it is assumed that any nitrogen contained in the fuel will convert to NO. The percentage of nitrogen in fuel however normally is low.

Two parameters to quantify the emissions of a diesel engine are the specific pollutant emission, *spe* (normally in g/kWh), and the pollutant emission ratio, *per* (normally in g/kg). The mass flow of pollutant emission $\dot{m}_{pe}$ can be any emission, i.e. CO_2, SO_x, NO_x, CO, HC, Soot (C) or Particulate Matter (PM). It is useful to relate the emission of a pollutant $\dot{m}_{pe}$ to the brake power of the engine. This way, the unwanted effect (pollution) is measured against a useful output (brake power). As a result, the definition for specific pollutant emission *spe* is similar to the definition for specific fuel consumption:

$$spe \stackrel{def}{=} \frac{\dot{m}_{pe}}{P_B} \quad [kg/Ws] \tag{7.44}$$

(Note that to obtain the usual unit g/kWh, the emission flow should be expressed as g/hr and the output power in kW). Equation (7.45) expresses a general relation of the form:

$$spi = specific\ pollutant\ index \stackrel{def}{=} \frac{pollutant\ mass\ generated}{ultimate\ useful\ product} \tag{7.45}$$

However, the definition of *ultimate* depends on the system boundary that is taken into consideration: obviously, for an engine builder the boundary is the engine itself and the ultimate useful product is brake power. In that case, equation (7.44) is adequate.

For a shipowner, however, the brake power of the engine is not the end; it is converted into the function *transportation of goods over a certain distance* by the ship and its installation. Obviously, for the shipowner the ultimate useful product can be expressed in ton-mile. Definition of a specific pollutant index in this way, i.e. as g/ton-mile, also would take into account the effects of the transmission losses, the propeller efficiency, the ship–propeller interaction and the hull resistance. It therefore would encourage overall system optimisation rather then engine optimisation. However, emission legislation for diesel engines, both for road transport (Euro III for instance) and for shipping (IMO: proposed annex VI to MARPOL) is expressed in g/kWh and therefore stops at the engine. On the other hand, to obtain reliable measurements of emissions in g/kWh is already complicated (on a test bed but certainly on board). The measurement of the number of ton-miles would be even more difficult in practical situations, thus preventing effective enforcement of such legislation.

Physical considerations suggest that there is a close relation between the production of pollutants and the actual combustion of fuel, rather than the generation of power. Let therefore the pollutant emission ratio *per* be defined as the ratio between the pollutant emission $\dot{m}_{pe}$ and the fuel consumption $\dot{m}_f$:

$$\text{per} \stackrel{\text{def}}{=} \frac{\dot{m}_{pe}}{\dot{m}_f} \qquad (7.46)$$

(Note that to obtain the usual unit g/kg the emission flow must be in g/hr and the fuel flow in kg /hr.)

The emission ratios for CO_2 and SO_2 are almost completely determined by the fuel composition, the latter being rather constant for fossil fuels:

- CO_2: approx. 3200 g/kg of fuel

- SO_2: approx. 20 g/kg of fuel for 1 % of S in the fuel

The pollutant emission ratio is not a specific pollutant index in the sense indicated in equation (7.45), since the nominator of *per*, i.e. fuel consumption $\dot{m}_f$, is not an *ultimate useful product*. The pollutant emission ratio is very useful for understanding emission from a physical or chemical point of view. However, judging emission from an environmental point of view requires a specific pollutant index, for instance the (power) specific pollutant emission *spe*.

The pollutant emission ratio and the specific pollutant emission are related with the specific fuel ratio as follows:

$$\text{spe} \stackrel{\text{def}}{=} \frac{\dot{m}_{pe}}{P_B} = \frac{\dot{m}_{pe}}{\dot{m}_f} \cdot \frac{\dot{m}_f}{P_B} = \text{per} \cdot \text{sfc} \qquad (7.47)$$

The specific pollutant emissions for several types of emission are often part of a diesel engine specification nowadays. For values of *sfc* between 160 and 220 g/kWh the pollutant emission ratios of some important emissions are converted to specific pollutant emission values in Table 7.2.

	pollutant emission ratio (per) in g/kg	specific pollutant emission (spe) in g/kWh
CO_2 (86% C in fuel)	3200	500–700
SO_x per % S in fuel	20	3.2–4.4
NO_x	40–100	6–22
HC (gaseous)	0.5–4	0.1–0.9
CO	2–20	0.3–4.4
Particulates (depending on fuel)	0.5–2	0.1–0.4

Table 7.2   Order of magnitude of diesel engine exhaust emissions. The *spe* has been determined using an *sfc* between 160 and 220 g/kWh.

7.5 Pressure charging

The goal of pressure charging is to obtain more power from a cylinder of given size, or in other words to increase the power density. To achieve this, more fuel will have to be combusted in the same volume, which requires more combustion air. If the density of air is increased, more mass can enter the cylinder. To increase the density, pressure needs to be increased and temperature decreased. This process is called pressure charging. For comparison, a naturally aspirating engine may have a mean effective pressure of 6 to 7 bar and a turbocharged engine of 10 to 30 bar, for identical cylinder size.

The charge of air is pre-compressed by a compressor before entering the cylinder. The compressor can be driven by the diesel engine itself (also called mechanically driven), by an electric motor or by an exhaust-gas driven turbine. The latter is most common. Mechanically driven compressors are sometimes used on board submarines where one can find significant underpressure in the inlet and backpressure in the exhaust receiver. An electric motor may be found on 2-stroke diesel engines, where, in the low power range, the exhaust-driven turbine does not develop enough power.

Today most engines have a charge system with an exhaust-driven turbine. This is referred to as turbocharging (patented in 1905 by Büchi and first practical application in 1923). To further increase the density of air, it is cooled after compression in a cooling system by low temperature water (or by air in case of smaller diesel engines for road transport).

7.5.1 Effect on mean effective pressure

As indicated in the introduction to this chapter, there is a direct effect of charge air pressure on mean effective pressure and thus power output of a pressure charged engine. In this section a general expression will be derived that relates mean effective pressure to charge air pressure (in fact density) and air–fuel ratio.

With the definition of overall engine efficiency, the mean effective pressure can be expressed in fuel heat input. Heat input is proportional to amount of injected fuel, which can be expressed in amount of combustion air by means of the air–fuel ratio. In formulae:

$$P_{me} \overset{def}{=} \frac{W_e}{V_s} \qquad \text{ref. (7.11)}$$

$$\eta_e \overset{def}{=} \frac{W_e}{Q_f} \qquad \text{ref. (7.13)}$$

$$Q_f \cong m_f \cdot h^L \qquad \text{ref. (7.16)}$$

$$afr \overset{def}{=} \frac{m_{ca}}{m_f} \qquad \text{ref. (7.34)}$$

Then by combining these, the mean effective pressure is directly related to the amount of combustion air that can be charged into the cylinder:

$$p_{me} = \eta_e \cdot \frac{m_{ca}}{V_S} \cdot \frac{h^L}{afr} \tag{7.48}$$

If the stroke volume would be filled with air of inlet receiver conditions (index 'c') the mass of air would, according to the ideal gas law, be equal to:

$$m = \frac{p_c \cdot V_S}{R \cdot T_c} \tag{7.49}$$

The total amount of air present in the cylinder m_{ca} normally is lower than the mass m above, because:

- temperature in the cylinder at the start of compression (inlet valve closes) normally is higher than in the inlet receiver.

- the cylinder volume at start of compression is less than the volume at BDC.

- some gas remaining from the previous stroke will still be present.

- on the other hand due to scavenging also the clearance volume (volume at TDC) will be charged with fresh air.

Put all the factors together into the *trapped air* efficiency:

$$\eta_{trap} \stackrel{def}{=} \frac{m_{ca}}{m} \tag{7.50}$$

Then the amount of air can be expressed in the air inlet receiver conditions:

$$m_{ca} = \eta_{trap} \cdot \frac{p_c \cdot V_S}{R \cdot T_c} \tag{7.51}$$

Substitute this into the expression for mean effective pressure to obtain a general expression:

$$p_{me} = \eta_e \cdot \eta_{trap} \cdot \frac{p_c}{R \cdot T_c} \cdot \frac{h^L}{afr} \tag{7.52}$$

From this expression the importance of a high charge pressure p_c and low charge air temperature T_c is directly visible. A low air–fuel ratio also is important, but when fuel is increased too much, the combustion will be incomplete and the engine even may produce visible smoke. The overall engine efficiency as well as the heat value of the fuel have a direct influence on the mean effective pressure. Last but not least, the filling of the cylinder with combustion air, as expressed by the trapped air efficiency, must be effective.

7.5.2   Turbocharging

When turbocharging according to the Büchi principle, the compressor is driven by a (gas) turbine that receives its gas power from the enthalpy flow of the exhaust gases. The turbine is located in the gas stream after an exhaust receiver which collects the exhaust gases of some or all of the cylinders of the engine. It usually has one stage and is of the axial flow type for the bigger turbochargers, and of the radial (or inward) flow type for small turbochargers. The compressor is located after an inlet filter, and it is feeding compressed air to an inlet receiver that is supplying air to some or all cylinders of the engine. It almost invariably is a one-stage centrifugal (or outward flow) compressor.

Usually, the turbine is directly coupled to the compressor and they are built together in a common housing: the turbocharger. The turbocharger could be considered as a small single shaft gas turbine without a combustion chamber. By using exhaust gases to power the turbine, a turbocharger is a fine example of waste heat usage.

The power necessary to drive a compressor in the turbocharger must be equal to the power delivered by the turbine. As introduced in Chapter 2, the power of a rotating machine, such as a compressor or a turbine, is:

$$P = \dot{m} \cdot \Delta h = \dot{m} \cdot c_p \cdot \Delta T \hspace{3cm} \text{ref. (2.9)}$$

This relationship shows the direct influence of mass flow on the output of the turbocharger. The temperature drop over the turbine is directly related to the pressure drop (Poisson, see Chapter 2). The pressure drop over the turbine depends on the flow area of the turbine and on the exhaust flow forced by the engine on the turbine. So, the output of the turbocharger mainly depends on the mass flow.

When the same equation is applied to the compressor, it shows that the power input will result not only in a pressure rise, but also in a temperature rise of the charge air. To lower the temperature and to increase the density a charge air cooler is required between the compressor and the inlet air receiver as shown in Figure 7.9.

A turbocharger may be operated on the constant-pressure principle or on the pulse principle. The differences between these principles lie in the design of the exhaust system of the engine. Just before the exhaust valve opens, the cylinder process ends with a relatively high pressure and temperature. During blow down, the cylinder pressure drops quickly to the exhaust receiver pressure. The pressure in a large receiver remains almost constant: the constant pressure system. The pressure in a relatively small receiver, on the other hand, has a pulsating character: the pulse system. See Figure 7.9.

Figure 7.9-A shows a constant pressure system. It features one big exhaust manifold, which collects the exhaust gases of all cylinders. The pressure in the manifold is relatively low and constant over the cycle, because the mass flow fluctuations, caused by the cylinders that intermittently exhaust into the receiver, are dampened out by the sheer size of the manifold. The turbine is supplied with a constant flow for which it can be designed optimally.

In a the pulse system, shown in Figure 7.9-B, up to three cylinders are connected to one turbine by a small exhaust pipe. The pressure in the manifold is low, which is advantageous for the scavenging process, until one of the cylinders opens its exhaust. At that instant, the pressure rises quickly, even higher than the charge pressure before the engine, giving the turbine a boost. The energy present in the exhaust gases is more effectively transported to the turbine. The pressure before the turbine is high and the blow down losses are much smaller than for the constant pressure system. The greater pressure ratio over the turbine however is counteracted by a lower efficiency of the turbine due to the increased flow losses as a result of the pulsating flow.

Besides the lower efficiency, another disadvantage of the pulse system is that not all cylinders can be connected to the same exhaust duct. During the scavenge period immediately following the blow down, no pulse from another cylinder can be allowed since this would cause back flow of exhaust gases into the cylinder and even into the inlet manifold where the pressure is lower than exhaust pulse peak pressure. In practice, only cylinders more than 240 degrees apart can be connected to one exhaust duct, so three cylinders of a 4-stroke engine at one duct as a maximum.

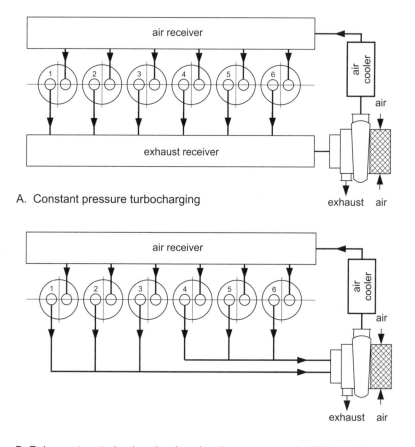

A. Constant pressure turbocharging

B. Pulse system turbocharging (combustion sequence 1-4-2-6-3-5-1)

Figure 7.9   Constant pressure and pulse system for a 6-cylinder 4-stroke engine.

7.5.3 Two-stage turbocharging

Single-stage turbochargers have a limited range up to 4 or 5 bar. In case of higher charge pressures two-stage charging must be considered. The principle of two-stage turbo-charging is shown in Figure 7.10. The two compressors independently run at different speeds. They are used in series, each connected to its own turbine. This results in two turbochargers in series: a high-pressure (HP) turbocharger and a low-pressure (LP) turbocharger. To further increase the density of the air, intercoolers are placed before the inlet receiver of the engine, and between the LP and the HP compressors. This extra intercooling increases the efficiency of the turbocharging system.

The disadvantages of high-efficiency turbocharging at high charge pressure are the added complexity of the duct system, the pressure losses related to the complex duct system, and the cost of such an installation.

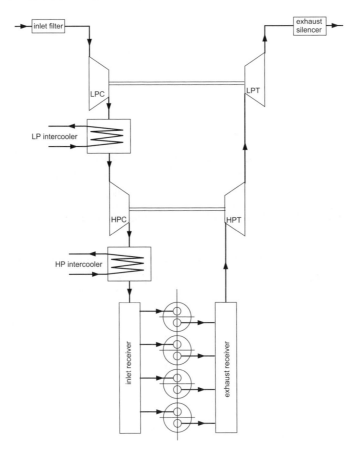

Figure 7.10   Principle diagram of two-stage turbo-charging: LPC and LPT form the low-pressure turbocharger and HPC and HPT the high-pressure turbocharger.

7.6   Operating envelope

In section 3.6.2, we introduced the drive characteristics of a diesel engine as a constant-torque drive. In this section, this will be examined in more detail using the theory that has been introduced in the previous sections of this chapter. Also examined are the consequences of turbocharging to the drive characteristics of a diesel engine.

7.6.1   *Naturally aspirating engine*

The limits of the operating envelope of a naturally aspirating diesel engine are indicated in Figure 7.11.

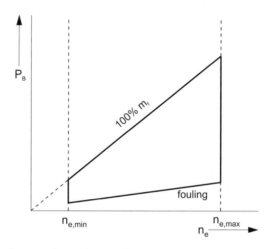

Figure 7.11   Operating envelope of naturally aspirating diesel engine.

The limits are as follows:

- The power is limited by the maximum fuel injected per cycle. This ideally is a straight line through the origin of the power-speed curve if it is assumed that the efficiency is constant, as in the torque-speed and power-speed curves that have already been introduced in section 3.6.2 (Figure 3.12). Efficiency has been defined by equation (7.13):

$$\eta_e \stackrel{\text{def}}{=} \frac{W_e}{Q_f} \qquad\qquad \text{ref. (7.13)}$$

With $Q_f \cong m_f \cdot h^L$ (equation (7.16)) and $P_B \stackrel{\text{def}}{=} \dfrac{W_e \cdot n_e \cdot i}{k}$ (equation (7.26)), this can be used to rewrite the expression for brake power:

$$P_B = \dfrac{\eta_e \cdot m_f \cdot h^L \cdot n_e \cdot i}{k} \left.\begin{array}{c} \\ \\ \end{array}\right\} \Rightarrow P_B = constant \cdot m_f \cdot n_e \qquad (7.53)$$

$$\eta_e \approx constant$$

Equation (7.53) shows that, if effective efficiency η_e is assumed to be constant, the delivered power is proportional to engine speed and to injected fuel. In reality however, effective efficiency is not a constant within the range of operational speeds, but varies slightly. Figure 7.12 shows a more realistic drive characteristic for a naturally aspirating engine compared to Figure 3.12.

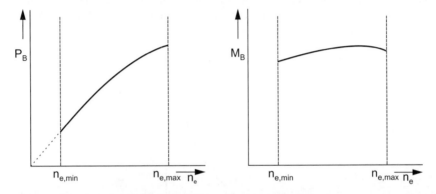

Figure 7.12   Drive characteristic of a naturally aspirating diesel engine taken into account the effect of efficiency

- Speed is limited to a maximum that is associated with inertia forces for which the rotating and translating parts (pistons, connecting rods, crankshaft but also the valves with their actuating mechanism) are designed.

- A diesel engine also has a minimum speed: below a certain speed, the engine will not run smoothly or may even stop altogether. This is caused by loss of compression and as a consequence failure of ignition. Minimum speed normally is 25 to 35 % of the nominal speed. When driving a ship with a fixed pitch propeller this also dictates a minimum ship speed.

- Below 25% to 40% torque, the combustion in the engine may become too "cold" and fouling of the cylinder will occur. Running a diesel engine at low power therefore is only permitted for a limited time.

7.6.2   One-stage turbocharged engine

Essentially, the turbocharged diesel engine has a constant-torque drive characteristic like the naturally aspirating engine. The limits of its operating envelope are the same as the limits in Figure 7.11. However, the operating envelope of the turbocharged engine has an additional limit that is associated with the performance of the turbocharger. Figure 7.13 shows the drive characteristic of a turbocharged engine.

The available air from the turbochargers causes an area in the low speed range of the drive characteristic in which maximum torque can no longer be achieved. The reason is that the lower engine speed causes a lower exhaust flow. The turbine mass flow then falls rapidly. Although specific exhaust energy, which is proportional to the temperature, is still high, the turbine cannot deliver sufficient power to the compressor, because the turbine pressure ratio drops with mass flow if the flow area remains constant. The compressor cannot maintain its original rotational speed, so the charge pressure drops. The mass of air in the cylinder, which is proportional to charge pressure, then drops as well. If injected fuel is maintained, the air–fuel ratio will drop and the air excess may become insufficient. Consequently, incomplete combustion would be the result and the exhaust temperature may become too high, causing thermal overload of the engine.

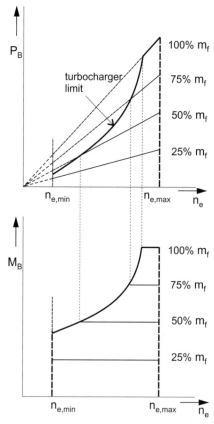

Figure 7.13   Drive characteristic of a one-stage turbocharged engine.

Another phenomenon associated with a decreased mass flow is compressor surge. In case of compressor surge, a low mass flow against a high backpressure causes a rotary compressor to be unstable (abrupt decrease of mass flow and pressure ratio). To prevent incomplete combustion and compressor surge, it is necessary to implement the turbocharger limit, which narrows the operating envelope of the diesel engine. Consequently, maximum torque is only available in the high-speed range, which can be a serious drawback of the turbocharger system.

7.6.3   Methods to broaden the engine characteristics

Figure 7.14 shows a propeller curve and the torque limitations of diesel engines qualitatively. The starting point is a naturally aspirating engine: Curve 2. To increase the power density of the engine, turbocharging is applied. Curve 3 is the torque-speed limit for an engine with a single-stage constant pressure turbocharging system. The available torque at lower engine speeds is reduced considerably. To broaden the operating envelope of a turbocharged engine several measures can be taken.

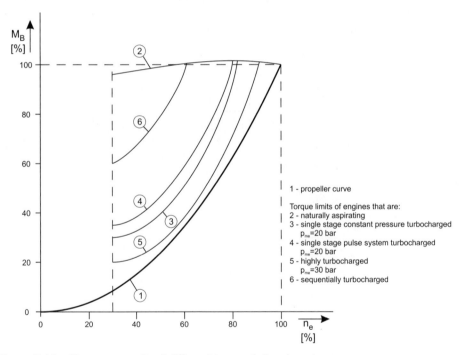

Figure 7.14   Torque capacity of different types of diesel engines.

As a first measure, the characteristic is broadened if the constant pressure system, Curve 3, is replaced by a pulse turbocharging system: Curve 4. Due to the smaller duct volume, high peak pressures will occur before the turbine, which will then produce more power to drive the compressor. The pulse system has the advantage of giving better charge at part load and thus a somewhat broader torque–speed curve.

For engines with a brake mean effective pressure of 20 to 22 bar, conventional turbocharging resulting in torque-speed limitations according to Curves 3 and 4 may be acceptable. However, an unacceptable situation occurs in case of high-pressure turbocharging where the charge air pressure is in the order of 4 bar and higher, or two-stage turbocharging with the same level of charge air pressure. In both cases, mean effective pressures of 30 bar may be reached resulting in a torque–speed limitation as in Curve 5. Such a limitation is unacceptable for almost every application because it leaves a margin between load and drive that is too small for acceleration or for operation at increased load. For advanced high-speed craft, the margin may be too small to overcome the hump that may be encountered in the resistance curve (as has been introduced in Chapter 4). Power plants including multiple engines or multiple shafts also require a wider margin in order to be able to run the engine against a considerably increased torque during single engine or single shaft operation.

The narrow operating envelope indicated by Curve 5 can be broadened by installing two or more constant pressure turbochargers in parallel: sequential turbocharging (Curve 6). Sequential turbocharging with two turbochargers is depicted in Figure 7.15.

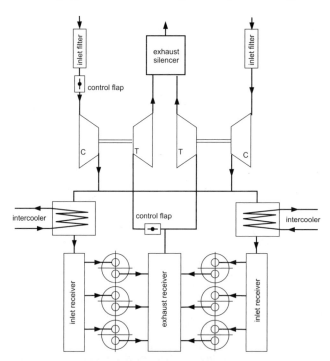

Figure 7.15   Schematic layout of single-stage, sequential turbocharging with two turbochargers in parallel.

The inlet receivers (if there is more than one) must be mutually connected. It is possible to switch off turbochargers sequentially when the load of the engine reduces. The smaller exhaust gas flow is led to the remaining turbine(s), thus increasing the pressure before the turbine(s). Consequently, they will be able to maintain speed and power to the remaining compressor(s). Sequential turbocharging widens the operating area in the engine characteristic, it improves the charge pressure at low loads and it reduces the risk of surge. Against these important advantages must be counted the complexity of the control system and the cost of more smaller turbochargers instead of a large one.

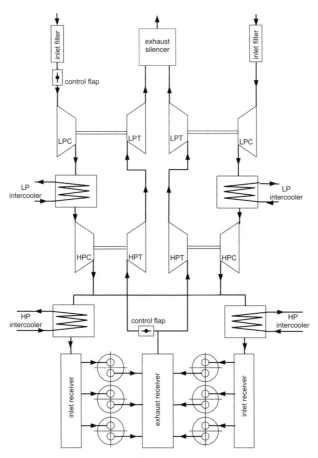

Figure 7.16   Schematic layout of two-stage, sequential turbocharging.

Two-stage turbocharging and *sequential* turbocharging are not the same:

- In case of sequential turbocharging, the turbochargers are placed in parallel and switched off and on sequentially with the objective to broaden the operating envelope;

■   In case of two-stage turbocharging, the turbochargers are placed in series with the objective to increase the mean effective pressure.

The combination of the two is also possible: two-stage, constant-pressure, sequential turbocharging results in high brake mean effective pressure at full load, without the disadvantages of a low torque limit at partial load. Two-stage sequential turbocharging is shown in Figure 7.16.

Other methods to improve the part load performance of a turbocharged diesel engine are the use of a waste gate system, a blow-off system or variable turbine geometry (VTG):

■   Waste gate.

A waste gate is a simple system that improves the part load performance of a turbocharged diesel engine by optimising the turbocharger for part load. This means that the throat area of the turbine is selected to be smaller than required for the mass flow of exhaust gases at nominal power of the engine, so that, at part load, a higher pressure will build up to drive the turbine. At higher engine speeds, the turbine cannot handle the flow anymore: the turbine pressure rises quickly and the turbocharger tends to overspeed. To avoid this, part of the exhaust gases are led round the turbine through a *waste gate*, see Figure 7.17.

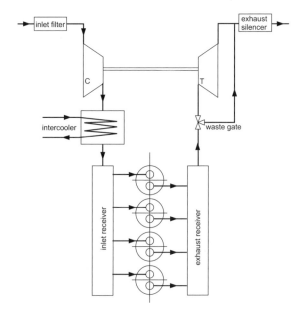

Figure 7.17   Single stage turbocharging with waste-gate to improve turbocharger performance.

It will be clear that such an improvement of part load performance will come at the cost of a non-optimal design point, i.e. the charge pressure and power of the engine in the design point could have been better. However, the high efficiency of the turbochargers nowadays, particularly of those of the bigger engines as used in marine applications, is such that the penalty can easily be accommodated. The advantages of the system are that it is simple and cheap, although it requires an additional control system.

- Blow off.

  An alternative is to blow off part of the charge air at low load of the engine. This is not so much intended for better part load performance but rather to avoid compressor surge at part load. There are two options here:

  - It is possible to completely bypass the engine and merge the bypass flow with the exhaust flow before the silencer. See Figure 7.18. This shifts the operating point in the compressor map away from the surge line.

  - It is also possible to let the blow off re-enter before the turbine. In that case, the flow through the turbine is the same, but the turbine inlet temperature is lowered.

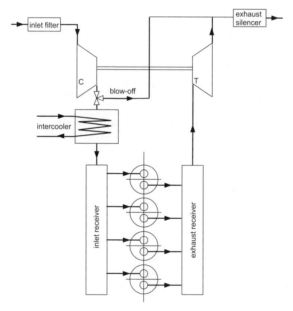

Figure 7.18   Single stage turbocharging with blow-off system to improve turbocharger performance.

- Variable turbine geometry (VTG).

  Another solution to widen the engine characteristic at low engine speeds is to provide the turbine with a variable throat area by adjusting the angle of the stator blades in the turbine inlet section. By decreasing the flow area in a turbine, a higher pressure can be maintained before the turbine. VTG has the same result as sequential turbocharging. The disadvantages of VTG are the vulnerability of the system (a rotating mechanism in a dirty environment), the complex control system and the additional costs. This solution seems promising for diesel engines of heavy-duty trucks, but for marine diesel engines, which are often running on heavy fuel oil, the fouling of the rotating mechanism of the inlet guide vanes seems to be a major disadvantage inhibiting wide application.

7.7   Power density

Power density is a measure of power per volume or per mass of an engine. It is important, particularly in marine applications and road transport, since weight and space are at a premium in a ship and a vehicle. For land-based power generation it is of less importance but not negligible. Power density also influences the initial (investment) costs of the engine. Power density and specific power are terms that are used interchangeably. Specific power can be related to several quantities: specific power related to swept volume, box volume or weight, and specific power related to bore area.

7.7.1   *Specific power related to swept volume*

The specific power related to total engine swept volume (β_{vs}) is defined as:

$$\beta_{VS} = \frac{P_B}{i \cdot V_S} \tag{7.54}$$

With the relationship between brake power and mean effective pressure,

$$P_B = \frac{p_{me} \cdot V_S \cdot n_e \cdot i}{k} \qquad \text{ref. (7.26)}$$

specific power related to swept volume can also be written as a function of mean effective pressure:

$$\beta_{VS} = \frac{p_{me} \cdot n_e}{k} \tag{7.55}$$

This expression shows that a high rotational speed and high mean effective pressure are directly proportional to a favourable power density. If the mean effective pressure and rotational speed would be the same for a 2-stroke engine and a 4-stroke engine, the power density of a 2-stroke engine would be twice the power density of a 4-stroke engine. In practice, however the mean effective pressure and speed are not the same for the two types of engine.

Power per litre swept volume is shown for some engines in Figure 7.19. As expected the power per tonne follows the same trend (Figure 7.20), as does the power per cubic metre of installed box volume (Figure 7.21).

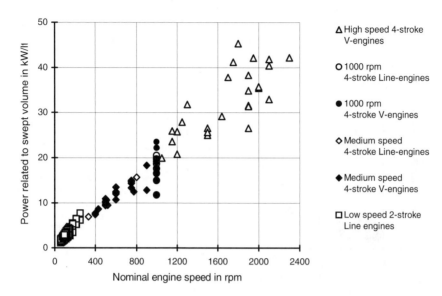

Figure 7.19   Trend of swept volume specific power for diesel engines as a function of nominal rotational speed (Year 2002).

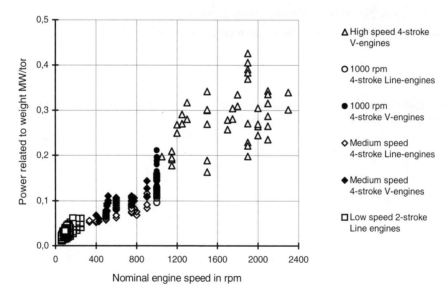

Figure 7.20   Trend of weight specific power for diesel engines as function of nominal rotational speed (Year 2002).

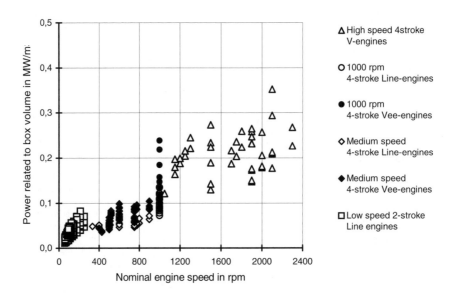

Figure 7.21   Trend of volume specific power for diesel engines as function of nominal rotational speed (Year 2002).

7.7.2   *Specific power related to bore area*

Power density can also be related to the total engine bore area A_B:

$$\beta_{AB} = \frac{P_B}{i \cdot A_B} \tag{7.56}$$

To substitute brake power P_B with an expression containing mean effective pressure and bore area, we use equations (7.26) and (7.2):

$$\left.\begin{array}{c} P_B = \dfrac{p_{me} \cdot V_S \cdot n_e \cdot i}{k} \\[2mm] V_S = A_B \cdot L_S \end{array}\right\} \Rightarrow P_B = \frac{p_{me} \cdot A_B \cdot L_S \cdot n_e \cdot i}{k} \tag{7.57}$$

And with mean piston speed defined as

$$c_m = 2 \cdot n_e \cdot L_S \qquad\qquad \text{ref. (7.41)}$$

Equation (7.57) can be rewritten in a way that can be compared with equation (7.26):

$$P_B = p_{me} \cdot A_B \cdot \frac{c_m \cdot i}{2k} \tag{7.58}$$

The specific power related to bore area can now be written as:

$$\beta_{AB} = \frac{P_B}{i \cdot A_B} = \frac{p_{me} \cdot c_m}{2 \cdot k} \tag{7.59}$$

Again, a high mean effective pressure turns out to be favourable but now *mean piston speed* is the other important factor instead of *rotational* speed. The technology parameter as introduced in equation (7.43) can be distinguished:

$$Technology\ parameter = p_{me} \cdot c_m \qquad\qquad \text{ref. (7.43)}$$

The more conservative low-speed engines have lower technology parameters, but it must not be forgotten that these engines also are 2-stroke engines, so every cycle counts a working stroke and its thermal load will be higher (as expressed by the factor *k* in equation (7.59).

7.7.3 *Maximum power for a given specification*

Equation (7.57) gives the impression that any power could be extracted from an engine, simply by increasing the number of cylinders, the engine speed, the bore area or the stroke length. However, there are limits to observe:

▪ The number of cylinders is limited by a maximum constructional length. In practice, this means that an in-line engine has 12 cylinders as maximum, and for a V-engine the limit seems to be 20 cylinders. Those limits are not absolute; 14 cylinder in-line engines are in study for container ships, and 24 cylinder V-engines have been built.

▪ The bore area, which obviously is directly related to bore diameter, is limited by the stroke–bore ratio. The stroke–bore ratio must be greater than one to obtain an acceptable geometrical shape of the combustion volume at TDC. (For Diesel engines, the geometrical shape is more critical than for Otto engines.)

▪ The (mean) piston speed is limited by the inertia forces associated with speed and for a 2-stroke engine by the scavenging process because the speed determines the time available for scavenging.

The limits accounted for: number of cylinders *i*, stroke–bore ratio λ_S and mean piston speed c_m, are parameters which must be selected during the design of the engine and for which there is only limited freedom. The bore area can be expressed in these parameters:

$$\left.\begin{aligned}
A_B &= \frac{\pi}{4} \cdot D_B{}^2 = \frac{\pi}{4} \cdot \frac{D_B{}^2}{L_S{}^2} \cdot \frac{L_S{}^2 \cdot n_e{}^2}{n_e{}^2} \\[2mm]
\lambda_S &= L_S / D_B \\[1mm]
c_m &= 2 \cdot n_e \cdot L_S
\end{aligned}\right\} \Rightarrow A_B = \frac{\pi}{16} \cdot \frac{c_m{}^2}{\lambda_S{}^2} \cdot \frac{1}{n_e{}^2} \tag{7.60}$$

Given the rotational engine speed, the mean piston speed limits the stroke length L_S and also the bore diameter D_B through the stroke–bore ratio. As a consequence of equation (7.60), the bore *diameter* will decrease with the nominal engine speed n_e.

The same three expressions in combination with equations (7.57) lead to an expression for brake power:

$$P_B = i \cdot \frac{\pi}{32} \cdot \frac{p_{me} \cdot c_m^3}{k \cdot \lambda_s^2} \cdot \frac{1}{n_e^2} \qquad (7.61)$$

This expression reveals that:

- The maximum power that can be obtained from an engine is proportional to the number of cylinders and to mean effective pressure. Since the mean effective pressure has almost doubled in the last twenty years, the maximum power from a given diesel engine has doubled in the same time frame.

- The maximum power decreases with the square of engine design speed. Therefore, high-speed engines may have a high power *density* but are limited in *absolute* power.

- For a large power, it would be best to select low values of the stroke–bore ratio. As argued before there are limits with respect to volume shape near TDC in view of combustion. Nevertheless, this explains why high-speed engines often have a relatively small stroke–bore ratio (just >1) in order to develop more power out of these small engines. Note that for low-speed engines a stroke–bore ratio of the order of one would result in very large cylinder diameters that have not been constructed.

- The dependency of brake power on the third power of mean piston speed is remarkable. This explains the urge to aim for high values of the mean piston speed for high speed engines even though there is a general belief that high speed is not favourable for cylinder wear and engine reliability.

When, for the main types introduced (low-speed, medium-speed and high-speed), typical values are assumed for mean effective pressure, mean piston speed and stroke–bore ratio, the maximum power can be calculated as a function of nominal rotational speed: see Figure 7.22. From this figure, it can be concluded that for high-speed engines, which are preferred for high speed because of their high power density, the maximum available power is very modest.

To further illustrate the validity of equation (7.61), Figure 7.23 shows the power per cylinder versus nominal engine speed of a number of actual diesel engines on the market. The general trend predicted in Figure 7.22 for total engine power is of course also found in the real data points of power per cylinder in Figure 7.23.

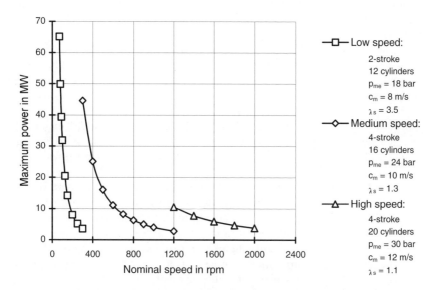

Figure 7.22   Maximum obtainable power for low-speed 2-stroke, medium-speed 4-stroke and high-speed 4-stroke engines, as a function of nominal engine speed.

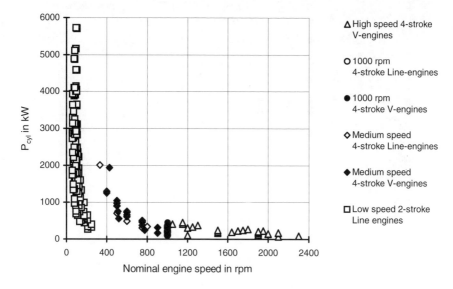

Figure 7.23   Plot of cylinder power versus nominal engine speed taken from a database of actual engines (Year 2002).

Looking at equation (7.61), it is interesting to also present the three main factors that determine cylinder power as a function of nominal engine speed: mean effective pressure (Figure 7.24), mean piston speed (Figure 7.25) and stroke–bore ratio (Figure 7.26).

Noteworthy in Figure 7.24 is the marked difference in mean effective pressure between 2-stroke and 4-stroke engines. Also note that 2-stroke engines can be specified at full rating with a mean effective pressure that is 18 to 19 bar or can be derated to a mean effective pressure around 16 or 12 bar. It is in the derated version that the efficiencies in Figure 7.6 may reach values of 52 to 54%.

From Figure 7.25 it can be concluded that the 2-stroke low-speed engines have a significantly lower mean piston speed than their 4-stroke counterparts. Also, within the 4-stroke engines, there is a general trend of increasing nominal engine speed with increasing mean piston speed.

The stroke–bore ratio in Figure 7.26 shows an enormous gap between the 2-stroke engines and the 4-stroke engines. The long stroke–bore ratios of low-speed engines have been dictated by the low propeller speeds chosen for large ships since the eighties of the last century and resulted in the universally adopted uni-flow scavenging system. For the 4-stroke engines there is a trend towards slightly increased stroke–bore ratio with a view on emissions (better shape of combustion volume at TDC). For the high-speed engines, the quest for power still keeps the stroke–bore ratio near unity.

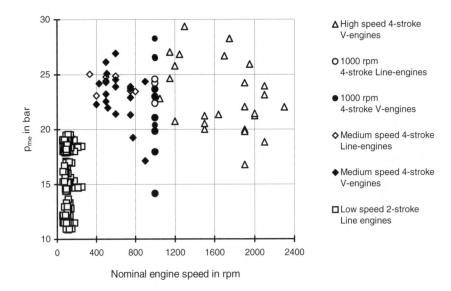

Figure 7.24   Plot of mean effective pressure versus nominal engine speed taken from a database of actual engines (Year 2002).

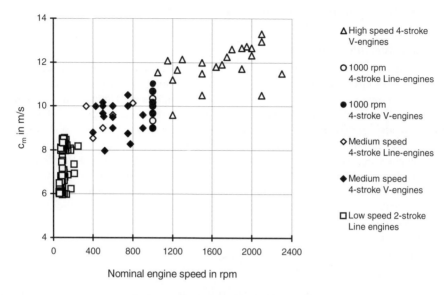

Figure 7.25   Plot of mean piston speed versus nominal engine speed taken from a database of actual engines (Year 2002).

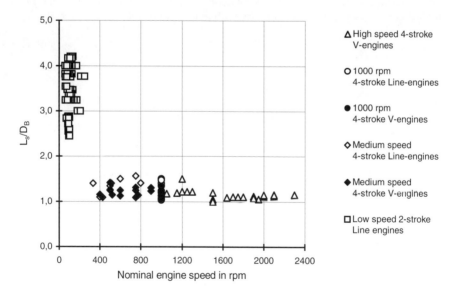

Figure 7.26   Plot of stroke–bore ratio versus nominal engine speed taken from a database of actual engines (Year 2002).

7.8   Thermodynamic analysis of the diesel engine

7.8.1   *Background: air–standard cycles*

The processes in internal combustion engines are complex. An accurate calculation method for these processes would require computer simulation to model the combustion, the change of composition of the medium, the irreversibilities associated with friction, the pressure and temperature gradients and the heat transfer between the gas and the wall. A simple method is preferred to predict trends and to carry out basic calculations. Air–standard cycles can be used to examine engines qualitatively.

Air–standard cycles are ideal cycle processes that approximate a real thermodynamic process by using air as the working fluid. Using basic thermodynamic principles, a standard cycle can be used for theoretical calculations. Even though values for mean effective pressure, temperature and pressure may be different from the value for an actual engine, this approach gives insight into the performance of the actual engine. Air–standard cycles for reciprocating engines are based on the following assumptions:

- The piston–cylinder assembly is a closed system: constant mass, no air or gas exchange with the environment, i.e. no scavenging.

- Combustion is considered as heat transfer from an external source occurring at constant minimum volume and/or constant maximum pressure, and heat rejection occurs at constant maximum volume, without gas exchange.

- The gas in the cycle is air, and it is modelled as a perfect gas, i.e. the ideal gas law holds and the specific heats do not vary with temperature (refer to Chapter 2):

$$p \cdot V = m \cdot R \cdot T \qquad\qquad \text{ref. (2.33)}$$

$$c_p = constant$$

$$c_v = c_p - R = constant$$

- All processes are internally reversible.

- Compression and expansion are isentropic (reversible adiabatic), i.e. Poisson's laws hold (refer to Chapter 2):

$$T \cdot V^{\kappa-1} = constant \qquad\qquad \text{ref. (2.47)}$$

$$p \cdot V^{\kappa} = constant \qquad\qquad \text{ref. (2.49)}$$

Where isentropic index κ is the ratio of specific heats

$$\kappa = \frac{c_p}{c_v} = constant \hspace{4cm} \text{ref. (2.44)}$$

- Compression starts at the volume at which expansion ends (not necessarily at BDC).

The following air–standard cycles are the cycles that are often used to model the processes in reciprocating internal combustion engines:

- Otto cycle for petrol engines.

- Diesel cycle for early diesel engines.

- Seiliger cycle or dual cycle for modern diesel engines.

Otto cycle

The air-standard Otto cycle is often used to simplify the processes in petrol engines (Otto engines). Figure 7.27 shows the p–v diagram and the T–s diagram. In the Otto cycle, heat is assumed to be added instantaneously when the piston is at TDC. The cycle consists of the following processes:

1-2	isentropic compression.
2-3	heat addition at constant volume (isochoric).
3-4	isentropic expansion.
4-1	heat rejection at constant volume.

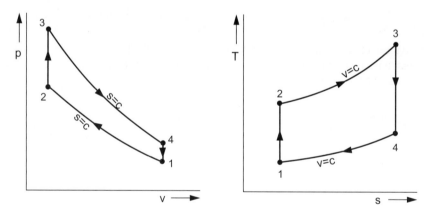

Figure 7.27 Air–standard cycle: Otto.

Diesel cycle

In a diesel cycle, it is assumed that heat is added during a constant pressure process that starts when the piston is at TDC. It used to be employed for the prediction of performance of the early diesel engines, where fuel mixed with air was injected over a longer period of time. The cycle can be used again for recent engines where high injection pressures allow for a late start of fuel injection. The cycle consists of the following processes:

1-2   isentropic compression.
2-3   heat addition at constant pressure (isobaric).
3-4   isentropic expansion.
4-1   heat rejection at constant volume.

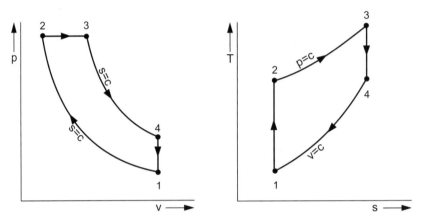

Figure 7.28   Air–standard cycle: Diesel.

Seiliger cycle

The Seiliger cycle is a combination of the Otto cycle and the Diesel cycle. It approximates the actual diesel process better as can be seen when comparing Figure 7.29 with the indicator diagram in Figure 7.4.

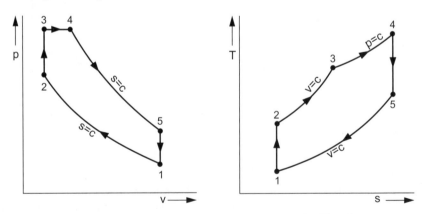

Figure 7.29   Air–standard cycle: 5-point Seiliger idealisation of a Diesel process.

Heat addition occurs in two steps, which is why it is often referred to as the dual cycle: first as the Otto cycle at constant volume, second as the Diesel cycle at constant pressure. The processes can be described as follows:

1-2   isentropic compression.
2-3   heat addition at constant volume (isochoric).
3-4   heat addition at constant pressure (isobaric).
4-5   isentropic expansion.
5-1   heat rejection at constant volume.

   In this introduction to the thermodynamic performance of a diesel engine, it suffices to model the processes in a diesel engine with a 5-point cycle. However, for more advanced considerations the 6-point dual cycle offers more refinement. In the 6-point cycle [Stapersma, 1996] combustion is modelled to occur over three stages: after isochoric and isobaric heat addition and expansion, heat addition continues isothermal before isentropic expansion starts. So, early and late combustion can be modelled adequately.

   If the air–standard cycles that have been introduced are compared, it is clear that both the Diesel and the Otto cycles can be derived from the Seiliger cycle by omitting either the heat addition at constant volume or the heat addition at constant pressure.

7.8.2   Qualitative comparison of the air–standard cycles

The air-standard cycles can be used to compare the performance of different processes qualitatively. The ideal thermodynamic efficiency has been defined in equation (7.20):

$$\eta_{td} \overset{def}{=} \frac{W_i}{Q_{in}} \qquad \text{ref. (7.20)}$$

For a cycle process, the indicated work (or net work output) of the trapped mass is equal to the net heat input:

$$W_i = W_{cycle} = Q_{cycle} = Q_{in} - Q_{out} \qquad \text{ref. (2.26)}$$

Therefore:

$$\eta_{td} = \frac{Q_{in} - Q_{out}}{Q_{in}} = 1 - \frac{Q_{out}}{Q_{in}} \qquad (7.62)$$

The thermodynamic efficiency can also be written in specific quantities, i.e. per unit mass:

$$\eta_{td} \overset{def}{=} \frac{w_i}{q_{in}} \qquad (7.63)$$

Therefore, in analogy with equation (7.62) the thermodynamic efficiency can be expressed in heat per unit mass only:

$$\eta_{td} = \frac{q_{in} - q_{out}}{q_{in}} = 1 - \frac{q_{out}}{q_{in}} \qquad (7.64)$$

As established in Chapter 2, work and heat are areas in the p–V and T–S diagrams, respectively. Consequently, specific work and specific heat input and output are areas in p–v and T–s diagrams, respectively.

Another aspect of the qualitative comparison will be the relation between the air–fuel ratio, or the air excess ratio, and the input heat. If the air–fuel ratio and the mass of air are kept constant in the processes that are compared, the fuel will have to be the same and consequently the input heat remains the same.

Comparing the Otto cycle to the Diesel cycle at constant compression ratio and constant input heat

Now consider an Otto cycle and a Diesel cycle, where compression ratio and input heat are identical. So, the area under the line 2–3 in a T–s diagram has to be the same for both the cycles. Figure 7.30 shows the p–v and T–s diagrams of the cycles.

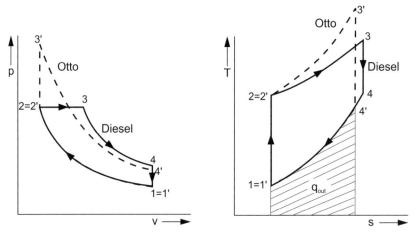

Figure 7.30   Comparison of an Otto and a Diesel cycle with identical heat input and compression ratio in p–v and T–s diagrams.

Since, in the T–s diagram, a line of constant volume is steeper than a line of constant pressure, the expansion process of the Otto cycle has to occur at a lower entropy in order to have equal areas under the lines 2'–3' and 2–3. From the T–s diagram, it can be concluded that heat leaving the cycle (q_{out}) of the Otto cycle is smaller than that of the Diesel cycle. Consequently, the efficiency of the Otto cycle is better, as shown by equation (7.64). This can also be expected because the temperature at which heat is added is higher for the Otto cycle.

This comparison, however, is not fully realistic. Instead of the compression ratio, the peak pressure should be kept identical in order to compare the processes on a fair basis. This is done next.

Comparing the Otto cycle to the Diesel cycle at constant peak pressure

If the maximum pressures are identical, the maximum forces in the engine are identical and consequently, the main structural components of the engines are comparable. In that case, the compression ratio of the Diesel cycle will be approximately twice that of the compression ratio of an Otto cycle. Again, the input heat is identical.

Figure 7.31 shows that q_{out} of the Otto cycle is bigger, so in this case the efficiency of the Otto process is worse than that of the Diesel cycle. It explains why, in practice, the efficiency of a petrol engine is lower than the efficiency of a diesel engine.

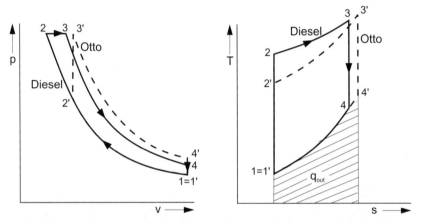

Figure 7.31   Comparison of an Otto and a Diesel cycle with identical heat input and peak pressure in p–v and T–s diagrams.

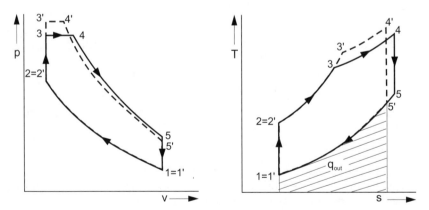

Figure 7.32   Comparison of two dual cycles with identical heat input when peak pressure (p_3) is increased in p–v and T–s diagrams.

Comparing Seiliger cycles: effect of increased peak pressure

The properties of a Seiliger cycle can also be examined qualitatively. The standard dual cycle is given in Figure 7.32. To compare the efficiency of this cycle to a cycle with increased peak pressure, a dotted line is added. The input heat is kept constant, so, in the T–s diagram, the area under line 2'–4' is equal to the area under 2–4. As demonstrated by the shaded area, the output heat of the cycle with increased peak pressure is less than that of the first cycle. So, see also equation (7.64), the thermodynamic efficiency increases as the maximum pressure increases.

Comparing Seiliger cycles: effect of increased compression ratio

The effect of the compression ratio on the thermodynamic efficiency of a cycle is examined by comparing a Seiliger cycle to a cycle with such a high compression ratio that all heat addition occurs at constant pressure; so, in fact to a Diesel cycle. Peak pressure and heat input are kept identical. In the T–s diagram in Figure 7.33, the areas under the lines 2'–4' and 2–4, i.e. input heat, are equal. Consequently, the output heat decreases as compression ratio increases. The thermodynamic efficiency increases as shown by equation (7.64).

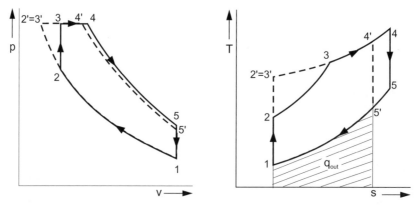

Figure 7.33   Comparison a dual cycle and a Diesel cycle with identical peak pressure and input heat in p–v and T–s diagrams.

From these comparisons, two important conclusions can be drawn with respect to the design of modern highly efficient diesel engines. The designer should:

▪ Choose a peak pressure as high as the construction of the engine allows.

▪ Design a fuel injection system, which predominantly gives a constant-pressure combustion enabling to set the compression ratio as high as possible. This kind of combustion is possible with modern injection systems using high fuel injection pressures.

Comparing Seiliger cycles: effect of turbocharging

In Figure 7.34 we compare a naturally aspirating engine with a turbocharged engine as if the processes take place in the same cylinder. This implies that the compression ratio and peak pressure are identical. Also, the air excess ratio and initial temperature are assumed to be the same in the two processes. Due to turbocharging, the initial pressure is higher and more mass is trapped in the cylinder.

First, examine the p–V diagram in Figure 7.34. Note that in this diagram the mass in cycle 1'–2'–3'–4'–5' is larger than in 1–2–3–4–5. The position of the turbocharged cycle relative to the original cycle will be substantiated. The initial pressure of the turbocharged cycle is higher and the cylinder volume does not change, so point 1' lies above point 1. Also, the compression ratios are the same, so the pressure at point 2' is higher than at point 2. Consequently, the line 2'–3' is shorter than 2–3 because, for this comparison, the peak pressure at 3' is identical to the pressure at 3. Heat addition 3'–4' is longer than 3–4; firstly because the heat added during stage 2'–3' is less, so, in order to add the same amount of heat, process 3'–4' needs to be longer, and secondly because more heat is added in the turbocharged cycle because more fuel will be combusted. Expansion returns the cycle to the volume in 5, where the pressure at 5' is higher than the pressure at 5.

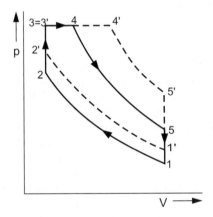

Figure 7.34   p–V diagram comparing the Seiliger cycles of a naturally aspirating engine and a turbocharged engine.

To examine the thermodynamic efficiency of both cycles, they are studied in specific quantities: see Figure 7.35. Both cycles are shown in a p–v diagram and a T–s diagram. Note that due to turbocharging more fuel will be combusted, so the total input heat Q_{in} is larger. However, the air excess is identical, so the air–fuel ratio will be the same: more fuel, more air and the input heat per unit mass q_{in} is identical. This is visualised in a T–s diagram: the areas under 2'–4' and 2–4 have to be equal.

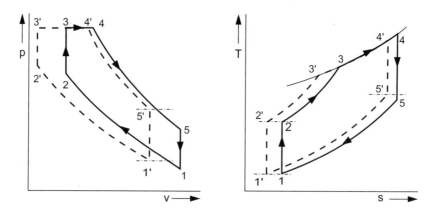

Figure 7.35   The p–v and T–s diagrams of two Seiliger cycles: a naturally aspirating engine and a turbocharged engine.

At the starting point 1', the pressure is higher than at 1. The specific volume is smaller because more mass is put into the same cylinder, so the volume per unit mass has decreased. The entropy at point 1' will be determined by examining the T–s diagram. The line of constant volume 1'–5' will lie above line 1–5 because the constant specific volume is smaller. Because the initial temperatures of the cycles are equal, point 1' must lie to the left of point 1.

The specific volume at point 2' is also smaller than at 2. The pressure is determined by the compression ratio, which is kept constant, so the pressure at point 2' is higher than at point 2. In the p–v diagram, line 3'–4' is a horizontal line at peak pressure. For the location of points 4' and 5', we return to the T–s diagram.

In the T–s diagram lines 1'–2' and 2'–3' can be drawn right away: 1'–2' has the same length as 1–2 because the process has the same compression ratio and consequently the same temperature rise, refer to equation (2.47). However, process 1'–2' occurs at lower entropy. Point 3' is found by extending line 3–4, which is a line of constant pressure, to the constant volume line through point 2'. Line 2'–3' lies at a lower constant specific volume parallel to line 2–3. Line 3'–4' lies at the same pressure as 3–4.

The location of point 4' is determined by shifting cycle 1'–2' to the right, so the lines of isentropic compression of both cycles coincide. In Figure 7.36 the points of the shifted cycle are points 1" to 5". The input heat per unit mass of the naturally aspirating engine and the (shifted) turbocharged engine are the same: consequently 4" lies to the right of point 4 in order to obtain equal areas under the lines 2–4 and 2"–4". Point 5" lies at the intersection of a line of constant entropy through point 4" and the line of constant volume 1–5. Having found these points, we can return to Figure 7.35 by shifting the cycle back to its original position. In the p–v diagram, the specific volume at point 5' is the same as at 1', so a line of constant volume can be drawn parallel to line 1–5.

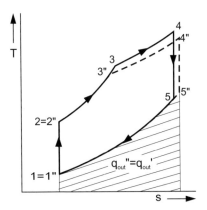

Figure 7.36   T–s diagram with turbocharged Seiliger cycle shifted to the right in order to compare areas representing heat per unit mass.

To examine the efficiency of both cycles, refer to the shifted turbocharged cycle in Figure 7.36. Having assured that the specific input heat is the same for both cycles, it can be seen that the specific output heat is larger for the turbocharged engine: consequently, the thermodynamic efficiency is lower as can be seen in equation (7.64). This adverse effect on the thermodynamic efficiency needs to be put in perspective:

- In practice, the peak pressure of a turbocharged engine will increase, adding a positive effect to the thermodynamic efficiency as concluded previously.

- The power delivered will be increased but the mechanical and heat losses will not increase in the same proportion; they tend to be absolutely equal thus relatively smaller.

So, the adverse effect on thermodynamic efficiency is counteracted by increasing peak pressures, and the mechanical and heat input efficiency improves: for the effective efficiency, as defined by equation (7.21), this means that turbocharging is not necessarily adverse but may even be favourable.

$$\eta_e = \eta_m \cdot \eta_{comb} \cdot \eta_q \cdot \eta_{td} \qquad \text{ref. (7.21)}$$

7.8.3   Analytic formulation of the Seiliger cycle

The processes of a Seiliger cycle can be described using the basic thermodynamic principles that have been introduced in Chapter 2. In Figure 7.37, the Seiliger cycle is shown. The volumes at Top Dead Centre and Bottom Dead Centre are indicated. The geometrical compression ratio relates the volume at Top Dead Centre to the total cylinder volume at Bottom Dead Centre: refer to equation (7.3):

$$\varepsilon \stackrel{\text{def}}{=} \frac{V_{BDC}}{V_{TDC}} \qquad \text{ref. (7.3)}$$

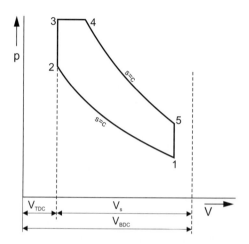

Figure 7.37   Exaggerated representation of the difference between V_1 and V_{BDC}.

Now in general:

$$V_1 < V_{BDC} \text{ (because intake closes after BDC) and } V_2 = V_{TDC}$$

So, the *effective* compression ratio that characterises the isentropic compression (stage 1–2) generally is smaller than the geometric compression ratio:

$$r_c \overset{def}{=} \frac{V_1}{V_2} \tag{7.65}$$

$$r_c < \varepsilon$$

The pressure rise at constant volume (2–3) is determined by a parameter a:

$$a \overset{def}{=} \frac{p_3}{p_2} \tag{7.66}$$

The isobaric expansion during combustion (3–4) is fixed by a parameter b:

$$b \overset{def}{=} \frac{V_4}{V_3} \tag{7.67}$$

The effective expansion ratio of the (isentropic) expansion phase (4-5) is by definition:

$$r_e \overset{def}{=} \frac{V_5}{V_4} = \frac{V_5}{V_3} \cdot \frac{V_3}{V_4} \tag{7.68}$$

If the expansion ends at the same volume as at which the compression begins then:

$$V_5 = V_1$$

By definition, the process between 2 and 3 occurs at constant volume:

$$V_3 = V_2$$

Then the effective expansion stroke turns out to be dependent on the previous parameters:

$$r_e = \frac{V_1}{V_2} \cdot \frac{V_3}{V_4} = \frac{r_c}{b} \tag{7.69}$$

Thus, the shape of the cycle is completely defined by the shape parameters:

$$r_c, a, b$$

With these parameters, the Seiliger cycle can be defined analytically in terms of a volume ratio φ, a pressure ratio π and a temperature ratio τ for each stage as presented in Table 7.3. Assuming perfect gas and equal fluid properties throughout, the isentropic index κ emerges as an additional parameter.

Stage	Volume ratio φ	Pressure ratio π	Temperature ratio τ
1 - 2	$\dfrac{V_1}{V_2} \overset{def}{=} r_c$	$\dfrac{p_2}{p_1} = r_c^{\kappa}$	$\dfrac{T_2}{T_1} = r_c^{\kappa-1}$
2 - 3	$\dfrac{V_3}{V_2} \overset{def}{=} 1$	$\dfrac{p_3}{p_2} \overset{def}{=} a$	$\dfrac{T_3}{T_2} = a$
3 - 4	$\dfrac{V_4}{V_3} \overset{def}{=} b$	$\dfrac{p_4}{p_3} \overset{def}{=} 1$	$\dfrac{T_4}{T_3} = b$
4 - 5	$\dfrac{V_5}{V_4} = \dfrac{r_c}{b}$	$\dfrac{p_4}{p_5} = \left(\dfrac{r_c}{b}\right)^{\kappa}$	$\dfrac{T_4}{T_5} = \left(\dfrac{r_c}{b}\right)^{\kappa-1}$
5 - 1	$\dfrac{V_5}{V_1} \overset{def}{=} 1$	$\dfrac{p_5}{p_1} = \dfrac{r_c^{\kappa} \cdot a}{\left(\frac{r_c}{b}\right)^{\kappa}}$ $= a \cdot b^{\kappa}$	$\dfrac{T_5}{T_1} = \dfrac{r_c^{\kappa-1} \cdot a \cdot b}{\left(\frac{r_c}{b}\right)^{\kappa-1}}$ $= a \cdot b^{\kappa}$

Table 7.3   Analytical definition of the Seiliger process.

7.8.4   Heat and work in the Seiliger cycle

Using the thermodynamic principles that were reviewed in Chapter 2, the heat and work associated with the Seiliger processes can be determined. Heat is added to the cycle during stages 2–3 and 3–4, while heat is rejected during stage 5–1. The cycle delivers work during the expansion of stages 3–4 and 4–5; it requires work during stage 1–2.

In this section specific work and specific heat input and output will be determined and expressed in the initial temperature, the specific heat, the isentropic index κ and the Seiliger parameters

Heat

The total theoretical heat input per kilogram of trapped mass is:

$$q_{in} = q_{23} + q_{34} \tag{7.70}$$

The contribution of the two combustion stages will be investigated. Consider the first law of thermodynamics for closed systems:

$$dU = \delta Q - \delta W \quad or \quad du = \delta q - \delta w \qquad \text{ref. (2.3)}$$

No work is transferred in stage 2–3, consequently the heat added in stage 2–3 is:

$$\left. \begin{aligned} du &= \delta q \\ du &= c_v \cdot dT \quad ref.\ (2.36) \end{aligned} \right\} \Rightarrow q_{23} = c_v \cdot (T_3 - T_2) \tag{7.71}$$

Using Table 7.3 this can be expressed in the three Seiliger parameters – a, b, r_c–, the initial temperature, the specific heat and the isentropic index, where the latter two are assumed constant for all stages.

$$q_{23} = c_v \cdot T_1 \cdot \frac{T_2}{T_1} \left(\frac{T_3}{T_2} - 1 \right) = c_v \cdot T_1 \cdot r_c^{\kappa-1} \cdot (a-1) \tag{7.72}$$

The heat added during stage 3–4 can be determined by using the second Gibbs equation:

$$dH = T \cdot dS + V \cdot dp \quad or \quad dh = T \cdot ds + v \cdot dp \qquad \text{ref. (2.21)}$$

As the heat addition is an isobaric process, which can also be considered reversible, it reduces to the following:

$$\left. \begin{aligned} dh &= T \cdot ds = \delta q \\ dh &= c_p \cdot dT \quad ref.\ (2.37) \end{aligned} \right\} \Rightarrow q_{34} = c_p \cdot (T_4 - T_3) \tag{7.73}$$

This can also be written as:

$$q_{34} = c_v \cdot \frac{c_p}{c_v} \cdot T_1 \cdot \frac{T_2}{T_1} \cdot \frac{T_3}{T_2} \left(\frac{T_4}{T_3} - 1 \right) = c_v \cdot T_1 \cdot \kappa \cdot r_c^{\kappa-1} \cdot a \cdot (b-1) \tag{7.74}$$

With equations (7.70), (7.72) and (7.74) the total specific heat input can be expressed non-dimensionally:

$$\frac{q_{in}}{c_v T_1} = r_c^{\kappa-1} \cdot \{(a-1) + \kappa \cdot a \cdot (b-1)\} \tag{7.75}$$

The specific heat output can also be expressed in the initial temperature, the specific heat, the isentropic index and the Seiliger parameters. Because the compression and expansion are assumed isentropic, the only heat rejection takes place during the exhaust stage (5–1):

$$q_{out} = |q_{51}| \tag{7.76}$$

With the first law of thermodynamics and equation (2.36), the heat rejected in stage 5–1 is determined. Note that the mathematical outcome will be a negative number.

$$|q_{51}| = c_v \cdot (T_5 - T_1)$$
$$= c_v \cdot T_1 \cdot \left(\frac{T_5}{T_1} - 1\right) = c_v \cdot T_1 \cdot \left(a \cdot b^\kappa - 1\right) \tag{7.77}$$

For a real engine, this heat is rejected by driving out the exhaust gases and taking in fresh and cool air. In non-dimensional form, the specific heat output is:

$$\frac{q_{out}}{c_v \cdot T_1} = a \cdot b^\kappa - 1 \tag{7.78}$$

Work

Likewise, the mass specific net work of the cycle can be calculated. First focus is on the work input.

$$w_{in} = |w_{12}| \tag{7.79}$$

For the compression stage, consider the first law of thermodynamics. Since heat transfer is assumed zero, the work is given by:

$$\left.\begin{aligned} du &= \delta q - \delta w \\ du &= c_v \cdot dT \ \textit{ref. (2.36)} \end{aligned}\right\} \Rightarrow w_{12} = -c_v \cdot (T_2 - T_1) \tag{7.80}$$

So,

$$|w_{12}| = c_v \cdot (T_2 - T_1)$$
$$= c_v \cdot T_1 \cdot \left(\frac{T_2}{T_1} - 1\right) = c_v \cdot T_1 \cdot (r_c^{\kappa-1} - 1) \tag{7.81}$$

The delivered work, or work output is:

$$w_{out} = w_{34} + w_{45} \tag{7.82}$$

Since the process is assumed to be reversible, use equation (2.15) for the first part of the work output:

$$\delta w = p \cdot dv \qquad\qquad \text{ref. 2.15}$$

Then:

$$
\begin{aligned}
w_{34} &= p_3 \cdot (V_4 - V_3) = R \cdot (T_4 - T_3) = (c_p - c_v) \cdot (T_4 - T_3) \\
&= c_v \cdot \left(\frac{c_p}{c_v} - 1 \right) \cdot T_1 \cdot \frac{T_2}{T_1} \cdot \frac{T_3}{T_2} \cdot \left(\frac{T_4}{T_3} - 1 \right) \\
&= c_v \cdot T_1 \cdot (\kappa - 1) \cdot r_c^{\ \kappa-1} \cdot a \cdot (b-1)
\end{aligned}
\qquad (7.83)
$$

Note that this solution can also be found when using the first law of thermodynamics and the solution for q_{34} from the previous section.

For the work delivered during stage 4–5, again consider the first law of thermodynamics:

$$
\left.
\begin{aligned}
du &= -\delta w \\
du &= c_v dT \quad \textit{ref. (2.38)}
\end{aligned}
\right\} \Rightarrow w_{45} = c_v \cdot (T_4 - T_5)
\qquad (7.84)
$$

$$
\begin{aligned}
w_{45} &= c_v \cdot T_1 \cdot \frac{T_2}{T_1} \cdot \frac{T_3}{T_2} \cdot \frac{T_4}{T_3} \cdot \left(1 - \frac{T_5}{T_4} \right) \\
&= c_v \cdot T_1 \cdot r_c^{\ \kappa-1} \cdot a \cdot b \cdot \left(1 - \frac{1}{\left(\dfrac{r_c}{b} \right)^{\kappa-1}} \right) = c_v \cdot T_1 \cdot (r_c^{\ \kappa-1} \cdot ab - ab^{\kappa})
\end{aligned}
\qquad (7.85)
$$

The net work of the cycle, indicated work w_i, is equal to:

$$w_i = w_{out} - w_{in} = w_{34} + w_{45} - \left| w_{12} \right| \qquad (7.86)$$

7.8.5   *Thermodynamic efficiency of the Seiliger cycle*

Making use of the equations derived in the previous section the ideal thermodynamic efficiency, as defined in equation (7.64), can be expressed in the Seiliger parameters a, b and r_c, and the isentropic index κ:

$$\eta_{td} = 1 - \frac{q_{out}}{q_{in}} = 1 - \frac{1}{r_c^{\ \kappa-1}} \cdot \frac{a \cdot b^{\kappa} - 1}{(a-1) + \kappa \cdot a \cdot (b-1)} \qquad (7.87)$$

Special cases occur when,

- $a = 1$; the Seiliger cycle describes a Diesel cycle:

$$\eta_{td,Diesel} = 1 - \frac{1}{r_c^{\kappa-1}} \cdot \frac{b^{\kappa}-1}{\kappa \cdot (b-1)} \tag{7.88}$$

- $b = 1$; the Seiliger cycle describes a Otto cycle:

$$\eta_{td,Otto} = 1 - \frac{1}{r_c^{\kappa-1}} \tag{7.89}$$

The thermodynamic efficiency of an Otto cycle does not depend on pressure ratio a, only on the compression ration r_c: the higher the compression ratio, the higher the efficiency. However, the compression ratio of an Otto engine is limited. In a real engine, the injected medium is a mixture of air and fuel. A compression ratio that is too high, i.e. a high end pressure and temperature, would result in early explosive combustion of the mixture. This *detonation* may lead to damage. To avoid detonation in a petrol engine, the fuel should have a sufficiently high anti-detonation quality, i.e. may not easily decompose or ignite itself (expressed in the octane number). Also, the compression ratio should be relatively low (7 to 8). Theoretically, the thermodynamic efficiency of an Otto engine with a compression ratio of 7 and an isentropic index κ of 1.40 is 0.54.

The thermodynamic efficiency of a Diesel cycle, on the other hand, depends on the compression ratio r_c and the volume ratio b. By comparing equations (7.88) and (7.89), it can be shown that at identical compression ratios, the efficiency of an Otto engine is better than that of a Diesel engine, as was qualitatively shown in section 7.8.2.

$$\left.\begin{array}{c} b > 1 \\ r_{c,Otto} = r_{c,Diesel} \end{array}\right\} \Rightarrow \eta_{td,Otto} > \eta_{td,Diesel}$$

However, the compression ratio of Diesel engines is much higher, i.e. 12 to 14, than the compression ratio of petrol engines. This explains the higher efficiencies of diesel engines compared to petrol engines: theoretically, the thermodynamic efficiency of a Diesel engine with compression ratio 14, volume ratio $b = 2.2$ and isentropic index κ of 1.40 is 0.58.

7.8.6 Mean indicated pressure of the Seiliger cycle

Like thermodynamic efficiency, mean indicated pressure can also be determined from the Seiliger parameters. The mean indicated pressure is by definition:

$$p_{mi} \overset{def}{=} \frac{W_i}{V_s} \tag{ref. (7.8)}$$

Indicated work is trapped mass times specific work:

$$W_i = m_1 \cdot w_i = \frac{p_1 \cdot V_1}{R \cdot T_1} \cdot w_i \tag{7.90}$$

With equation (7.90), mean indicated pressure can be written in non-dimensional form:

$$\frac{p_{mi}}{p_1} = \frac{V_1}{V_S} \cdot \frac{w_i}{R \cdot T_1} \tag{7.91}$$

The volume ratio that appears in this relation expresses the fact that the initial volume is different from the swept volume:

$$\frac{V_1}{V_S} = \frac{V_1}{V_2} \cdot \frac{V_{TDC}}{V_{BDC} - V_{TDC}} = \frac{r_c}{\varepsilon - 1} \tag{7.92}$$

The factor which makes specific work non-dimensional, is equal to:

$$R \cdot T_1 = \left(c_p - c_v\right) \cdot T_1 = \left(\kappa - 1\right) \cdot c_v \cdot T_1 \tag{7.93}$$

So, by combining equations (7.91) to (7.93), the mean indicated pressure can be expressed in specific work as:

$$\frac{p_{mi}}{p_1} = \frac{1}{\kappa - 1} \cdot \frac{r_c}{\varepsilon - 1} \cdot \frac{w_i}{c_v \cdot T_1} \tag{7.94}$$

The indicated work can be expressed in the input heat:

$$w_i = \eta_{td} \cdot q_{in}$$

So, with the equations derived in previous sections the specific indicated work can be expressed non-dimensionally:

$$\frac{w_i}{c_v T_1} = \eta_{td} \cdot \left[r_c^{\kappa - 1} \cdot \left\{ (a - 1) + \kappa \cdot a \cdot (b - 1) \right\} \right] \tag{7.95}$$

Now substitute this expression for specific work in equation (7.94) in order to obtain an expression for mean indicated pressure that is non-dimensional and that only contains Seiliger parameters and the thermodynamic efficiency (which could also be expressed in Seiliger parameters as shown in equation (7.87)):

$$\frac{p_{mi}}{p_1} = \frac{\eta_{td}}{\kappa - 1} \cdot \frac{r_c}{\varepsilon - 1} \cdot \left[r_c^{\kappa - 1} \cdot \left\{ (a - 1) + \kappa \cdot a \cdot (b - 1) \right\} \right] \tag{7.96}$$

7.8.7   Effect of design limitations to the Seiliger parameters

When we look at equations (7.87) and (7.96), it seems that by changing the Seiliger parameters, the performance can be improved. However, there are limitations in the design of turbocharged diesel engines: the maximum pressure and the air excess during combustion. These limitations have an effect on the extent to which the cycle can be *shaped* by the Seiliger parameters.

First, consider the maximum peak pressure. In the qualitative considerations in section 7.8.2, it was shown that a high peak pressure increases the thermodynamic efficiency. The limit of the pressure is dictated by the dimensioning of cylinder head, piston, connecting rod, crankshaft and bearings. The peak pressure p_{max} is chosen by the designer within the limits of technology and costs of the engine.

The designer also specifies the charge pressure p_1 and the pressure rise during combustion, expressed by shape parameter a. The charge pressure is dictated by the turbocharger technology. In section 7.8.2 it has been shown, for given charge and peak pressures, that if the compression ratio increases, i.e. parameter a decreases, the thermodynamic efficiency increases. The pressure rise during combustion is determined by the fuel injection system. Design of these systems is aimed at late injection at high pressure, thus decreasing a.

After the designer has set those variables, i.e. p_{max}, p_1 and a, the effective compression ratio r_c turns out to be a dependent variable:

$$p_{max} = p_3 = a \cdot r_c^{\kappa} \cdot p_1 \Rightarrow r_c = \left(\frac{p_{max}}{a \cdot p_1} \right)^{\frac{1}{\kappa}} \tag{7.97}$$

The other limitation, the air excess ratio, determines the conditions for combustion and must be carefully selected, among others in view of the fuel to be burned. The relations between the air–fuel ratio, the heat input and the air excess ratio need to be determined:

$$afr \overset{def}{=} \frac{m_{ca}}{m_f} = m_{ca} \cdot \frac{h^L}{Q_f} \tag{7.98}$$

$$Q_{in} = \eta_{comb} \cdot \eta_q \cdot Q_f \qquad \text{ref. (7.19)}$$

If equation (7.19) is used, the relation between input heat and air–fuel ratio can be found:

$$afr = m_{ca} \cdot \frac{h^L}{Q_f} = \frac{m_{ca}}{Q_{in}} \cdot \eta_{comb} \cdot \eta_q \cdot h^L = \eta_{comb} \cdot \eta_q \cdot \frac{h^L}{q_{in}} \tag{7.99}$$

And consequently, the relation between the input heat and the air excess ratio is:

$$\lambda = \frac{afr}{\sigma} = \eta_{comb} \cdot \eta_q \cdot \frac{h^L}{\sigma \cdot q_{in}} \tag{7.100}$$

If complete combustion is assumed, i.e. combustion efficiency is one, the air excess ratio may be written as:

$$\lambda = \eta_q \cdot \frac{h^L}{\sigma \cdot q_{in}} \tag{7.101}$$

Now substitute the expression for the input heat as given by equation (7.75):

$$\lambda = \eta_q \cdot \frac{h^L}{\sigma \cdot c_v \cdot T_1} \cdot \frac{1}{r_c^{\kappa-1} \cdot \left((a-1) + \kappa \cdot a \cdot (b-1)\right)} \tag{7.102}$$

If combustion pressure rise parameter a and the air excess ratio are selected, parameter b is a dependent parameter:

$$b = \frac{\left\{ \left(\eta_q \cdot \frac{h^L}{\lambda \cdot \sigma \cdot c_v \cdot T_1} \cdot \frac{1}{r_c^{\kappa-1}} \right) - (a-1) + \kappa \cdot a \right\}}{\kappa \cdot a} \tag{7.103}$$

So, equations (7.97) and (7.103) show that the parameters set by the designer, the charge pressure, the maximum pressure, the pressure rise during combustion and the air excess ratio, determine the Seiliger cycle that describe the diesel process. Consequently, the thermodynamic efficiency and the mean indicated pressure can be determined with the expressions in equations (7.87) and (7.96).

7.8.8   *Performance of the Diesel engine*

The theoretical framework derived in the previous sections can be used to draw some general conclusions about the thermodynamic performance of the turbocharged diesel cycle. Charge pressures up to 5 bar have been investigated while the peak pressures is kept at distinct values of 120, 180 and 300 bar.

Figure 7.38 illustrates the increase of the mean indicated pressure with increasing charge pressure for different peak pressures as given by equation (7.96). Observe that the effect of the peak pressure on mean indicated pressure is far less than that of the charge pressure.

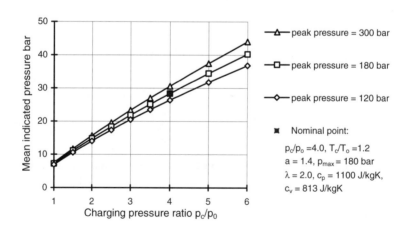

Figure 7.38   Ideal mean indicated pressure of a Seiliger cycle.

Figure 7.39 illustrates the effect of peak and charge pressure to the thermodynamic efficiency of a Seiliger cycle as given by equation (7.87). The figure shows what has already been shown in section 7.8.2:

- Increasing the charge pressure has a negative effect on thermodynamic efficiency (see also Figure 7.35).

- Increasing the peak pressure is a way to compensate the efficiency loss caused by the higher charge pressure, because the thermodynamic efficiency increases with increasing peak pressure (see also Figure 7.32)

Both effects often occur in the same engine since increasing the charge pressure at constant peak pressure would result in a compression ratio that is too low for auto-ignition (see limit line in Figure 7.39).

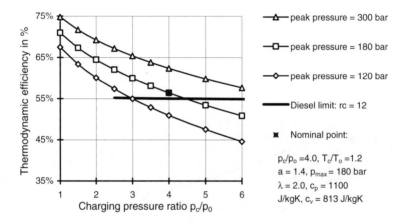

Figure 7.39   Ideal thermodynamic efficiency of Seiliger cycle.

Consider equation (7.21) to evaluate the overall efficiency of a diesel engine.

$$\eta_e = \eta_m \cdot \eta_{comb} \cdot \eta_q \cdot \eta_{td} \qquad \text{ref. (7.21)}$$

If the power of a given engine is increased considerably by increasing the charge pressure, the mechanical and heat losses tend to increase at a lower rate than the power. In other words, the mechanical efficiency and heat input efficiency as defined will *increase* with *increasing* charge pressure see Figure 7.40.

So, an important conclusion can be drawn from equation (7.21): the overall effective efficiency is the result of two opposing effects: an increase of charge pressure will cause the thermodynamic efficiency to decrease and the mechanical and the heat efficiency to increase. The two effects more or less compensate each other. The net result is shown in Figure 7.41. The figure shows lines of different peak pressures. For each peak pressure, there tends to be an optimum value of the charge pressure. Peak pressure as such remains the important parameter to improve efficiency in any case.

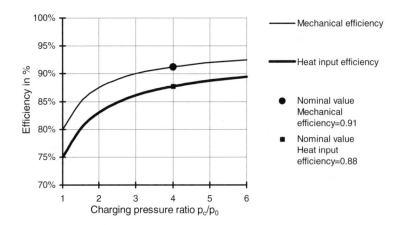

Figure 7.40   Mechanical and heat losses of a diesel engine expressed as partial
efficiency versus charge pressure.

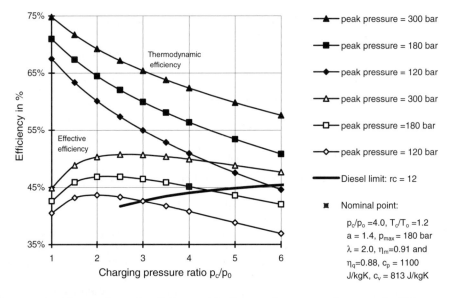

Figure 7.41   Thermodynamic efficiency of Seiliger cycle compared to overall efficiency of
diesel engine.

The mean effective pressure can be found by multiplying the mean indicated pressure by
the mechanical efficiency. Mean indicated pressure and mean effective pressure are
shown in Figure 7.42.

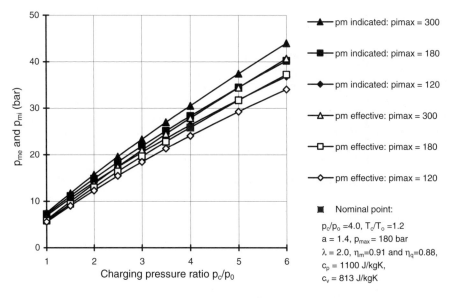

Figure 7.42   Ideal mean indicated pressure of Seiliger cycle compared to mean effective pressure of diesel engine.

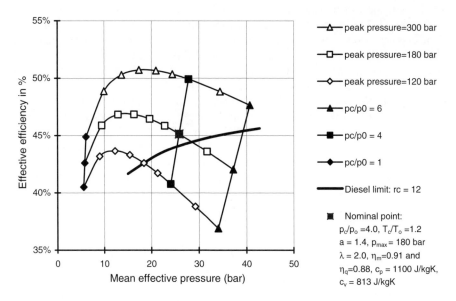

Figure 7.43   Trade-off of efficiency and mean effective pressure for several values of the charge pressure and peak pressure.

The results for mean effective pressure and overall efficiency can be brought together in a trade-off picture with both parameters at the axes. The charge pressure, together with peak pressure, are then running parameters along the curves; see Figure 7.43.

Now it is clear that when the charge pressure is increased there comes a moment (say at 1.5 or 2 bar) where it is necessary to increase peak pressure as well in order to maintain overall efficiency. This is exactly what can be seen in the development of modern turbocharged engines today. Charge pressures have reached values of 3 to 4 bar with peak pressures of 150 to 180 bar. While charge pressures continue to increase to 5 bar, the peak pressure for which modern engines are designed is 200 to 220 bar. A further discussion of these issues can be found in [Grimmelius, 1999].

7.9   Construction and installation

7.9.1   Construction

This section gives an overview of some types of diesel engines currently found in marine prime mover applications:

- MAN B&W K98MC (6 cylinders: 34320kW – 12 cylinders: 68640 kW, at 94 rpm).

- Wärtsilä 46 in-line and V-configuration.

- MTU 20V 1163.

Figure 7.44 shows a cross-section of the K98MC 2-stroke diesel engine of MAN B&W. The engine can be delivered as a 6 to 12 cylinder in-line engine, developing an output power of 34320 to 68640 kW. Its mean effective pressure is 18.2 bar and the nominal engine speed is 94 rpm. As can be seen in the cross-section the engine is a crosshead (1) engine. From the size of the exhaust receiver (2), it is clear that the engine is charged by a constant pressure turbocharging system. The turbocharger (3), air receiver (4), air cooler (5) and air intake ports (6) are shown as well.

Each cylinder has one exhaust valve (7) (hydraulically actuated to open and with an air spring (8) to close the valve) leaving room for three radially distributed fuel injectors (atomisers) connected to a high-pressure fuel pump. The three injectors ensure that an amount of fuel (about the contents of a beer glass) is injected in a relatively short time (some milliseconds). On the right hand side of the cylinder the hydraulic actuator of the exhaust valve and the camshaft (9) are found. Note that the camshaft has two cams (not shown) one for the fuel injector and one for the exhaust valve (10).

The piston (11) is oil-cooled. The cooling oil is supplied through the piston rod (12). The oil supply is connected to the crosshead through telescopic piping. The cylinder head (13), the liner and the exhaust valve house are water-cooled.

All main bolts are hydraulically tightened to ensure correct pre-tensioning of these bolts and to maintain the stress variations within acceptable limits. This refers to the main bearing caps of the crankshaft, the connecting rod bearings, the cylinder head bolts, the anchor bolts, which connect the bedplate (17), the frame of the crosshead (18) and the cylinder block (19). As an example, one of the bolts (16) is indicated.

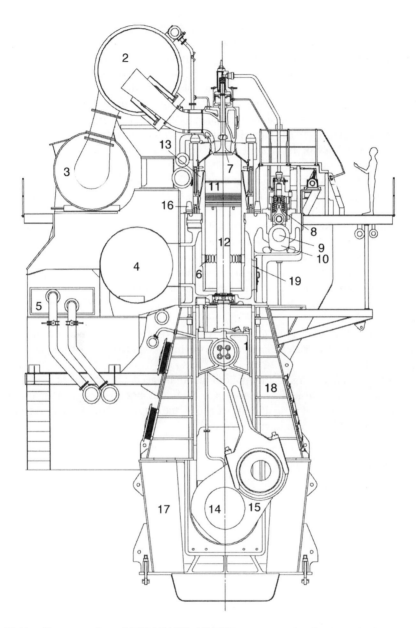

Figure 7.44   Cross section of MAN B&W's K98MC: an example of a 2-stroke low-speed diesel engine. (Courtesy of MAN B&W Diesel A/S: K98MC Project Guide 1998).

Figure 7.45 and Figure 7.46 show cross-sections of the Wärtsilä 46, 4-stroke diesel engines in in-line and V-configuration respectively. This engine can be delivered in 6, 8 or 9 cylinders in-line and in 12, 16 or 18 cylinders in V-configuration (5430-25650 kW at 500 rpm). It is a medium-speed trunk piston engine. Note that the cylinders of an in-line engine are identical to the V-engine. Only the frame of both engines is different.

The size of the exhaust receivers (as shown in the cross-section of the V-engine) reveals that the turbocharging uses the pulse system. Each cylinder has two air intake valves and two exhaust valves. The exhaust valves can only be seen in the V-engine cross-section. The fuel injector is located in the centre of cylinder cover, between the four valves.

The air intake receiver is located on the right side for the in-line engine, and for the V-engine in the middle between the cylinder rows. In the cross-section of the line engine the turbocharger can be distinguished.

As in the MAN B&W engine discussed in the foregoing, the piston of this engine is cooled with oil. The cooling oil has to travel a long way since it is supplied to the caps of the main crankshaft bearing, from which it flows into the bearing. From the bearing, it enters the crankshaft in channels; through the channels it flows to the crankpin and then to the connecting rod. Finally, it gets to the channels in the piston through the piston pin. Therefore, oil pressures will have to be high. The cylinder liner and cover are water-cooled.

On the left side of the engine (for the V-engines on either side), a camshaft is shown. It has three cams: one for the exhaust valves, one for the intake valves and one for the fuel pump.

The piping arrangements of the modern medium-speed engines are much less than the arrangements of the 2-stroke low-speed engines. In the modern designs the cooling water and oil piping is integrated in the structure of the engine. The advantages are a neat looking engine and lower production costs.

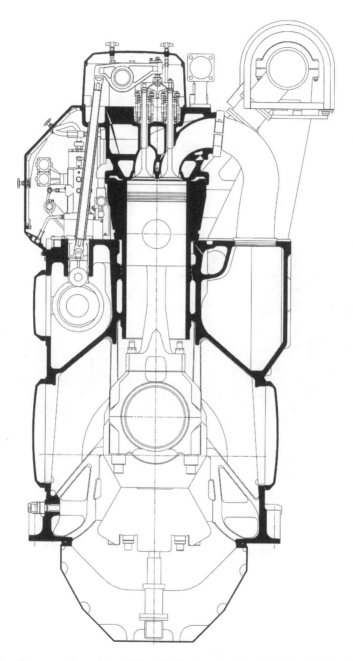

Figure 7.45   Cross-section of the Wärtsilä 46 4-stroke diesel engine; in-line. (Courtesy of Wärtsilä NSD Corporation).

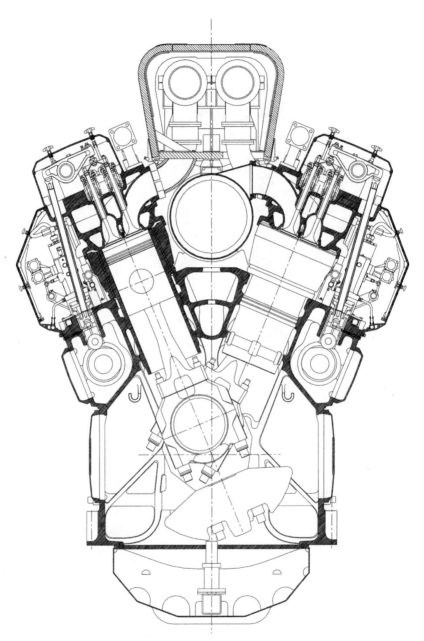

Figure 7.46   Cross-section of the Wärtsilä 46 4-stroke diesel engine; V-configuration.
(Courtesy of Wärtsilä NSD Corporation).

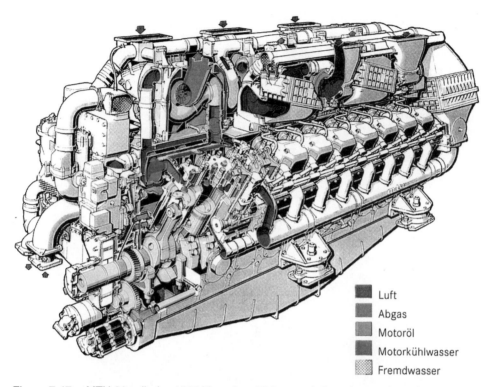

Luft
Abgas
Motoröl
Motorkühlwasser
Fremdwasser

Figure 7.47   MTU 20 cylinder 1163 V-engine: high-speed, 4-stroke, trunk engine with sequential turbocharging. (Courtesy of MTU).

Figure 7.47 shows a high-speed engine by MTU. It is a 4-stroke, trunk piston, 20 cylinder V-engine. Combustion air is supplied using a two-stage sequential turbocharging system. Note the considerable volume on top of the engine to accommodate all (10) turbochargers and charge air coolers. Also note two (of six) silencer blocks, by which the engine can be resiliently mounted on its foundation.

7.9.2   *Installation*

Diesel engines can either be rigidly or resiliently mounted to their foundation. Low-speed 2-stroke engines normally are rigidly mounted. Because the ship's construction is not very stiff and low-speed engines are heavy, the alignment of these huge engines (in particular of the crankshaft bearings) requires careful handling.

High-speed engines are resiliently mounted to isolate noise and vibration. Airborne noise of high-speed engines is such that there have been (naval) applications where an acoustical enclosure has been fitted. For naval applications, a double elastic mounting may also be necessary to attenuate the structure borne noise. Resilient mounting is becoming common practice for medium-speed engines too, in particular for cruise ships and ferries, where passenger comfort is an issue.

The engine room ventilation must be sized to supply the air to the engines, because most diesel engines take their intake air directly from the engine room. Consequently, the air may be relatively hot. To avoid these drawbacks, diesel engines are sometimes provided with their own air inlet ducts. Notwithstanding a smaller ventilation system, the total duct volume will be larger in that case. Also, the (under-)pressure before the engine may be somewhat lower, but since temperature will be lower as well, intake air density in general will be higher than in case of air supply from the engine room.

7.10 Exercises

Exercise 1

A diesel engine designer is interested to know the effect of turbocharging on mean effective pressure and power. The engine he is investigating is a 4-stroke diesel engine with 12 cylinders. Additionally, it has a rotational speed of 1000 rpm, a mean piston speed of 10 m/s and its stroke–bore ratio is 1.3.

He estimated the following data (which may assumed reasonable):

- Thermodynamic efficiency   56%
- Mechanical losses   approximately 10%
- Heat losses   approximately 10%
- Charge pressure   3 bar <u>over</u>pressure in inlet receiver
- Charging is reasonably effective   95%
- Inlet receiver temperature   50 °C
- Air excess ratio   2
- Lower heat value of fuel h^L_{MDO} 42,700 kJ/kg
- Stoichiometric fuel air ratio σ 14.5:1
- Gas constant air/exhaust gas R   0.287 kJ/kg

A). *Calculate engine efficiency, mean effective pressure and power output*
B). *If an engine of the same size would not be turbocharged, what would be the efficiency, mean effective pressure and power, keeping the assumptions unaltered.*
C). *What assumption(s) would you change, in what direction and how much, and how much would that affect your answers?*

Exercise 2

For a ship a 4-stroke diesel engine is required with the following outline specification:

- Power   9000 kW
- Maximum speed   600 rpm

According to the manufacturer the following data apply to his state-of-the-art cylinder design and pressure charging technology:

- Mean piston speed   10 m/s
- Brake Mean Effective Pressure: 24 bar

From a viewpoint of maintenance there is a preference for the lowest number of cylinders without going to extreme constructional dimensions. Therefore following alternatives are considered:

- Number of cylinders   8 or 12

A). Calculate for both number of cylinders:
- *Stroke length, bore diameter and stroke–bore ratio*
- *Power per litre swept volume*
- *Wear index*

B). Which number of cylinders has your preference and why?

The power density of the engine discussed before is considered too low. Therefore it is decided to specify the *same power*, 9000 kW, from a *high speed* instead of a medium speed engine:

- High speed   1200 rpm

The specification still is for a 4-stroke engine and at first it is assumed that cylinder design and pressure charging have the same technological parameters. Tentatively, the number of cylinders must be increased, therefore the following alternatives are considered:

- Number of cylinders   12 or 20

C). Calculate for both number of cylinders:
- *Stroke length, bore diameter and stroke–bore ratio*
- *Power per litre swept volume*
- *Wear index*

D). Does any of the selected number of cylinders lead to a feasible engine?

The basic specification for a high speed 4-stroke engine remains 9000 kW at 1200 rpm. The practical maximum of 20 cylinders will be investigated in more detail. In order to improve the engine, the cylinder design and pressure charging are modified in two steps. First mean piston speed is increased:

- Mean piston speed   12 m/s

Then charge pressure is increased resulting in:

- Brake Mean Effective Pressure: 30 bar

E). Calculate for the increased mean piston speed:
- *Stroke length, bore diameter and stroke–bore ratio*
- *Power per litre swept volume*
- *Wear index*

F). As E) but for the increased mean effective pressure:
G). Comment on the trend of the results.

The ship owner is interested to see what a 2-stroke *low speed* alternative would look like.

- Power   9000 kW

- Low speed   120 rpm

According to the manufacturer, the following data apply to a 2-stroke state-of-the-art cylinder design and pressure charging technology:

- Mean piston speed   8 m/s

- Brake Mean Effective Pressure: 18 bar

From a maintenance point of view, there is a preference for the lowest number of cylinders. Because there is a feeling that the number of cylinders could be lower than for the medium- and high-speed engines, the following alternatives are considered:

- Number of cylinders   12 or 6

H). Calculate for both numbers of cylinders:
- *Stroke length, bore diameter and stroke–bore ratio*
- *Power per litre swept volume*
- *Wear index*

I). Which number of cylinders has your preference and why? Also comment on the differences with the 4-stroke cases.

Exercise 3

The brochure of a diesel engine manufacturer gives the following information for a 4-stroke, turbocharged, 6-cylinder diesel engine. The maximum brake power of the engine is 4800 kW at a nominal engine speed of 500 rpm. The specific fuel consumption is 186.5 g/kWh, when running on marine diesel oil (MDO), with a lower heating value of 42,700 kJ/kg. The engine is also capable of running on heavy fuel oils. These data are valid for nominal ambient conditions: air temperature 25 ^{0}C (298 K) and a pressure of 1 bar.

The cylinder bore is 400 mm, the stroke length 600 mm and the compression ratio is 13. Further the charge air pressure (absolute) and the maximum firing pressure are derived from diagrams in the brochure: 4 bar and 180 bar respectively.

A ship owner considers to use this engine as propulsion prime mover in a container feeder ship. He has decided to run the engine on a heavy fuel oil (HFO), with a lower heating value of 41,000 kJ/kg. The price of this fuel is 150 Euro/1000 kg. Besides the price of purchase of the engine, he wants to evaluate the technical merits of this engine. Therefore he decides to calculate and estimate a number of technical parameters on the basis of which he can make his judgements. He wants to determine:

- *A). the mean effective pressure, the mean piston speed and the technology parameter,*
- *B). the engine efficiency, the specific fuel consumption, the fuel flow, the fuel cost per kWh and per hour,*
- *C). the air mass flow, the specific air consumption, the air fuel ratio during combustion, the air excess ratio and the total air excess ratio,*
- *D). the temperatures and the pressures in the cylinder during a process cycle,*

E). the specific heat input, the specific heat output and the specific work (per kg of
      trapped air),

F). the mean indicated pressure,

G). the thermodynamic, mechanical, heat input and indicated efficiencies.

Where applicable, he will use the Seiliger cycle as a comparison process. Assume the
following characteristics, which are a good average for the range of temperatures during
compression and expansion:

$$c_p = 1.100 \ kJ/kg$$

$$c_v = 0.813 \ kJ/kg$$

$$R = c_p - c_v = 0.287 \ kJ/kg$$

$$\kappa = \frac{c_p}{c_v} = 1.353$$

In order to make the calculations he has estimated the following parameters:

▪ For the scavenging process the engine uses 10 % more air than used for combustion,

▪ The air temperature in the cylinder at the start of compression is, due to heat input
    during the flow process through the cylinder head, 60 ^{0}C above the air temperature
    after the air cooler. As the air temperature after the cooler is given as 55 ^{0}C (328 K),
    this start temperature for the cylinder process is $T_1 = 115 \ ^0C$ (388 K).

▪ It may be assumed that the effective compression ratio is (almost) equal to the
    geometric compression ratio because this is a four stroke engine.

▪ The volume ratio for the constant pressure heat addition in the Seiliger process is
    1.65. Note that this is not the most logical parameter to be estimated. It is easier to
    make a good guess for the heat input efficiency (Figure 7.36). However, in order to
    make the calculations in this exercise more straightforward the volume ratio has been
    given.

▪ The stoichiometric air fuel ratio is $\sigma = 14.5 \ kg/kg$.

Calculate the parameters stated under A) to G), on which the shipowner wants to make
his judgements.

Solution Exercise 1

- The mechanical and heat losses are both approximately 10%, so mechanical and heat efficiency are both 0.9. Consequently the effective engine efficiency is:

$$\eta_e = 0.9 \cdot 0.9 \cdot 0.56 = 0.454 = 45.4\%$$

- To determine the mean effective pressure, first realise that work is converted heat, which is converted chemical energy in fuel. The amount of the chemical energy is determined by the available amount of air through the air-fuel ratio. The cylinder fills with air of absolute pressure 3+1=4 bar and temperature of 273+50=323 K.

Consequently, theoretically the mass trapped in the volume is:

$$m = \frac{p \cdot V_s}{R \cdot T} = \frac{4 \cdot 10^5 \cdot V_s}{287 \cdot 323} = 4.315 \cdot V_s \text{ kg}$$

The swept volume will not need to be determined numerically at this stage, because p_{me} is work over swept volume, so it will be eliminated later. As charging is 95% effective, the actual amount of fresh combustion air is less than the trapped mass as calculated theoretically.

$$m_{ca} = 0.95 \cdot m = 4.10 \cdot V_s \text{ kg}$$

The air excess ratio is 2 and the stoichiometric air-fuel ratio is 14.5, so the air fuel ratio is 29. The amount of fuel consequently is:

$$m_f = \frac{m_{ca}}{29} = 0.141 \cdot V_s \text{ kg}$$

The heat associated with this amount of fuel is:

$$Q_f = m_f \cdot 42700 = 6035 \cdot V_s \text{ kJ}$$

The useful work output is less and can be determined with the effective efficiency as calculated under A).:

$$W_e = \eta_e \cdot Q_f = 2740 \cdot V_s \text{ kJ}$$

The mean effective pressure is effective work divided by swept volume so:

$$p_{me} = 2740 \text{ kPa} = 27.4 \text{ bar}$$

- To determine the brake power, we first need to calculate some other parameters, such as the stroke length:

$$L_S = \frac{c_m}{2 \cdot n_e / 60} = 0.3 \text{ m}$$

- The bore diameter now follows from the stroke-bore ratio, which is 1.3 :

$$D_B = \frac{L_S}{1.3} = 0.231 \text{ m}$$

The swept volume can now be determined:

$$V_s = \frac{\pi}{4} \cdot D_B^{\,2} \cdot L_s = 0.0126 \text{ m}^3$$

The work done by each cylinder is:

$$W_e = p_{me} \cdot V_s = 2740 \cdot 10^3 \cdot 0.0126 = 34.5 \cdot 10^3 \text{ J}$$

The cycle frequency for a 4-stroke 12 cylinder engine equals:

$$f = \frac{n_e \cdot 12}{60 \cdot k} = 100 \text{ Hz}$$

So, the brake power is:

$$P_B = W_e \cdot f = 3450 \cdot 10^3 \text{ W} = 3450 \text{ kW}$$

B).

- Keeping the assumptions unaltered, the mechanical and heat efficiency remain both 0.9. Consequently the effective engine efficiency would be the same:

$$\eta_e = 0.9 \cdot 0.9 \cdot 0.56 = 0.454 = 45.4\%$$

- No turbocharging means that the charge pressure is lowered to 1 bar. The mass trapped theoretically in the swept volume then is:

$$m = \frac{p \cdot V_S}{R \cdot T} = \frac{1 \cdot 10^5}{287 \cdot 323} = 1.079 \cdot V_S$$

- This is of course a factor 4 less than in case A. This also applies to the actual amount of fresh combustion air and consequently, since air fuel ratio is assumed not to alter, also to the amount of fuel. But then heat and effective work will be smaller by a factor 4 too, as well as the mean effective pressure ratio:

$$p_{me} = \frac{2740}{4} = 685 \text{ kPa} = 6.85 \text{ bar}$$

- Assuming the same engine speed, power also is a factor 4 less than in case A):

$$P_B = \frac{3450 \cdot 10^3}{4} = 862 \cdot 10^3 \text{ W} = 862 \text{ kW}$$

C).

- Mechanical and heat losses: although power of the non turbocharged engine is considerable lower than the turbocharged engine it is not likely that the mechanical losses and heat losses will also be lower by a factor 4. In fact they have a tendency to remain the same in absolute sense. Consequently, the mechanical and heat losses as a percentage of ideal work and ideal heat input will be considerably higher than the assumed 10%. A view on Figure 7.40 would suggest 20% for the mechanical losses and 25% for the heat losses.

- Another question would be what peak pressure one would allow in the non-turbocharged engine. If it would be possible to keep the same peak pressure, for instance by increasing the compression ratio, the thermodynamic efficiency would be much better. But the compression ratio could become excessive and peak pressure for a non-turbocharged engine normally will be lower.

- The effect to the overall engine efficiency therefore is the result of the opposing effects of increased mechanical and heat losses and better thermodynamic efficiency. A view on Figure 7.43 would suggest that it would be 41% for a peak pressure of 120 bar instead of the 45% found in case A and used in case B, i.e. lower by a factor 1.1.

- The trapped air efficiency of a non-turbocharged engine will be worse than for a turbocharged engine since it is not possible to have an overpressure across the engine and hence scavenging is less effective. It could well be that the assumed 95% for the trapped air efficiency would drop to 80%, i.e. lower by a factor 1.20. This would translate directly into amount of fresh air, amount of fuel and heat input lower by the same factor. Combined with the somewhat lower engine efficiency, the effective work would be lower by the product of the two factors, i.e. 1.1 x 1.2 = 1.3. The mean effective pressure:

$$p_{me} = \frac{685}{1.3} = 526 \text{ kPa} = 5.3 \text{ bar}$$

- This is a typical value for diesel engines of the pre-turbocharger era. The engine power would be only:

$$P_B = \frac{862 \cdot 10^3}{1.3} = 663 \cdot 10^3 \text{ W} = 663 \text{ kW}$$

This of course is considerably less then the figure found in A).

Solution Exercise 2

A).
- The stroke length is determined by the speed of the engine (in revolutions per second) and the mean piston speed:

$$L_s = \frac{c_m}{2 \cdot n_e} = \frac{10}{2 \cdot \frac{600}{60}} = 500 \text{ mm}$$

- The bore diameter needs to be determined from the swept volume which can be found from the mean effective pressure and the effective work. The effective work using 8 or 12 cylinders can be determined:

$$W_{e,8} = \frac{P_B \cdot k}{n \cdot i} = \frac{9000 \cdot 2}{10 \cdot 8} = 225 \text{ kJ (8 cylinders)}$$

$$W_{e,12} = \frac{P_B \cdot k}{n \cdot i} = \frac{9000 \cdot 2}{10 \cdot 12} = 150 \ kJ \ (12 \ cylinders)$$

(The second subscript of the parameters indicates the number of cylinders.)

The mean effective pressure has been given: 24 bar = $2.4 \cdot 10^6$ Pa, this results in the following swept volumes:

$$p_{me} = \frac{W_{e,8}}{V_s} \rightarrow V_{s,8} = \frac{W_{e,8}}{p_{me}} = \frac{225 \cdot 10^3}{2.4 \cdot 10^6} = 0.09375 \ m^3$$

$$p_{me} = \frac{W_{e,12}}{V_s} \rightarrow V_{s,12} = \frac{W_{e,12}}{p_{me}} = \frac{150 \cdot 10^3}{2.4 \cdot 10^6} = 0.0625 \ m^3$$

So the bore diameters are:

$$V_{s,8} = \frac{1}{4} \cdot \pi \cdot D_{B,8}^2 \cdot L_s \rightarrow D_{B,8} = \sqrt{\frac{V_{s,8} \cdot 4}{\pi \cdot L_s}} = 0.489 \ m$$

$$V_{s,12} = \frac{1}{4} \cdot \pi \cdot D_{B,12}^2 \cdot L_s \rightarrow D_{B,12} = \sqrt{\frac{V_{s,12} \cdot 4}{\pi \cdot L_s}} = 0.400 \ m$$

- And the stroke–bore ratios:

$$\left(\frac{L_s}{D_B} \right)_8 = 1.02$$

$$\left(\frac{L_s}{D_B} \right)_{12} = 1.25$$

The ratio belonging to the 8 cylinder engine will result in a relatively flat top volume, so the stroke-bore ratio of the 12 cylinder engine is preferred. A flat top volume will have a negative impact on the fuel injection and vaporisation.

- The powers per litre swept volume are:

$$\beta_{VS,8} = \frac{P}{V_{s,8} \cdot i} = \frac{9000}{0.09375 \cdot 8} = 12 \ MW/m^3 = 12 kW/l$$

$$\beta_{VS,12} = \frac{P}{V_{s,12} \cdot i} = \frac{9000}{0.0625 \cdot 12} = 12 \ MW/m^3 = 12 kW/l$$

- Now the wear indices can be determined:

$$i \cdot D_{B,8} \cdot p_{me} \cdot c_m = 8 \cdot 0.489 \cdot 24 \cdot 10 = 939 \ (for \ 8 \ cylinders)$$

$$i \cdot D_{B,12} \cdot p_{me} \cdot c_m = 12 \cdot 0.400 \cdot 24 \cdot 10 = 1152 \ (for \ 12 \ cylinders)$$

B).
- The 12 cylinder engine has a more attractive stroke–bore ratio so this is a better alternative, although there is a penalty in wear.

C).
- The only parameter which has changed is the number of revolutions, the mean piston speed is still 10 m/s so the stroke length is:

$$L_s = \frac{c_m}{2 \cdot n_e} = \frac{10}{2 \cdot \dfrac{1200}{60}} = 250 \ mm$$

- In order to determine the bore diameter we need to calculate the effective work using 12 or 20 cylinders:

$$W_{e,12} = \frac{P_B \cdot k}{n \cdot i} = \frac{9000 \cdot 2}{20 \cdot 12} = 75 \ kJ \ (12 \ cylinders)$$

$$W_{e,20} = \frac{P_B \cdot k}{n \cdot i} = \frac{9000 \cdot 2}{20 \cdot 20} = 45 \ kJ \ (20 \ cylinders)$$

The mean effective pressure is still 24 bar $= 2.4 \cdot 10^6$ Pa, this results in the following swept volumes:

$$p_{me} = \frac{W_{e,12}}{V_{s,12}} \rightarrow V_{s,12} = \frac{W_{e,12}}{p_{me}} = \frac{75 \cdot 10^3}{2.4 \cdot 10^6} = 0.03125 \ m^3$$

$$p_{me} = \frac{W_{e,20}}{V_s} \rightarrow V_{s,20} = \frac{W_{e,20}}{p_{me}} = \frac{45 \cdot 10^3}{2.4 \cdot 10^6} = 0.01875 \ m^3$$

So the bore diameters are:

$$V_{s,12} = \frac{1}{4} \cdot \pi \cdot D_{B,12}^2 \cdot L_s \rightarrow D_{B,12} = \sqrt{\frac{V_{s,12} \cdot 4}{\pi \cdot L_s}} = 0.400 \ m$$

$$V_{s,20} = \frac{1}{4} \cdot \pi \cdot D_{B,20}^2 \cdot L_s \rightarrow D_{B,20} = \sqrt{\frac{V_{s,20} \cdot 4}{\pi \cdot L_s}} = 0.309 \ m$$

- And the stroke–bore ratios:

$$\left(\frac{L_s}{D_B}\right)_{12} = 0.625$$

$$\left(\frac{L_s}{D_B}\right)_{20} = 0.809$$

- Now the wear indices can be determined:

$$i \cdot D_{B,12} \cdot p_{me} \cdot c_m = 12 \cdot 0.400 \cdot 24 \cdot 10 = 1152 \ (for \ 12 \ cylinders)$$

$$i \cdot D_{B,20} \cdot p_{me} \cdot c_m = 20 \cdot 0.309 \cdot 24 \cdot 10 = 1483 \ (for \ 20 \ cylinders)$$

D).

–   Neither one of the engines are feasible because of their extremely low stroke–bore ratios.

E).

–   The stroke length at 1200 rpm has changed because of the altered piston speed :

$$L_s = \frac{c_m}{2 \cdot n_e} = \frac{12}{2 \cdot \frac{1200}{60}} = 300 \; mm$$

–   The effective work using 20 cylinders can be determined:

$$W_e = \frac{P_B \cdot k}{n \cdot i} = \frac{9000 \cdot 2}{20 \cdot 20} = 45 \; kJ$$

The mean effective pressure has been given: 24 bar = $2.4 \cdot 10^6$ Pa, this results in the following swept volume:

$$p_{me} = \frac{W_e}{V_s} \Rightarrow V_s = \frac{W_e}{p_{me}} = \frac{45 \cdot 10^3}{2.4 \cdot 10^6} = 0.01875 \; m^3$$

So the bore diameter is:

$$V_s = \frac{1}{4} \cdot \pi \cdot D_B^2 \cdot L_s \Rightarrow D_B = \sqrt{\frac{V_s \cdot 4}{\pi \cdot L_s}} = 0.282 \; m$$

And the stroke–bore ratio:

$$\left(\frac{L_s}{D_B} \right) = 1.06$$

Which is a reasonable value that has been used on some MTU high-speed engines.

–   The power per litre swept volume is:

$$\beta_{VS} = \frac{P}{V_s \cdot i} = \frac{9000}{0.01875 \cdot 20} = 24 \; MW / m^3 = 24 kW / 1$$

–   Now the wear index can be determined:

$$i \cdot D_B \cdot p_{me} \cdot c_m = 20 \cdot 0.282 \cdot 24 \cdot 12 = 1624$$

This is a really high value!

F).

–   The stroke length at increased p_{me} remains unchanged:

$$L_s = \frac{c_m}{2 \cdot n_e} = \frac{12}{2 \cdot \frac{1200}{60}} = 300 \; mm$$

–   The effective work is also unchanged:

$$W_e = \frac{P_B \cdot k}{n \cdot i} = \frac{9000 \cdot 2}{20 \cdot 20} = 45 \; kJ$$

The mean effective pressure is now changed to 30 bar = $3.0 \cdot 10^6$ Pa, this results in the following swept volume:

$$p_{me} = \frac{W_e}{V_s} \rightarrow V_s = \frac{W_e}{p_{me}} = \frac{45 \cdot 10^3}{3.0 \cdot 10^6} = 0.0150 \; m^3$$

So the bore diameter is:

$$V_s = \frac{1}{4} \cdot \pi \cdot D_B^2 \cdot L_s \rightarrow D_B = \sqrt{\frac{V_s \cdot 4}{\pi \cdot L_s}} = 0.252 \; m$$

And the stroke–bore ratio:

$$\left(\frac{L_s}{D_B} \right) = 1.19$$

Which is a very normal value for a stroke/bore ratio.

– The power per litre swept volume is:

$$\beta_{VS} = \frac{P}{V_s \cdot i} = \frac{9000}{0.0150 \cdot 20} = 30 \; MW/m^3 = 30 \; kW/l$$

– And the wear index which is also higher:

$$i \cdot D_B \cdot p_{me} \cdot c_m = 20 \cdot 0.252 \cdot 30 \cdot 12 = 1814$$

G).

– From the previous steps it is now clear why high speed engines tend to have as much cylinders as possible and also have in general high mean piston speeds. The reason is that a requirement to develop a certain power (which still is low in comparison to what can be achieved with medium speed engines) would otherwise lead to unacceptable stroke/bore ratios. Increasing the mean effective pressure by high pressure turbocharging makes things easier, as was shown. The price however is a very high wear index.

H).

– The stroke length is determined by the speed of the engine (in revolutions per second) and the mean piston speed:

$$L_s = \frac{c_m}{2 \cdot n_e} = \frac{8}{2 \cdot \frac{120}{60}} = 2 \; m$$

– The bore diameter needs to be determined from the swept volume which can be found from the mean effective pressure and the effective work. The effective work using 6 or 12 cylinders can be determined:

$$W_{e,6} = \frac{P_B \cdot k}{n \cdot i} = \frac{9000 \cdot 1}{2 \cdot 6} = 750 \ kJ \ (6 \ cylinders)$$

$$W_{e,12} = \frac{P_B \cdot k}{n \cdot i} = \frac{9000 \cdot 1}{2 \cdot 12} = 375 \ kJ \ (12 \ cylinders)$$

The mean effective pressure has been given: 18 bar = $1.8 \cdot 10^{-6}$ Pa, this results in the following swept volumes:

$$P_{me} = \frac{W_{e,6}}{V_s} \rightarrow V_{s,6} = \frac{W_{e,6}}{P_{me}} = \frac{750 \cdot 10^3}{1.8 \cdot 10^6} = 0.417 \ m^3$$

$$P_{me} = \frac{W_{e,12}}{V_s} \rightarrow V_{s,12} = \frac{W_{e,12}}{P_{me}} = \frac{375 \cdot 10^3}{1.8 \cdot 10^6} = 0.208 \ m^3$$

So the bore diameters are:

$$V_{s,6} = \frac{1}{4} \cdot \pi \cdot D_{B,6}^2 \cdot L_s \rightarrow D_{B,6} = \sqrt{\frac{V_{s,6} \cdot 4}{\pi \cdot L_s}} = 0.515 \ m$$

$$V_{s,12} = \frac{1}{4} \cdot \pi \cdot D_{B,12}^2 \cdot L_s \rightarrow D_{B,12} = \sqrt{\frac{V_{s,12} \cdot 4}{\pi \cdot L_s}} = 0.364 \ m$$

–   And the stroke–bore ratios:

$$\left(\frac{L_s}{D_B}\right)_6 = 3.88$$

$$\left(\frac{L_s}{D_B}\right)_{12} = 5.49$$

–   The powers per litre swept volume are:

$$\beta_{VS,6} = \frac{P}{V_{s,6} \cdot i} = \frac{9000}{0.417 \cdot 6} = 3.6 \ MW / m^3 = 3.6 \ kW / l$$

$$\beta_{VS,12} = \frac{P}{V_{s,12} \cdot i} = \frac{9000}{0.208 \cdot 12} = 3.6 \ MW / m^3 = 3.6 \ kW / l$$

–   Now the wear indices can be determined:

$$i \cdot D_{B,6} \cdot P_{me} \cdot c_m = 6 \cdot 0.515 \cdot 18 \cdot 8 = 445 \ (for \ 6 \ cylinders)$$

$$i \cdot D_{B,12} \cdot P_{me} \cdot c_m = 12 \cdot 0.364 \cdot 18 \cdot 8 = 629 \ (for \ 12 \ cylinders)$$

I.)   The 6 cylinder engine has a lower wear index and will be shorter, so this is the best alternative. Further, the stroke-bore ratio is very high. It has been shown that the wear index of a two-stroke engine is lower than the wear index of a four-stroke engine, so the two stroke engine requires less maintenance because of its lower wear. On the other hand, a two stroke engine is larger and has less power per swept volume.

Solution Exercise 3

A).

- The *mean effective pressure* can be calculated with equation (7.26):

$$p_{me} = k \cdot \frac{P_B}{i \cdot n_e \cdot V_S} = 2 \cdot \frac{4800 \times 10^3}{6 \cdot \frac{500}{60} \cdot 0.0754} = 25.4 \times 10^5 \ N/m^2 = 25.4 \ bar$$

where $V_s = \frac{\pi}{4} \cdot D_B^2 \cdot L_s = \frac{\pi}{4} \cdot 0.4^2 \cdot 0.6 = 0.0754 \ m^3$

- The *mean piston speed* follows from equation (7.41):

$$c_m = 2 \cdot n_e \cdot L_s = 2 \cdot 500 \cdot 0.6 = 10 \ m/s$$

- The *technology parameter* is defined as:

$$p_{me} \cdot c_m = 25.4 \cdot 10 = 254 ,$$ which is a state of the art (relatively high) figure for a medium speed diesel engine of 500 rpm (see Figure 7.7).

B).

- The *engine efficiency* follows from equation (7.33):

$$\eta_e = \frac{3.600.000}{sfc_{no\,min\,al} \cdot h_{MDO}^L} = \frac{3.600.000}{42700 \cdot 186.5} = 0.452$$

This is a state of the art figure for medium speed diesel engines.

- The *sfc* with the fuel used on board the ship follows from the same equation, but now with the lower heating value of the used HFO. It is assumed that the engine efficiency does not change with the use of another fuel:

$$sfc_{HFO} = \frac{3.600.000}{\eta_e \cdot h_{HFO}^L} = \frac{3.600.000}{0.452 \cdot 41000} = 194.2 \ g/kWh$$

- The *fuel mass flow* can be calculated with:

$$\dot{m}_f = sfc \cdot P_B = 194.2 \cdot 4800 = 932 \times 10^3 \ g/h = 0.259 \ kg/s$$

- *Fuel cost* per kWh follow from:

$$sfc \cdot fuel \ price = 194.2 \cdot \frac{150}{10^6} = 0.0291 \ Euro/kWh$$

This is a reasonably low figure. Compare it, for instance, with the price of an electrical kWh, as delivered by the electricity company to a household: approximately 0.09 Euro/kWh.

- *Fuel cost* per running hour follows from:

$$fuel \ flow \cdot fuel \ price = 0.259 \cdot 3600 \cdot \frac{150}{1000} = 139.86 \ Euro/hour$$

C).

- The *air consumption* can be estimated by calculating the mass of air in the cylinder at the start of the compression process. Assuming that the maximum cylinder volume (V_{BDC}) is completely filled with fresh air at charge pressure and intake temperature, the following can be calculated:

$$V_{BDC} = V_S \cdot \frac{\varepsilon}{\varepsilon - 1} = 0.0754 \cdot \frac{13}{12} = 0.0817 \ m^3 \ .$$

This relation can be derived from (7.3) and the definition of V_{BDC}.

$$\rho_{air,1} = \frac{p_1}{RT_1} = \frac{4 \times 10^5}{287 \cdot 388} = 3.59 \ kg/m^3 \qquad \text{ref. (2.32)}$$

- The mass of (trapped) combustion air in the cylinder is now:

$$m_{ca} = V_{BDC} \cdot \rho_{air,1} = 0.0817 \cdot 3.59 = 0.293 \ kg \ .$$

- This leads to the *combustion air mass flow* for the complete engine, by multiplying cylinder air mass with the engine firing frequency:

$$\dot{m}_{ca} = m_{ca} \cdot n_e \cdot \frac{i}{k} = 0.293 \cdot \frac{500}{60} \cdot \frac{6}{2} = 7.34 \ kg/s$$

- The *total air mass flow* also includes the air flow for scavenging of the cylinders. This requires an additional 10 %:

$$\dot{m}_{air,in} = 1.10 \cdot 7.34 = 8.07 \ kg/s \ .$$

- The *specific air consumption*:

$$sac = \frac{m_{air,in}}{P_B} = \frac{8.07 \cdot 3600}{4800} = 6.05 \ kg/kWh \ .$$

This is a relatively low figure for a medium speed diesel engine (ref. section 7.4.4)

- The *air fuel ratio during combustion* follows from:

$$afr = \frac{\dot{m}_{ca}}{\dot{m}_f} = \frac{7.34}{0.259} = 28.3 \ kg/kg$$

- The *air excess ratio* is defined as the available mass of air for combustion divided by the stoichiometric mass of air needed for combustion:

$$\lambda = \frac{afr}{\sigma} = \frac{28.3}{14.5} = 1.96$$

- The *total air excess* ratio takes also the scavenging air into account:

$$\lambda_{tot} = 1.10 \cdot 1.96 = 2.15$$

This figure seems just adequate for a medium speed diesel engine running on heavy fuel oil (see section 7.4.4).

From now on the calculations do not concern the actual engine, but the comparison process, the air-standard Seiliger cycle.

D). The *pressures and temperatures during a cylinder cycle* can be calculated using the relations given in Table 7.3 (it is assumed that $r_c = \epsilon$):

$p_1 = 4\ bar$ $\qquad\qquad$ $T_1 = 388\ K$

$p_2 = p_1 \cdot \epsilon^\kappa = 3.5 \cdot 13^{1.353} = 128.6\ bar$ $\qquad$ $T_2 = T_1 \cdot \epsilon^{\kappa-1} = 388 \cdot 13^{0.353} = 960\ K$

$p_3 = 180\ bar$ $\qquad\qquad$ $T_3 = a \cdot T_2 = 1.4 \cdot 960 = 1343\ K$

$a = \dfrac{p_3}{p_2} = \dfrac{180}{128.6} = 1.40$

$p_4 = p_3 = 180\ bar$ $\qquad\qquad$ $T_4 = b \cdot T_3 = 1.65 \cdot 1343 = 2216\ K$

$p_5 = p_4 \cdot \left(\dfrac{\epsilon}{b}\right)^\kappa = 180 \cdot \left(\dfrac{1.65}{13}\right)^{1.353} = 11\ bar$ $\qquad$ $T_5 = T_4 \left(\dfrac{\epsilon}{b}\right)^{\kappa-1} = 1069\ K$

E). The *specific heat input, output and indicated work* can be calculated, using the temperatures calculated in the previous part:

$$q_{in} = q_{2,3} + q_{3,4} = c_v \cdot (T_3 - T_2) + c_p \cdot (T_4 - T_3)$$
$$= 0.813 \cdot (1343 - 960) + 1.100 \cdot (2216 - 1343) = 1272.1\ kJ/kg$$
$$q_{out} = q_{5,1} = c_v \cdot (T_5 - T_1) = 0.813 \cdot (1069 - 388) = 553.7\ kJ/kg$$
$$w_i = q_{in} - q_{out} = 1272.1 - 553.7 = 718.4\ kJ/kg$$

F). The *mean indicated pressure* can be calculated with (7.96), but it is much easier to use the definition of mean indicated pressure:

$$p_{mi} = \frac{W_i}{V_s} = \frac{w_i \cdot m_{ca}}{V_s} = \frac{718.4 \times 10^3 \cdot 0.293}{0.0754} = 2.79 \times 10^6\ N/m^2 = 27.9\ bar$$

G). The *thermodynamic efficiency* of the Seiliger cycle can be calculated using (7.88), but again it is easier to use the definition of efficiency:

$$\eta_{td} = \frac{w_i}{q_{in}} = \frac{718.4}{1272.1} = 0.565$$

- The *mechanical efficiency* of the engine can now be calculated with:

$$\eta_m = \frac{p_{me}}{p_{mi}} = \frac{25.4}{27.9} = 0.910$$

- The *heat input efficiency* can be calculated with (7.21), when the combustion efficiency is assumed to be 1 (which should be almost the case for an engine with a good fuel injection system):

$$\eta_q = \frac{\eta_e}{\eta_m \cdot \eta_{comb} \cdot \eta_{td}} = \frac{0.452}{0.910 \cdot 1 \cdot 0.565} = 0.879$$

- The *indicated efficiency* follows also from (7.21)

$$\eta_i = \eta_{comb} \cdot \eta_q \cdot \eta_{td} = 1 \cdot 0.879 \cdot 0565 = 0.497$$

The meaning of the calculated efficiencies is recapitulated. Useful mechanical energy W_e is 45.2 % (η_e) of the chemical energy Q_f, supplied with the fuel. The losses can also be expressed as a fraction of the chemical energy Q_f : 54.8 %, i.e. $1 - \eta_e$, of the supplied chemical energy is lost in different forms:

- $1 - \eta_{comb}$ of the chemical energy is lost, if $\eta_{comb} < 1$. It represents a very small portion of the fuel that will not be combusted.

- 12.1 % (= $1 - \eta_q$) of the generated heat Q_{comb} entering the cylinder process of an actual engine is lost during the process, due to cooling of the cylinder walls and piston crown. This cooling happens during compression, combustion and expansion. The heat leaving the cylinder goes into cooling water and cooling oil. In this example, 12.1 % of Q_{comb} equals 12.1 % of the chemical energy Q_f, because complete combustion ($\eta_{comb} = 1$) is assumed.

  In the Seiliger cycle, it is assumed that compression and expansion are isentropic (reversible adiabatic) processes and also that all added heat (Q_{in}) remains in the process. Consequently, the heat lost due to cooling, is left out of the calculations. The Seiliger cycle only considers Q_{in}, which equals chemical energy multiplied with η_{comb} and η_q.

- The heat in exhaust gases that leave the actual engine amount to 43.5 % ($1 - \eta_{td}$) of the net heat input Q_{in}. This can be expressed as a share of the chemical energy contained in the fuel:

  $$0.435 \cdot \eta_{comb} \cdot \eta_q = 0.382 \cdot 1 \cdot 0.879 = 38.2 \% \text{ of } Q_f$$

  In the actual engine this heat is partly used to drive the turbine of the turbocharger and is partly lost with the exhaust gas going into the funnel. In the Seiliger cycle this heat is removed from the process by a heat flow to the environment (process 5–1).

- 9.0 % (= $1 - \eta_m$) of the indicated work W_i are mechanical losses: friction of the piston in the cylinder liner, friction in bearings and energy needed to drive the fuel injection pumps and valve gear. On high speed engines the power needed to drive cooling water and lubrication pumps is also included in the mechanical efficiency. This loss equals:

  $$0.09 \cdot \eta_i = 0.09 \cdot 0.497 = 4.5 \% \text{ of } Q_f$$

  The mechanical efficiency also includes the pump losses, i.e. the energy associated with the intake and exhaust strokes. For a naturally aspirating engine, they are indeed losses (the pressure in the cylinder during exhaust is higher than during air intake). For a turbocharged engine, on the other hand, they are positive and contribute to the engine power. Consequently, the mechanical losses will be smaller than for a non-turbocharged engine.

7.11 References and further reading

Diesel, 1913

Rudolf Diesel: *"Die Entstehung des Dieselmotors"*, Julius Springer, Berlin 1913. Herausgegeben: Steiger, 1984 ISBN 3-921564-70-0

Grimmelius, 1999

H. Grimmelius and D. Stapersma: *"The potential of the turbocharged diesel engine"*, Advanced Marine Machinery Systems MARPOWER 99, Newcastle upon Tyne, March 1999

Harrold, 1989

A. F. Harrold: *"Development of merchant ship propulsion machinery over the past 25 years"*, Trans I MarE, Vol 101, pp. 1-16, 1989

Harrington, 1992

R. L. Harrington et al.: *"Marine engineering"*, pp 91–97 & 100–106: Chapter III *Diesel engines* by Alan L. Rowen

Heywood, 1988

John B. Heywood: *"Internal Combustion Engine Fundamentals"*, McGraw-Hill, New York, International Edition, 1988

Kytölä, 1998

J. Kytölä (Wärtsilä NSD Corporation): *"Design and Performance of a Large-Bore Medium-speed Engine"*, 22nd CIMAC Congress (Volume 1), Copenhagen 1998

Merker, 1991

G. Merker and H. Klotz (MTU): *"Entwicklungsstand hochafgeladener, schnellaufender 4-takt Dieselmotoren"*, MTU Focus, 1/1991

Paro, 1993

D. Paro, G. Liljenfeldt and D. Jay: *"The future potential of the diesel process"*, 20th CIMAC Conference, London 1993

Stapersma, 1996

D. Stapersma: *"Diesel Engines, A fundamental approach to performance analysis, turbocharging, combustion, emissions and heat transfer"*, Diesel Engines A Part I: Performance analysis and turbocharging, Delft University of Technology/R.Nl.N.C., 1996.

Chapter 8

Gas Turbines

8.0   Learning goals

After studying this chapter, the student should be able to:

- *Describe the working principles of the gas turbine.*

- *Apply the Brayton cycle to calculate gas turbine performance for the simple cycle and the regenerative cycle.*

- *Explain the influence of the pressure ratio and of the temperature ratio on efficiency and power density.*

- *Explain the influence of compressor, turbine and heat exchanger losses on gas turbine performance (efficiency and power density).*

- *Explain the operating envelope of a twin-shaft gas turbine and the influence of power on sfc.*

- *Describe the effect of ambient conditions and intake and exhaust losses on power and fuel consumption.*

- *Describe the necessary measures for installation on board: acoustical enclosure, air filtration, up- and down-takes and fuel treatment.*

8.1   Introduction

In Chapter 6 the gas turbine has been discussed briefly. A gas turbine basically consists of a compressor, a combustion chamber, a turbine and inlet- and exhaust ducts.

Two important performance parameters for gas turbines are power density and fuel economy. Naturally fuel economy is an important parameter for both user and environment. The power density provides an indication of the gas turbine's volume and weight. It is especially important for applications where space and weight are limited as is the case for the transport sector. Therefore, when evaluating the suitability of a gas turbine for a critical application (such as a fast ship) power density could become more stringent than fuel economy. Apart from the power density and fuel economy the economics of the solution will be determined by the initial costs, maintenance costs and the reliability of the engine.

In this chapter a basic thermodynamic analysis will be given for the simple cycle and the regenerative cycle, both ideal and with losses. Based on this analysis the critical parameters for power density and fuel economy will be explained as well as methods for optimising the performance.

This chapter concludes by paying attention to some practical implications of the installation of gas turbines on board of ships such as the power–speed envelope, the sensitivity to ambient conditions and intake and exhaust losses, air filtration, acoustic measures and design of inlet and exhaust ducts.

8.2   Working principle

Gas turbines transform chemical energy stored in fuels into mechanical energy at the output shaft. This conversion process takes place in two steps: first chemical energy is converted into thermal energy by means of a combustion reaction of the fuel with the working medium, air, and then thermal energy is converted into mechanical energy.

During this energy conversion the working fluid, air, is subjected to the following processes:

- Air inlet.

- Compression from atmospheric pressure to the combustion pressure (in the order of 10 to 30 bar).

- Combustion at constant pressure up to a high temperature (state-of-the-art is typically in the range of 1200 to 1500 degrees Kelvin) after fuel is injected into the combustion chamber.

- Expansion to atmospheric pressure.

- Exhaust.

As mentioned in section 6.2.2, a simple cycle gas turbine may have one or two shafts, see Figure 8.1. The single and twin-shaft cycles are thermodynamically equivalent. In ship propulsion plants the twin-shaft arrangement is most commonly used. Compared to the single shaft gas turbine and also to the diesel engine, the twin-shaft gas turbine has the advantage that its operating envelope is much wider, since output speed can freely change without disturbing the compressor operation.

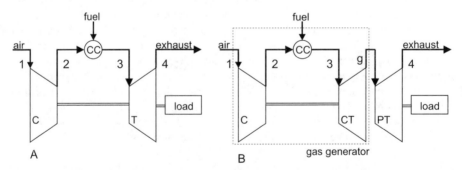

Figure 8.1   Simple cycle gas turbines: A) single shaft concept in which the turbine *T* drives the compressor *C* and the load, B) twin-shaft concept in which the compressor turbine *CT* drives the compressor *C* and the free power turbine *PT* drives the load.

The cycle considered is an open cycle, which means that fresh atmospheric air enters the system continuously and energy is added to the system by combustion of fuel in the working fluid itself, i.e. internal combustion. The products of the combustion are expanded in the turbine and leave the system through the exhaust.

8.3   The ideal simple Brayton cycle

In order to evaluate the actual gas turbine, it is frequently compared with an ideal air–standard cycle: the Brayton cycle. The assumption of an ideal Brayton cycle will imply the following:

- Compression and expansion processes are reversible and adiabatic, i.e. isentropic.
- The change of kinetic energy of the working fluid between inlet and outlet of each component is taken into account by using total temperature and pressure all over.
- There are no pressure losses in the inlet ducting, combustion chambers, heat exchangers, intercoolers, exhaust ducting, and ducts connecting the components.
- The working fluid has the same composition throughout the cycle and is a perfect gas with constant specific heats.
- Heat is added to the working fluid from an external source instead of internal combustion as in the actual process.
- Heat is extracted from the working fluid with a heat sink instead of discharging the working fluid to the environment as in the actual process.
- The mass flow is constant throughout the cycle, i.e. the mass addition by fuel is neglected.

Note that similar assumptions were made for the Seiliger cycle in the previous chapter.

In Figure 8.2, both the flow scheme and the T–s diagram of an ideal Brayton cycle are shown, as well as the station numbering that will be adopted. Table 8.1 describes the processes that can be distinguished in the diagram.

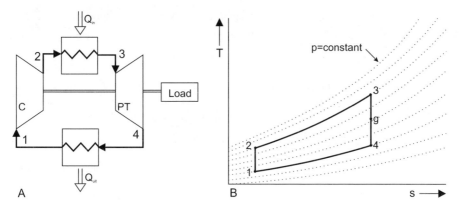

Figure 8.2   An ideal Brayton cycle gas turbine.

Process	Description
1-2	Isentropic compression in the compressor.
2-3	Heat addition at constant pressure.
3-4	Isentropic expansion through a turbine back to compressor inlet pressure.
4-1	Heat discharge at constant pressure.

Table 8.1   Description of processes in the Brayton cycle.

For the ideal case, pressure losses in intake and exhaust ducting as well as in the combustion chamber are neglected. The pressure ratio across the compressor π_C is then equal to that of the turbine π_T:

$$\pi \overset{def}{=} \pi_C = \frac{p_2}{p_1} = \frac{p_3}{p_4} = \pi_T \tag{8.1}$$

The pressure ratio π of the process will typically vary between 10 and 30.

The other important parameter of the gas turbine cycle is the maximum temperature ratio which is defined as:

$$\tau \overset{def}{=} \frac{T_3}{T_1} \tag{8.2}$$

For marine applications air intake temperature T_1 is approximately 300 K. Turbine entry temperature T_3 mainly depends on the temperature resistance of the turbine's inlet blades; approximately 1250 K for state of the art engines.

8.3.1   Work and heat

The amounts of work and heat added to or delivered by the processes will be determined.

Work

The power required for the compression stage (process 1–2) is proportional to the mass flow and the increase of the specific enthalpy:

$$P = \dot{W} = \dot{m} \cdot (h_i - h_e) \qquad\qquad \text{ref. (2.9)}$$

The increase of the enthalpy of a perfect gas can be expressed in the temperature difference of the working fluid (as given by equation (2.41)). For the compression process this leads to an expression for power that is formally negative ($T_1 < T_2$):

$$P_{12} = \dot{m} \cdot c_p \cdot (T_1 - T_2) \tag{8.3}$$

Take the absolute value, then the compressor work per kilogram of air going through the machine is defined as:

$$w_C \overset{\text{def}}{=} \frac{P_C}{\dot{m}} = \frac{|P_{12}|}{\dot{m}} = c_p \cdot (T_2 - T_1) \tag{8.4}$$

The power developed during expansion of the hot gases (process 3-4) can also be described by equation (2.9). The power delivered by the turbine process expressed in a temperature difference then is:

$$P_{34} = \dot{m} \cdot c_p \cdot (T_3 - T_4) \tag{8.5}$$

The power delivered by the turbine is used to (1) drive the compressor and (2) drive the load. The work of the turbine per kilogram air going through the machine is defined as:

$$w_T \overset{\text{def}}{=} \frac{P_T}{\dot{m}} = \frac{P_{34}}{\dot{m}} = c_p \cdot (T_3 - T_4) \tag{8.6}$$

The compressor and turbine work according to equations (8.4) and (8.6) can be expressed in temperature ratios:

$$w_C = c_p \cdot (T_2 - T_1) = c_p \cdot T_1 \cdot \left(\frac{T_2}{T_1} - 1 \right) \tag{8.7}$$

$$w_T = c_p \cdot (T_3 - T_4) = c_p \cdot T_3 \cdot \left(1 - \frac{T_4}{T_3} \right) = c_p \cdot T_1 \cdot \left(\frac{T_3}{T_1} \right) \cdot \left(1 - \frac{T_4}{T_3} \right) \tag{8.8}$$

Apart from the maximum temperature ratio of the cycle as introduced in 8.3, the temperature ratios over the compressor and turbine can be recognised in these expressions. The temperature ratios can be transformed into pressure ratios by using Poisson's p–T relation (refer to equation (2.48)):

$$\tau_C \overset{\text{def}}{=} \frac{T_2}{T_1} = \left(\frac{p_2}{p_1} \right)^{\frac{\kappa-1}{\kappa}} = \pi^{\frac{\kappa-1}{\kappa}} \tag{8.9}$$

$$\tau_T \overset{\text{def}}{=} \frac{T_3}{T_4} = \left(\frac{p_3}{p_4} \right)^{\frac{\kappa-1}{\kappa}} = \pi^{\frac{\kappa-1}{\kappa}} \tag{8.10}$$

Note that in this ideal case the temperature ratio over compressor and turbine are equal; this will not be the case when, in the next section, component losses are taken into account.

In order to simplify the expressions for work, substitute equations (8.2), (8.9) and (8.10) into equations (8.7) and (8.8). Work has been made non-dimensional by dividing by $c_p \cdot T_1$:

$$\frac{w_C}{c_p \cdot T_1} = \pi^{\frac{\kappa-1}{\kappa}} - 1 \tag{8.11}$$

$$\frac{w_T}{c_p \cdot T_1} = \tau \cdot \left(1 - \frac{1}{\pi^{\frac{\kappa-1}{\kappa}}} \right) \tag{8.12}$$

Heat

The heat addition (process 2-3) is proportional to the mass flow rate and the increase of the specific enthalpy:

$$\dot{Q} = \dot{m} \cdot \left(h_e - h_i \right) \qquad \text{ref. (2.10)}$$

By expressing the enthalpy difference in a temperature difference, heat addition can be calculated:

$$\dot{Q}_{23} = \dot{m} \cdot c_p \cdot \left(T_3 - T_2 \right) \tag{8.13}$$

Or the input heat per kilogram air going through the machine:

$$q_{in} \overset{\text{def}}{=} \frac{\dot{Q}_{in}}{\dot{m}} = \frac{\dot{Q}_{23}}{\dot{m}} = c_p \cdot \left(T_3 - T_2 \right) \tag{8.14}$$

The heat flow in the fourth stage of the Brayton cycle, the heat rejection, is determined in the same way as the heat addition:

$$q_{out} \overset{\text{def}}{=} \frac{\dot{Q}_{out}}{\dot{m}} = \frac{\left| \dot{Q}_{41} \right|}{\dot{m}} = c_p \cdot \left(T_4 - T_1 \right) \tag{8.15}$$

The heat input flow as given by equation (8.14) and the heat rejection flow as given in equation (8.15) can be expressed in temperature ratios:

$$q_{in} = c_p \cdot \left(T_3 - T_2 \right) = c_p \cdot T_1 \cdot \left(\frac{T_3}{T_1} - \frac{T_2}{T_1} \right) \tag{8.16}$$

$$q_{out} = c_p \cdot \left(T_4 - T_1 \right) = c_p \cdot T_1 \cdot \left(\frac{T_4}{T_1} - 1 \right) = c_p \cdot T_1 \cdot \left(\frac{T_4}{T_3} \right) \left(\frac{T_3}{T_1} - \frac{T_3}{T_4} \right) \tag{8.17}$$

Subsequently, the input and output heat can be expressed using the parameters π and τ by using equations (8.2), (8.9) and (8.10):

$$\frac{q_{in}}{c_p \cdot T_1} = \tau - \pi^{\frac{\kappa-1}{\kappa}} \tag{8.18}$$

$$\frac{q_{out}}{c_p \cdot T_1} = \frac{1}{\pi^{\frac{\kappa-1}{\kappa}}} \cdot \left(\tau - \pi^{\frac{\kappa-1}{\kappa}} \right) \tag{8.19}$$

The heat input and output per unit mass are areas in a T–s diagram, as illustrated in Figure 8.3. The heat input equals the area under line 2–3 and the heat output equals the area under line 4–1.

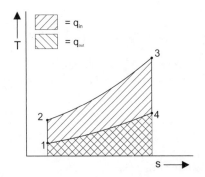

Figure 8.3   Heat input and output for the ideal Brayton cycle.

8.3.2 *Power density*

A numerical indicator for power density is the specific power [kJ/kg], which is the brake power [kW] divided by the mass flow rate of air [kg/s]:

$$\beta_m \overset{def}{=} \frac{P_B}{\dot{m}_{air}} \tag{8.20}$$

This quantity is a good indicator of weight and volume of the core engine and also of the intake and exhaust ducts. The volume and weight of the core engine, however, are only a fraction of the installation volume and weight of the total engine since the bedframe and the acoustical enclosure are not included. The volume of smaller gas turbines is especially dominated by the size of the acoustical enclosure. So in that case, the specific power is a poor indicator of specific installation volume because the real volume is no longer proportional with the air mass flow.

Note that specific power for a gas turbine is equal to the inverse of specific air consumption same as defined for the diesel engine:

$$sac \overset{def}{=} \frac{\dot{m}_{air}}{P_B} \tag{ref. (7.40)}$$

If mechanical losses are neglected, the power output P_B is equal to the ideal cycle output P_{cycle} that can be calculated by subtracting compressor power from the turbine's total developed power:

$$P_B = P_{cycle} = P_T - P_C \tag{8.21}$$

The cycle power of the gas turbine can be compared to the indicated power of the diesel engine; refer to equation (7.23). Because the mechanical losses in the gas turbine are essentially smaller than in the diesel engine, the cycle power, in practice, is almost equal to the brake power.

The output power of a twin-shaft simple cycle is the power delivered by the power turbine:

$$P_{cycle} = P_{PT} = \dot{m} \cdot c_p \cdot \left(T_g - T_4\right) \tag{8.22}$$

The power turbine entry temperature T_g is determined by the condition that the power delivered by the compressor turbine must just be sufficient to drive the compressor:

$$P_{CT} = P_C = \dot{m} \cdot c_p \cdot \left(T_3 - T_g\right) \tag{8.23}$$

Together with equation (8.3) this equation fixes the power turbine entry temperature T_g. The enthalpy of the stream of gas in point g represents the *gas power* which is converted into *brake power* in the free power turbine.

For both single shaft and twin-shaft gas turbines, the power density is:

$$\beta_m = w_{cycle} = \frac{P_{cycle}}{\dot{m}} = \frac{P_T}{\dot{m}} - \frac{P_C}{\dot{m}} = w_T - w_C \tag{8.24}$$

Or, using the expressions for ideal compressor and turbine work for the Brayton cycle:

$$\frac{w_{cycle}}{c_p \cdot T_1} = \tau \cdot \left(1 - \frac{1}{\pi^{\frac{\kappa-1}{\kappa}}}\right) - \left(\pi^{\frac{\kappa-1}{\kappa}} - 1\right) \tag{8.25}$$

This expression can also be written as the multiplication of two factors:

$$\frac{w_{cycle}}{c_p \cdot T_1} = \left(\tau - \pi^{\frac{\kappa-1}{\kappa}}\right) \cdot \left(1 - \frac{1}{\pi^{\frac{\kappa-1}{\kappa}}}\right) \tag{8.26}$$

From this equation, it can be seen that the specific power is zero for two specific values of the pressure ratio:

$$\pi = 1 \text{ and } \pi = \tau^{\frac{\kappa}{\kappa-1}} \tag{8.27}$$

Considerations of continuity require that a maximum specific power will occur between those two values. Taking the derivative with respect to pressure ratio and putting this to zero yields:

$$\frac{\partial w_{cycle}}{\partial \pi} = 0 \rightarrow \pi^{\frac{\kappa-1}{\kappa}} = \sqrt{\tau} \tag{8.28}$$

Figure 8.4 shows the specific power of a typical ideal simple cycle for $\tau = 4$ and $\tau = 5$ where it can be seen that for higher temperature ratios, the maximum values increase and occur at higher pressure ratio.

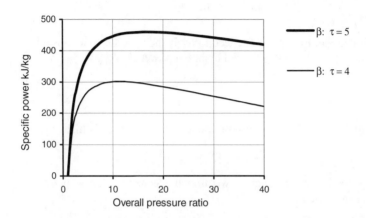

Figure 8.4   Specific power versus overall pressure for the ideal Brayton cycle.

The two values mentioned in equation (8.27) are the operating limits for the ideal Brayton cycle. Therefore, all possible ideal Brayton cycles will lie between these two values. To illustrate this, the two limits have been drawn in Figure 8.5. Also shown are two cycles, *A* and *B*, that lie between them.

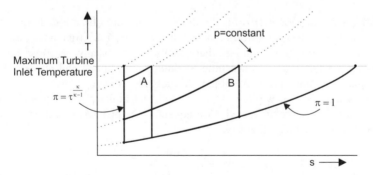

Figure 8.5   Ideal Brayton cycles with the same turbine inlet temperatures.

When comparing specific output power, it must be concluded that, cycle *B* with a moderate pressure ratio performs better than cycle *A* with a relative high pressure ratio, as shown in Figure 8.4. When comparing thermodynamic efficiency however, cycle *A* is better than cycle *B* as will be explained in the next section.

8.3.3   The thermodynamic efficiency

The efficiency of a gas turbine in general is by definition:

$$\eta_e \overset{def}{=} \frac{P_B}{\dot{Q}_f} \tag{8.29}$$

The most direct way to express fuel economy is the specific fuel consumption (normally in g/kWh), i.e. fuel flow [g/hr] divided by brake power [kW]:

$$sfc = \frac{\dot{m}_f}{P_B} \qquad\qquad ref. (7.32)$$

The link between specific fuel consumption and the efficiency is made by:

$$\dot{Q}_f = \dot{m}_f \cdot h^L \qquad\qquad ref. (7.16)$$

and thus, as for the diesel engine, we find the general relation between specific fuel consumption and efficiency:

$$sfc = \frac{\dot{Q}_f}{P_B \cdot h^L} = \frac{1}{\eta_e \cdot h^L} \qquad\qquad ref. (7.33)$$

If heat losses to the wall and losses as a result of incomplete combustion are neglected, the heat of the fuel flow is equal to the thermodynamic heat addition:

$$\dot{Q}_{in} = \dot{Q}_f \tag{8.30}$$

Compare this with equation (7.19) for the diesel engine and observe that equation (8.30) does neither exhibit a heat input efficiency, nor a combustion efficiency. For a real gas turbine, contrary to the diesel engine, there really is hardly any heat loss (combustion chamber is not cooled and residence time of fluid is very short) and also combustion is almost complete (continuous combustion, light fuels).

In the previous section, we have already seen that brake power equals cycle power when mechanical losses are neglected. Consequently, the efficiency of a Brayton cycle is equal to the thermodynamic efficiency:

$$\eta_e = \eta_{td} \overset{def}{=} \frac{P_{cycle}}{\dot{Q}_{in}} \tag{8.31}$$

This is the equivalent of equation (7.20), which defines thermodynamic efficiency for the diesel engine. Note that the diesel engine was analysed in terms of work and heat *per cycle*. Whereas the gas turbine has been analysed in terms of work and heat *per second*, i.e. power and heat flow, because it is a continuous flow machine. As in section 8.3.1

power and heat flow can be divided by mass flow to obtain mass specific work and heat. This leads to a definition of thermodynamic efficiency, which is equal to the one given in Chapter 7 for the diesel engine:

$$\eta_{td} \overset{def}{=} \frac{w_{cycle}}{q_{in}}$$

ref. (7.63)

And by the same reasoning as in Chapter 7:

$$\eta_{td} = \frac{q_{in} - q_{out}}{q_{in}} = 1 - \frac{q_{out}}{q_{in}}$$

ref. (7.64)

Now remember:

$$\frac{q_{in}}{c_p \cdot T_1} = \tau - \pi^{\frac{\kappa-1}{\kappa}}$$

ref. (8.18)

$$\frac{q_{out}}{c_p \cdot T_1} = \frac{1}{\pi^{\frac{\kappa-1}{\kappa}}} \cdot \left(\tau - \pi^{\frac{\kappa-1}{\kappa}} \right)$$

ref. (8.19)

$$\frac{w_{cycle}}{c_p \cdot T_1} = \left(\tau - \pi^{\frac{\kappa-1}{\kappa}} \right) \cdot \left(1 - \frac{1}{\pi^{\frac{\kappa-1}{\kappa}}} \right)$$

ref. (8.26)

By substitution of these in equation (7.63) or (7.64), the efficiency of the ideal cycle reduces to a simple expression:

$$\eta_{td} = 1 - \frac{1}{\pi^{\frac{\kappa-1}{\kappa}}}$$

(8.32)

Remarkably, the efficiency for the ideal Brayton cycle process depends only on the pressure ratio π and not on the temperature ratio τ. Using equation (8.32), it is possible to plot efficiency versus the overall pressure ratio. This is done in Figure 8.6.

Now revisit Figure 8.5 where it was claimed that cycle A, although having lower specific power, had a better efficiency. This can qualitatively be explained by observing that in cycle *A* the heat output area is much smaller relative to the net work area than in cycle *B*. Figure 8.6 shows that thermodynamic efficiency increases with an increasing pressure ratio π.

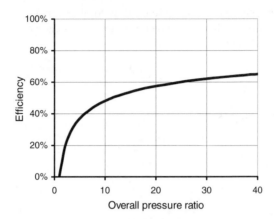

Figure 8.6   Thermodynamic efficiency versus overall pressure ratio for the ideal
                 Brayton cycle.

Looking at Figure 8.6 it may seem that the thermodynamic efficiency of the ideal Brayton cycle approaches 100% if the pressure ratio π approaches infinity. However, equation (8.27) showed that the pressure ratio of the ideal Brayton cycle has a limit value of $\tau^{\frac{\kappa}{\kappa-1}}$ where output power is zero. At this limit the efficiency has, according to equation (8.32), reached a value of:

$$\eta_{td} = 1 - \frac{1}{\pi^{\frac{\kappa-1}{\kappa}}} = 1 - \frac{1}{\tau} = 1 - \frac{T_1}{T_3}$$

Note that this is the Carnot efficiency as given in equation (2.31).

8.4   The simple cycle with losses

Up till now T–s diagrams and calculations were shown for the ideal Brayton cycle. In a real gas turbine, however, a number of losses play a role:

- Friction and incidence losses of the fluid flowing through the compressor and turbine.
- Pressure losses in all ducting associated with the gas turbine: intake ducting, ducting between the components, in the combustion chamber and in the exhaust ducts.
- Combustion losses due to incomplete combustion of the fuel.
- Heat losses to the environment from compressor, turbine and combustion chamber.
- Mechanical losses: losses in bearings, power loss due to PTO for auxiliary equipment such as fuel and lubricating oil pumps.

As the losses in the compressor and turbine are by far the most important, only these will be evaluated in this section. Note that in the following sections, the efficiency and the power density will be determined for theoretical cycles. Consequently, the efficiency is still referred to as thermodynamic efficiency. Because the most important losses have been accounted for (efficiency of the compressor and the turbine), the thermodynamic efficiency of the theoretical cycle is a fairly good approximation for the efficiency of a real gas turbine, even though a number of losses have not been included.

8.4.1   Work and heat

In case the compression and the expansion are still adiabatic, but with internal friction, the processes are no longer isentropic and the entropy must increase as shown in Figure 8.7. Compression between pressures p_1 and p_2 now takes place along an oblique line. The result is a higher temperature T_2 than in case of isentropic compression along a vertical line: $T_2 > T_{2s}$. So, more compression power is needed, see also equation (8.4). During the expansion process in the turbine between pressures p_3 and p_4 the entropy increases as well, so the temperature at the outlet of the turbine will be higher then in a cycle without losses: $T_4 > T_{4s}$ (where it is assumed that $p_2 = p_3$ and $p_4 = p_1$ as there still are no other pressure losses). This means that expansion power has decreased, see also equation (8.5).

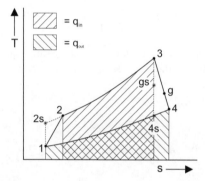

Figure 8.7   T-s diagram for the Brayton cycle with losses.

The ideal Brayton cycle is indicated in Figure 8.7 by cycle 1-2s-3-4s-1. The cycle with losses is cycle 1-2-3-4-1. The amount of heat added to the cycle with losses, i.e. the area under the line 2-3 is smaller than the amount of heat added to the ideal cycle, i.e. the area under the line 2s-3. On the other hand, more heat is rejected during process 4-1 of the cycle with losses than during process 4s-1 of the ideal cycle, as can be seen when comparing the area under line 4-1 to the area under line 4s-1. Consequently, the net work output of the cycle with losses is less than the work output of the ideal cycle and the efficiency is also less. This can be shown analytically:

$$q_{out} : \quad q_{41} > q_{4s,1}$$

$$q_{in} : \quad q_{23} < q_{2s,3}$$

So:

$$w_{cycle} = q_{in} - q_{out} : \quad q_{23} - q_{41} < q_{2s,3} - q_{4s,1}$$

$$\eta_{td} = 1 - \frac{q_{out}}{q_{in}}: \quad 1 - \frac{q_{41}}{q_{23}} < 1 - \frac{q_{4s,1}}{q_{2s,3}}$$

The basic expression for work and heat are the same as for the ideal cycle:

$$w_C = c_p \cdot (T_2 - T_1) = c_p \cdot T_1 \cdot (\tau_C - 1) \qquad\qquad \text{ref. (8.7)}$$

$$w_T = c_p \cdot (T_3 - T_4) = c_p \cdot T_1 \cdot \tau \cdot \left(1 - \frac{1}{\tau_T}\right) \qquad\qquad \text{ref. (8.8)}$$

The exit temperature T_2 and T_4, however, are different due to the losses in the compressor and the turbine. The losses can be expressed numerically by assuming that the actual compression and expansion are polytropic processes instead of isentropic processes. It is still assumed that the pressure ratios for the turbine and the compressor are the same:

$$\pi = \pi_C = \frac{p_2}{p_1} = \frac{p_3}{p_4} = \pi_T \qquad\qquad \text{ref. (8.1)}$$

The assumption of polytropic compression and expansion requires that the isentropic index κ is replaced by a polytropic index n_C, so the temperature ratio over the compressor is:

$$\tau_C = \pi^{\frac{n_C - 1}{n_C}} \qquad\qquad (8.33)$$

The new exponent n_C may be calculated by introducing the polytropic compressor efficiency η_c:

$$\frac{n_C - 1}{n_C} = \frac{1}{\eta_C} \cdot \frac{\kappa - 1}{\kappa} \qquad\qquad (8.34)$$

For $\eta_C < 1$ the resulting exponent in Poisson's law will increase, i.e. $n_c > \kappa$. Therefore, the temperature rise for a given pressure ratio will be higher than for the ideal case. As a result, the work required for compression will be higher:

$$\frac{w_C}{c_p \cdot T_1} = \pi^{\frac{n_C - 1}{n_C}} - 1 \qquad\qquad (8.35)$$

For polytropic expansion, process 3-4, delivered work can be calculated like-wise. First introducing the polytropic index n_T for the expansion process inside the turbine:

$$\tau_T = \pi^{\frac{n_T - 1}{n_T}} \qquad\qquad (8.36)$$

The new exponent n_T may be calculated by introducing the polytropic turbine efficiency η_T:

$$\frac{n_T - 1}{n_T} = \eta_T \cdot \frac{\kappa - 1}{\kappa} \tag{8.37}$$

(Note the differences between the expressions for polytropic efficiencies of the compressor and the turbine: this way the efficiency of both machines is less than one.)

For $\eta_T < 1$ the exponent in Poisson's law is smaller than for the isentropic case, i.e. $n_T < \kappa$. As a result the temperature drop for a given pressure ratio is less, thus decreasing the work output:

$$\frac{w_T}{c_p \cdot T_1} = \tau \cdot \left(1 - \frac{1}{\pi^{\frac{n_T - 1}{n_T}}} \right) \tag{8.38}$$

The heat flow in the combustion chamber also changes. First consider the input heat flow of an ideal cycle:

$$q_{in} = c_p \cdot T_1 \cdot \left(\frac{T_3}{T_1} - \frac{T_2}{T_1} \right) = c_p \cdot T_1 \cdot \left(\tau - \pi^{\frac{\kappa - 1}{\kappa}} \right) \qquad \text{ref. (8.16)}$$

By using the polytropic relationship for the temperature ratio of the compressor this results in:

$$\frac{q_{in}}{c_p \cdot T_1} = \left(\tau - \pi^{\frac{n_C - 1}{n_C}} \right) \tag{8.39}$$

So, the input heat flow decreases relative to the ideal cycle.

8.4.2 Performance

For the Brayton cycle with losses, efficiency and specific power can be calculated as was done previously in sections 8.3.1-8.3.3 for an ideal cycle. The only difference is that delivered turbine power and required compressor power have changed due to the polytropic compression and expansion. Specific power for the non-ideal simple cycle gas turbine is obtained by substitution of equations (8.35) and (8.38) into equation (8.24). The non-dimensional form of specific power is obtained by dividing specific power by a measure for the enthalpy of the intake mass flow:

$$\frac{w_{cycle}}{c_p \cdot T_1} = \tau \cdot \left(1 - \frac{1}{\pi^{\frac{n_T - 1}{n_T}}} \right) - \left(\pi^{\frac{n_C - 1}{n_C}} - 1 \right) \tag{8.40}$$

Specific power curves for both the ideal cycle and cycle with losses are shown in Figure 8.8.

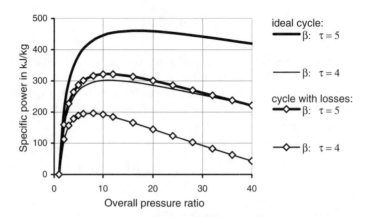

Figure 8.8   Specific power versus overall pressure ratio for the simple cycle gas
                 turbine with losses. Polytropic efficiency of compressor η_c = 0.90 and for
                 turbine η_T = 0.85. No pressure losses included.

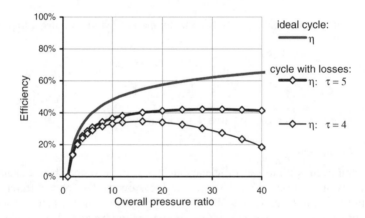

Figure 8.9   Efficiency versus overall pressure ratio for the simple cycle gas turbine
                 with losses. Polytropic efficiency of compressor η_c = 0.90 and for turbine
                 η_T = 0.85. No pressure losses included.

The efficiency of the Brayton cycle is also altered when assuming polytropic
compression and expansion. Substituting equations (8.39) and (8.40) into equation (7.63)
gives:

$$\eta_{td} \overset{def}{=} \frac{W_{cycle}}{q_{in}} = \frac{\tau \cdot \left(1 - \dfrac{1}{\pi^{\frac{n_T-1}{n_T}}}\right) - \left(\pi^{\frac{n_C-1}{n_C}} - 1\right)}{\tau - \pi^{\frac{n_C-1}{n_C}}} \qquad (8.41)$$

Efficiency curves for both the ideal cycle and cycle with losses are shown in Figure 8.9

Due to the introduction of losses, gas turbine performance has drastically been altered. Taking a closer look at Figure 8.8 and Figure 8.9 shows that both efficiency and specific power are at a significantly lower level. So, the ideal Brayton cycle as shown in Figure 8.2 is far too optimistic for determining actual gas turbine performance.

Another interesting phenomenon is that total efficiency for the simple cycle with losses also depends on the temperature ratio τ and that optimum efficiency is reached at a lower pressure ratio π than was the case for the ideal cycle. For example, the optimum efficiency for the simple cycle with losses is reached at overall pressure ratio $\pi = 18$, for a temperature ratio $\tau = 4$. Whereas the optimum efficiency for the ideal Brayton cycle is reached at the cycle's maximum pressure ratio limit as defined by equation (8.27) and it is not dependent on the temperature ratio.

Figure 8.8 and Figure 8.9 are still theoretical as some losses have been neglected during performance evaluation; actual performance curves for both specific power and efficiency will show somewhat lower values.

8.5 Advanced cycles

The simple cycle gas turbine is well established in industry and finds its application in the marine sector as well. The basic analysis, given in the previous sections, has shown that power density is the strong point of the gas turbine and this is the main reason for its application in naval ships and fast ferries. Also emissions are low; this has opened the market for the application of gas turbines in cruise ships. The weak point, however, remains the low thermodynamic efficiency of the simple cycle when compared to its direct competitors: the diesel engine in the marine market and the steam installation in land-based power plants. Therefore a trend towards improving the basic thermodynamics of the gas turbine cycle can be seen: advanced cycles of increasing complexity are advocated. Sometimes the term *complex cycles* is used instead of *advanced cycles*.

Measures to improve the efficiency and specific power of a gas turbine are:

- First stage of heating of the compressed air by means of the hot exhaust gases in a heat exchanger, i.e. recuperation.
- Cooling of the air between compression stages, i.e. inter-cooling.
- Additional fuel heat input between expansion stages, i.e. reheat.

In combination with variable geometry blades in turbine and/or compressor the result may be a gas turbine with relatively high performance both at full and part load. Unfortunately, the gas turbine as a unit will become heavier and possibly reacting slower to load steps, due to the time lag associated with a heat exchanger.

A first example of an advanced cycle is the regenerative cycle, where a heat exchanger has been added in order to use the waste heat of the exhaust gases. A full analysis of the basic theory of the regenerative cycle will be given in this section.

As for the simple cycle, the regenerative cycle shows different optima for efficiency and specific work. Moreover, the optimum efficiency for the simple cycle and of the regenerative cycle will prove to be different. In general, each advanced cycle that is proposed can be expected to have different optima. This leads to the issue of cycle optimisation and a short introduction to this complicated matter will be given in this section.

With this knowledge in hand an outlook into the potential of other advanced cycles will be presented. The section will be concluded with a particular promising advanced cycle, the inter-cooled regenerative cycle.

8.5.1 The ideal regenerative cycle

A short introduction to regenerative cycles was previously provided in chapter 6.2.2. The general idea behind the regenerative cycle, see Figure 8.10, is that the heat in the exhaust gases can be used to heat the compressed air in a heat exchanger, thus diminishing the heat that needs to be supplied by the fuel in the combustion chamber.

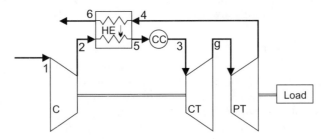

Figure 8.10   Flow scheme for the regenerative cycle.

Adding a heat exchanger (HE) that transfers the heat of the exhaust to the first stage of the heating process before the combustion chamber does not alter the expressions for the power of the compressor and turbine. Therefore the expression for the specific power of the regenerative cycle is the same as for the simple cycle. This includes the occurrence of an optimum value at a certain pressure ratio for given temperature ratio.

$$\frac{w_C}{c_p \cdot T_1} = \pi^{\frac{\kappa-1}{\kappa}} - 1 \qquad\qquad \text{ref. (8.11)}$$

$$\frac{w_T}{c_p \cdot T_1} = \tau \cdot \left(1 - \frac{1}{\pi^{\frac{\kappa-1}{\kappa}}} \right) \qquad\qquad \text{ref. (8.12)}$$

$$\frac{W_{cycle}}{c_p \cdot T_1} = \left(\tau - \pi^{\frac{\kappa-1}{\kappa}} \right) \cdot \left(1 - \frac{1}{\pi^{\frac{\kappa-1}{\kappa}}} \right) \qquad \text{ref. (8.26)}$$

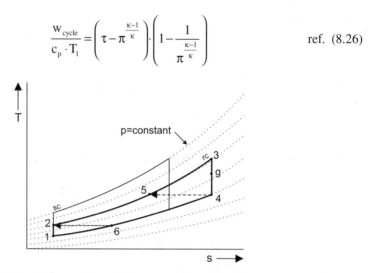

Figure 8.11   The T–s diagram of an ideal regenerative cycle (RC) compared to the simple cycle (SC).

Examining the two cycles shown in Figure 8.11, two major differences can be recognised between the two cycles:

- The heat added to the cycle by means of fuel is less in a regenerative cycle: $(T_3 - T_5)_{reg.cyc} < (T_3 - T_2)_{sim.cyc}$. So, the fuel economy for the regenerative cycle is better than for the simple cycle. As a result the regenerative cycle has potential to improve total efficiency.

- In a regenerative cycle, the temperature after the turbine must be higher than the temperature after the compressor in order to make heat exchange possible: $T_4 > T_2$. The pressure ratio of the regenerative cycle is therefore lower than the pressure ratio of the simple cycle ($\pi_{sim.cyc} > \pi_{reg.cyc}$).

The expression for total heat addition is basically the same for both cycles:

$$q_{23} = \frac{\dot{Q}_{23}}{\dot{m}} = c_p \cdot (T_3 - T_2) \quad \dot{Q}_{23} = \dot{m} \cdot c_p \cdot (T_3 - T_2) \qquad \text{ref. (8.13)}$$

The heat added in process 2–3 is the sum of the heat added in the combustion chamber and the heat added in the heat exchanger:

$$q_{23} = q_{in} + q_{HE} \qquad (8.42)$$

For an ideal counter flow heat exchanger with infinite area, the air after the compressor can be heated up to the gas exhaust temperature after the last turbine:

$$T_5 = T_4 \ and \ T_6 = T_2$$

So, the heat added in the heat exchanger is:

$$q_{HE} = \frac{\dot{Q}_{HE}}{\dot{m}} = c_p \cdot (T_5 - T_2) = c_p \cdot (T_4 - T_2) \tag{8.43}$$

Therefore, the heat input in the combustion chamber (i.e. from the fuel) is:

$$q_{in} = \frac{\dot{Q}_{in}}{\dot{m}} = c_p \cdot (T_3 - T_5) = c_p \cdot (T_3 - T_4) \tag{8.44}$$

The heat input can be written in non-dimensional form as:

$$\frac{q_{in}}{c_p \cdot T_1} = \frac{T_3}{T_1} - \frac{T_4}{T_1} = \frac{T_3}{T_1} - \frac{T_4}{T_3} \cdot \frac{T_3}{T_1} = \tau \cdot \left(1 - \frac{1}{\pi^{\frac{\kappa-1}{\kappa}}} \right) \tag{8.45}$$

Then, the thermodynamic efficiency of the ideal regenerative cycle is, using equation (7.63):

$$\eta_{td} \overset{def}{=} \frac{w_{cycle}}{q_{in}} = \frac{\beta_m}{q_{in}} = \frac{\left(\tau - \pi^{\frac{\kappa-1}{\kappa}} \right) \cdot \left(1 - \frac{1}{\pi^{\frac{\kappa-1}{\kappa}}} \right)}{\tau \cdot \left(1 - \frac{1}{\pi^{\frac{\kappa-1}{\kappa}}} \right)} = \frac{\left(\tau - \pi^{\frac{\kappa-1}{\kappa}} \right)}{\tau}$$

This can be rearranged:

$$\eta_{td} = 1 - \frac{\pi^{\frac{\kappa-1}{\kappa}}}{\tau} \tag{8.46}$$

The efficiency of the ideal regenerative cycle thus depends on pressure ratio *and* temperature ratio. Moreover the efficiency now *decreases* with pressure ratio. So, contrary to the simple non-regenerative cycle, one must opt for a cycle with a *low* pressure ratio. The physical background is that at a low pressure ratio the exhaust temperature is high, which is favourable for use of waste heat. On the other hand, the temperature after compression is low; this offers ample opportunity for heat exchange between the two flows.

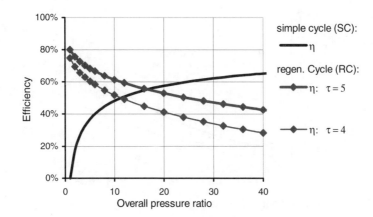

Figure 8.12   The thermodynamic efficiency of the ideal regenerative cycle compared to the efficiency of the ideal simple cycle.

The efficiency of the regenerative cycle is higher than the efficiency of the simple cycle when $T_4 > T_2$. It can be proven that the pressure ratio π should be less than $\tau^{\frac{\kappa}{2(\kappa-1)}}$. In Figure 8.12, π equals $\tau^{\frac{\kappa}{2(\kappa-1)}}$ at the intersection points of the curves of the simple and the regenerative cycles. For higher pressure ratios the regenerative cycle is counter-productive: in a heat exchanger heat would be lost instead of added.

8.5.2   *The regenerative cycle with losses*

As for the simple cycle the component losses need to be dealt with. The losses in the compressor and the turbine are captured in the polytropic efficiencies. For a heat exchanger with finite dimensions the temperature of the heated air T_5 will be less than the exhaust temperature T_4. The losses in the heat exchanger are captured in the heat exchanger efficiency η_{HE}: the ratio of the real temperature increase of the air (T_5-T_2) to the maximum possible value (T_4-T_2):

$$\eta_{HE} = \frac{(T_5 - T_2)}{(T_4 - T_2)} \tag{8.47}$$

Note that η_{HE} strictly speaking is not an efficiency but an effectiveness: it does not stand for an energy *loss* but merely expresses the fact that the heat exchange area of a real heat exchanger is not infinite.

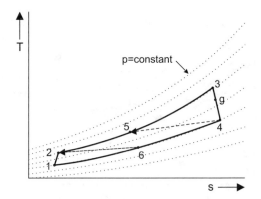

Figure 8.13   The T–s diagram for the regenerative cycle with losses.

Figure 8.13 shows the component losses in a T–s diagram. During compression and expansion the entropy increases, and the dashed lines representing heat exchange are no longer horizontal. The expressions for compressor and turbine power do not change compared to the simple cycle with losses, neither does the expression for specific power:

$$\frac{w_C}{c_p \cdot T_1} = \pi^{\frac{n_C - 1}{n_C}} - 1 \qquad \qquad \text{ref. (8.35)}$$

$$\frac{w_T}{c_p \cdot T_1} = \tau \cdot \left(1 - \frac{1}{\pi^{\frac{n_T - 1}{n_T}}} \right) \qquad \qquad \text{ref. (8.38)}$$

$$\frac{w_{cycle}}{c_p \cdot T_1} = \tau \cdot \left(1 - \frac{1}{\pi^{\frac{n_T - 1}{n_T}}} \right) - \left(\pi^{\frac{n_C - 1}{n_C}} - 1 \right) \qquad \qquad \text{ref. (8.40)}$$

The heat added to the cycle is:

$$q_{in} = \frac{\dot{Q}_{in}}{\dot{m}} = c_p \cdot \left[(T_3 - T_2) - \eta_{HE} \cdot (T_4 - T_2) \right] \qquad \qquad (8.48)$$

The heat input can be written in non-dimensional form in the usual way:

$$\frac{q_{in}}{c_p \cdot T_1} = \left(\frac{T_3}{T_1} - \frac{T_2}{T_1} \right) - \eta_{HE} \cdot \left(\frac{T_4}{T_1} - \frac{T_2}{T_1} \right)$$

$$= \left(\frac{T_3}{T_1} - \frac{T_2}{T_1} \right) - \eta_{HE} \cdot \left(\frac{T_4}{T_3} \cdot \frac{T_3}{T_1} - \frac{T_2}{T_1} \right)$$

Or after substitution of the polytropic relations (equations (8.33) and (8.36)) and the overall temperature ratio:

$$\frac{q_{in}}{c_p \cdot T_1} = \left(\tau - \pi^{\frac{n_C-1}{n_C}} \right) - \eta_{HE} \cdot \left(\frac{\tau}{\pi^{\frac{n_T-1}{n_T}}} - \pi^{\frac{n_C-1}{n_C}} \right)$$

$$= \tau \cdot \left(1 - \frac{\eta_{HE}}{\pi^{\frac{n_T-1}{n_T}}} \right) - \left(1 - \eta_{HE}\right) \cdot \pi^{\frac{n_C-1}{n_C}}$$

(8.49)

With equations (8.40) and (8.48), the thermodynamic efficiency of the regenerative cycle with losses can be calculated:

$$\eta_{td} = \frac{W_{cycle}}{q_{in}} = \frac{\beta_{\dot{m}}}{q_{in}} = \frac{\tau \cdot \left(1 - \dfrac{1}{\pi^{\frac{n_T-1}{n_T}}} \right) - \left(\pi^{\frac{n_C-1}{n_C}} - 1 \right)}{\tau \cdot \left(1 - \dfrac{\eta_{HE}}{\pi^{\frac{n_T-1}{n_T}}} \right) - \left(1 - \eta_{HE}\right) \cdot \pi^{\frac{n_C-1}{n_C}}}$$

(8.50)

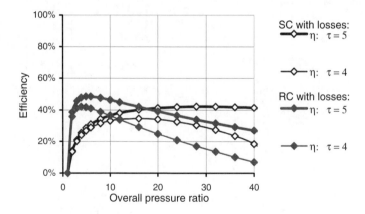

Figure 8.14   The thermodynamic efficiency for the simple cycle and regenerative cycle including losses. ($\eta_c = 0.90$, $\eta_T = 0.85$, $\eta_{HE} = 0.80$ and no pressure losses included).

Figure 8.14 is an illustration of this complicated expression, showing the total efficiency of the regenerative cycle including losses as a function the pressure ratio. The curves of the simple cycle with losses are also shown for an easy comparison between the two cycles. Two important conclusions may be drawn from Figure 8.14:

▪ The optimum total efficiency for the regenerative cycle proves to be higher than that of the simple cycle.

▪ The optimum for regenerative cycles is clearly reached in the lower pressure ratio range.

8.5.3   The Inter-Cooled Regenerative cycle

ICR cycle stands for Inter-Cooled Regenerative cycle. In short this implies that a cooler has been added to the regenerative cycle, as shown in Figure 8.15. This type of gas turbine uses a low pressure spool (a low pressure compressor driven by a low pressure turbine) and a high pressure spool. A power turbine is used to drive the load.

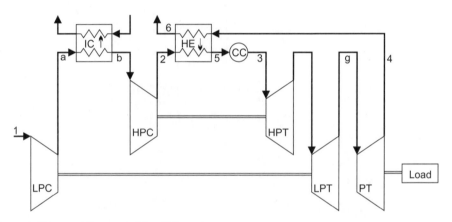

Figure 8.15   Diagram of the ICR cycle

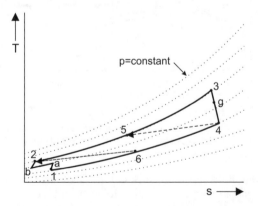

Figure 8.16   The T–s diagram of an Inter-Cooled Regenerative cycle.

The inter-cooler between the low pressure and the high pressure compressor reduces the required compressor power, and consequently it increases the net work of the cycle. Thus the power density has increased.

The decrease of the compressor outlet temperature does not increase fuel consumption: as for the basic regenerative cycle the first part of the heat addition is taken from the exhaust and not supplied by fuel as indicated by Figure 8.16. A comprehensive overview of the performance potential will be given in section 8.5.5.

A picture of this gas turbine is presented in Figure 8.17. For the inter-cooler the airflow must deviate from the axial gas path through the gas turbine. The heat exchanger has a by-pass which is used in case of problems and which enables the gas turbine to be run up to normal power (but at higher fuel consumption of course).

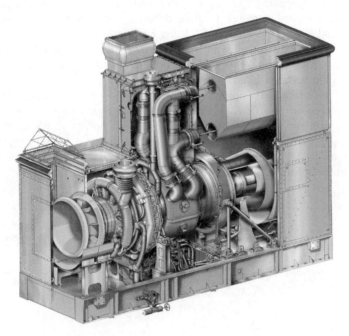

Figure 8.17   3D-cutaway view of a 22 MW ICR Rolls-Royce WR 21 gas turbine. (Courtesy of Rolls-Royce).

8.5.4   Cycle optimisation

From the considerations in the previous sections, it can be concluded that the main parameters that influence the specific power and overall efficiency of a gas turbine are:

- The maximum temperature ratio ($\tau = T_3/T_1$), i.e. the temperature before inlet of the turbine(s) relative to the temperature of the environment.

- The maximum pressure ratio ($\pi = p_2/p_1$), i.e. the pressure after the compressor(s) relative to the environmental pressure.

Furthermore, the efficiencies of the turbomachinery have a major impact: for good performance they must be as high as possible. This also applies to the heat exchanger effectiveness. Although not shown in the previous simplified discussion, pressure losses in the flow path deteriorate both specific power and efficiency and must also be kept as low as possible.

The highest value of the maximum *temperature* ratio will in general give the best performance in terms of specific power and efficiency. The thermal load of the turbine blades forms the limit and a maximum temperature ratio of 5 already requires very advanced blade-cooling techniques. This also explains the amount of research that has been put into new materials for turbine blades and the development of advanced blade-cooling by bleed air taken from the compressor.

The maximum *pressure* ratio of a gas turbine, however, should not be chosen as high as possible. In the foregoing analysis it has been shown that the pressure ratio must be optimised; the optimum however is quite different for maximum specific work and maximum overall efficiency. This could clearly be seen in Figure 8.8 and Figure 8.9. For the simple cycle the optimum value for specific power (i.e. the 'smallest' engine) requires a pressure ratio between 10 and 15 while the optimum value for the efficiency is reached for a pressure ratio between 20 and 40.

In order to understand why optimising with respect to specific power is different from optimising with respect to efficiency, the simple cycle for the two optima has been drawn in a T–s diagram; see Figure 8.18. In the cycle with optimum efficiency the higher pressure ratio causes the combustion heat to be delivered at a higher temperature level which (refer to the Carnot efficiency) is much more favourable. The turbomachinery losses prevent the optimum from lying at an even higher pressure ratio.

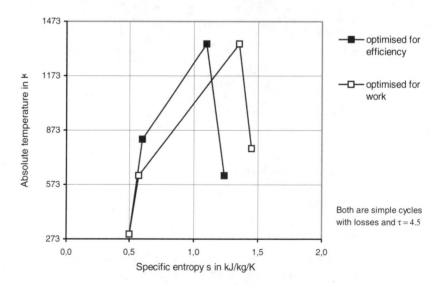

Figure 8.18   T-s diagram for a Simple Cycle Gas Turbine optimised for efficiency (ETAOPT) and specific work (WORKOPT) respectively.

There is an elegant way to put both optima in one graph, which amongst others can be found in [Wilson, 1984]. Efficiency and specific power are put on the vertical and horizontal axis respectively, see Figure 8.19. In this trade-off picture, lines for several constant maximum temperature ratios are entered whereby the pressure ratio is a running parameter along these (strongly curved) lines. A few lines of constant pressure ratio are entered as well thus completing the grid. The reader may verify that the information contained in Figure 8.8 and Figure 8.9 for the simple cycle is directly transformed into Figure 8.19. The two optima now can be seen directly as the horizontal tangent (optimum for the efficiency) and the vertical tangent (optimum for specific work) of the constant temperature lines. In particular the plot shows that a trade-off must be made between efficiency and specific power, i.e. between a gas turbine with low specific fuel consumption and a small engine.

This may be the place to compare the trade off plot for the gas turbine, Figure 8.19, with the same type of plot for the diesel engine in Figure 7.43. Apart from the fact that power density for the gas turbine is in work per unit mass, while for the diesel engine it is in work per unit volume (mean effective pressure), other differences are:

- for a gas turbine the *overall cycle temperature* is the main parameter influencing the attainable efficiency. For the diesel engine this is the *peak cylinder pressure*.

- for a gas turbine for each value of the maximum temperature the *cycle pressure ratio* can be optimised both with respect to efficiency and power density. For the diesel engine for each value of the peak pressure the *charge pressure* can be optimised with respect to efficiency only.

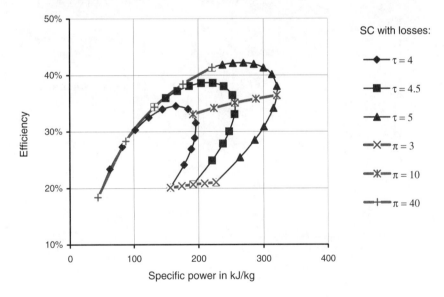

Figure 8.19   Trade-off between efficiency and specific power for a Simple Cycle Gas Turbine. (η_c = 0.90 and η_T = 0.85. No pressure losses included.

The same can be done for the regenerative cycle. The recuperation of exhaust heat by addition of a heat exchanger changes the relative position of the optima completely: the optimum efficiency now is reached at much lower pressure ratios between 3 and 8 as shown in Figure 8.14. This is a favourable characteristic of the regenerative gas turbine since it means simple turbomachinery and thus a cheap gas turbine can be used. With a radial compressor and turbine even a single stage is possible. The heat exchanger on the other hand adds to complexity.

The position of the optimum for the specific power has not changed (still at pressure ratios between 10 and 15 refer to Figure 8.8). For a real case, however, specific power of the regenerative gas turbine will be slightly less than that of the simple cycle due to the pressure loss of the heat exchangers (both at air and gas side). In practice, the specific *installation* weight of the regenerative gas turbine will be greater due to the weight of the heat exchanger itself.

The explanation of the reversal of the optima becomes clear when looking at the T-s diagram: see Figure 8.20. The heat exchanger only is effective in case of a considerable temperature difference between the exhaust temperature of the turbine(s) and the exit temperature of the compressor(s). This is only possible when the the pressure ratio of the engine is small and the T-s diagram is shallow.

Again the result can be presented in one trade-off graph: see Figure 8.21. In this figure the direction for which the pressure ratio increases along the curves has reversed when compared to Figure 8.19. This effect is shown for just one temperature ratio in Figure 8.22.

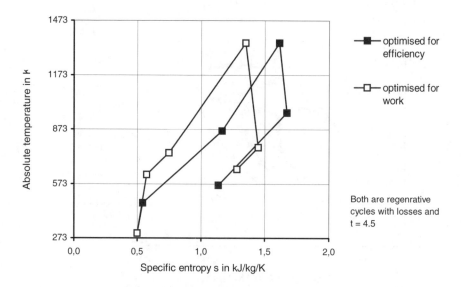

Figure 8.20   T-s diagram for the Regenerative Gas Turbine optimised for efficiency and specific work respectively.

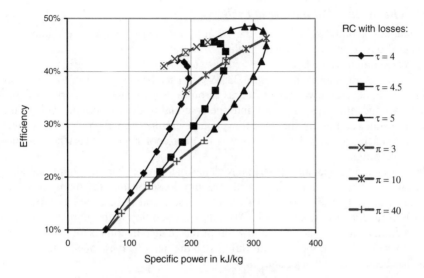

Figure 8.21   Trade-off between efficiency and specific power for a Regenerative Gas Turbine ($\eta_c = 0.90$, $\eta_T = 0.85$, $\eta_{HE} = 0.80$ and no pressure losses included).

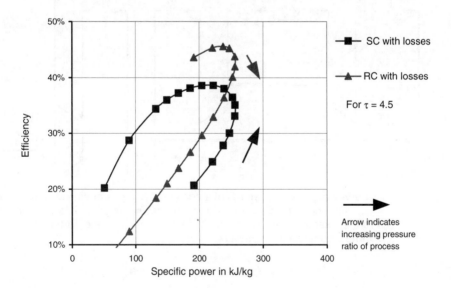

Figure 8.22   Trade-off between efficiency and specific power of the Simple Cycle Gas Turbine and the Regenerative Gas Turbine.

8.5.5   *The potential of advanced cycles*

The techniques as outlined before were used in [Stapersma, 1999] to investigate all sorts of advanced gas turbine cycles with features such as inter-cooling between compressor stages, recuperation of heat from the exhaust and reheat between turbine stages. The different options are shown in Figure 8.23. A cycle analysis resulted in the overview of the potential of several advanced cycle gas turbines as presented in the trade-off plot of Figure 8.24. Since this was a research into the potential of the gas turbine cycle in the far future, the values chosen for the overall cycle temperature ratio, the polytropic efficiency of the turbomachinery and the effectiveness of inter-cooler and exhaust heat exchanger were relatively high.

The analysis in [Stapersma, 1999] goes somewhat further than the simplified analysis given in the previous sections. First of all pressure losses in the flow path are included. Furthermore the polytropic efficiencies of compressors and turbines are assumed to be a (decreasing) function of pressure ratio. Also, the heat addition in the combustion chamber is calculated in a more precise way allowing for the change in composition and associated change in specific heat of the working fluid. Also the mass increase due to the addition of the fuel has been taken into account.

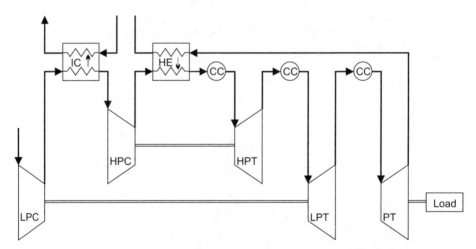

Figure 8.23   Survey of possible features of a complex cycle gas turbine showing inter-cooling of the air between compressor stages, heating of the compressed air in an exhaust heat exchanger and furthermore two reheat combustion chambers.

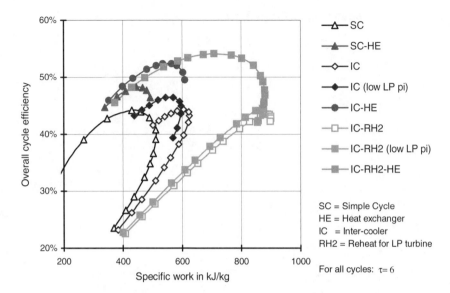

Figure 8.24 Comparison of several complex cycle gas turbines; $\eta_C=\eta_T=0.9$, decreasing with increase of pressure ratio; effectiveness of exhaust heat exchanger and inter-cooler: $\eta_{HE}=0.9$.

From this comparison, it can be concluded that if one is not prepared to accept the complexity of a second combustion chamber (RH = reheat), the cycle with inter-cooling between compressor stages (IC = Inter-cooling) *combined* with regeneration of heat from the exhaust (HE = Heat exchanger) offers the best potential. This is the Inter-Cooled Regenerative cycle (ICR) that has already been presented in Figure 8.15.

Again this cycle may be optimised for maximum work output or for maximum efficiency; see the T-s diagram in Figure 8.25. Strictly speaking the optimisation for an inter-cooled cycle must be carried while varying both the overall pressure ratio and the ratio of the HP and LP compressor ratios:

$$v = \frac{\pi_{LPC}}{\pi_{HPC}}$$

For the ICR cycle, the optimum for specific work and efficiency are both found for almost equal HP and LP compressor pressure ratios. For the inter-cooled cycle without recuperation maximum efficiency will only be found if the LP compressor pressure ratio is much lower that the HP compressor pressure ratio, as shown in Figure 8.24. The same is also true for the intercooled cycle with one stage of reheat

The performance potential of the ICR cycle is shown in Figure 8.26. As a reference, an ICR gas turbine has been included that is available for marine application (Rolls Royce WR 21). From the figure it can be concluded that the pressure ratio is chosen between the values for optimum specific power and optimum overall efficiency, but closer to the latter (the selected pressure ratio in fact is 11.5 which is rather low thanks to the adoption of the heat exchanger).

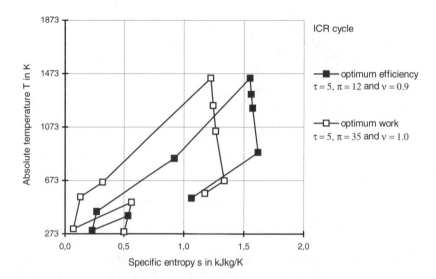

Figure 8.25   T-s diagram of an ICR cycle gas turbine (See also Figure 8.15).

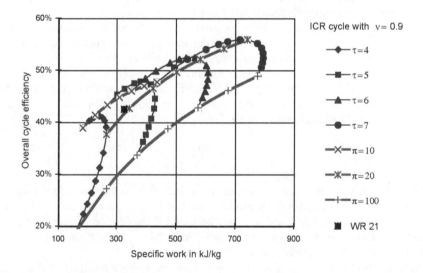

Figure 8.26   Trade-off between overall efficiency and specific power of an advanced cycle gas turbine ; ICR cycle.

8.6 The operating envelope

The drive characteristics of the free power turbine have already been given in section 3.6.2. In this section, the torque–speed and power–speed characteristics are studied in more detail.

8.6.1 The power–speed curve

Figure 8.27 shows the torque–speed curves for the output turbine of a single-shaft gas turbine and of a separate power turbine. For comparison the torque–speed curve of a naturally aspirating diesel engine is also shown.

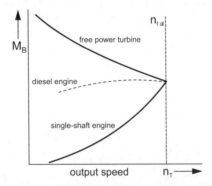

Figure 8.27   Torque–speed characteristics of the single and twin-shaft gas turbines.

In a single-shaft gas turbine, the speeds of the compressor, the turbine and the load are linked. If the speed of the load decreases, so will the speed of the compressor. Consequently, the mass flow and associated power decrease. As power decreases faster than the speed, so will the torque.

The speed of the power turbine of a twin-shaft turbine may change irrespective of the speed of the gas generator. If the compressor runs at a fixed speed, the gas generator develops a constant gas power. If the output speed (load and power turbine) decreases, this will not affect the compressor speed so the gas power will hardly be affected and the output power remains constant. Consequently, a reduction in output speed results in an increase in torque.

The power–speed curve of the free turbine is favourable for loads that do not require constant speeds: within a wide range of speed, power is maintained. It is possible to develop high power even at low speeds. If a gas turbine is used to drive a propeller, the propeller load curve can be followed and at each point there is sufficient power reserve for accelerating the ship. Also there is room for increased resistance in which case the propeller curve shifts to higher values.

A typical output power–speed characteristic of an existing gas turbine (Rolls Royce Spey SM1A) is included: see Figure 8.28. Lines of constant fuel flow are indicated. The limit curve of maximum fuel seems a parabolic curve with a flat top near nominal speed, the latter causing almost constant power behaviour around the nominal point. The parabolic shape of the limiting envelope for a gas turbine with free power turbine is almost exact and can be derived from first principles with the assumption that the power turbine behaves according to Euler's pump curve and that the mass flow of the gas generator is proportional to fuel flow. As a consequence the turbine torque almost linearly increases at decreasing output speed.

Gas turbines in general are not rotationally reversible. Consequently, reversing a ship with a mechanically driven propeller requires a gearbox to reverse rotation (reversible gearing with clutches) or a propulsor that can provide reverse thrust (controllable pitch propeller or waterjet with thrust deflector).

For some gas turbines the rotation can be specified for clockwise and anti-clockwise direction (i.e. the blading of the power turbine is produced in two symmetrical versions). If this is not the case, a solution must be found in case of a twin-shaft ship where both shafts normally have opposing directions of rotation (either inward or outward). The solution could be an extra pair of gears in one of the gearboxes.

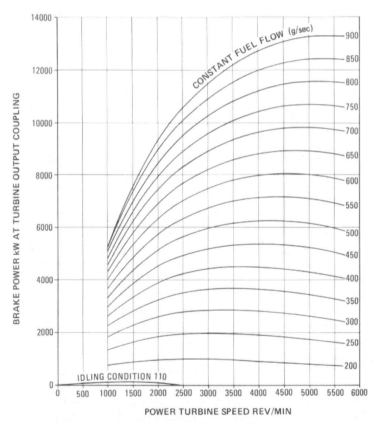

Figure 8.28   Power–speed characteristic for a simple cycle gas turbine with free power turbine with lines of constant fuel.

8.6.2 *Fuel consumption*

Figure 8.28 shows lines of constant fuel consumption. Fuel consumption divided by power is the specific fuel consumption *sfc*. Figure 8.29 gives values for *sfc* along the propeller curve (for other trajectories of the engine characteristic the curve usually lies somewhat higher).

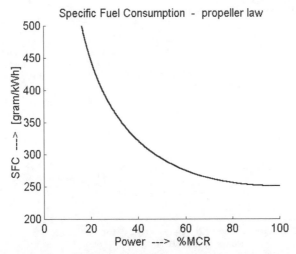

Figure 8.29   Specific fuel consumption of simple cycle gas turbine at part load along the propeller law.

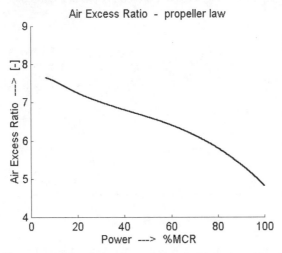

Figure 8.30   Air excess ratio of simple cycle gas turbine at part load along the propeller law.

Figure 8.29 shows that *sfc* of a gas turbine increases sharply at part load. The fundamental cause for this is that the air consumption of a gas turbine decreases much slower than the fuel consumption as can been concluded from the air excess ratio that increases sharply at part load in Figure 8.30. The air excess acts to cool the gases and therefore the gas turbine cannot maintain the turbine inlet temperature, for which it was designed, at part load. From the previous thermodynamic discussions the deteriorating effect on the overall engine efficiency will be clear.

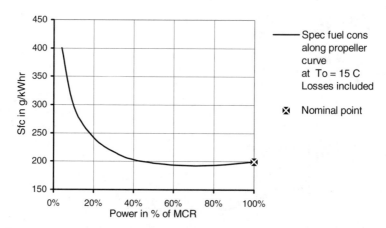

Figure 8.31   Specific fuel consumption of the ICR gas turbine with variable blade geometry at the turbine; part load curve along the propeller law.

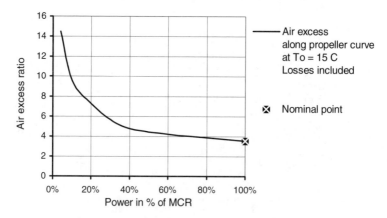

Figure 8.32   Air excess ratio of ICR gas turbine with variable blade geometry at the turbine; part load curve along the propeller law.

A method to maintain turbine inlet temperature is to control the amount of air through the engine by means of variable geometry of the stator blading in the turbine. By decreasing the area, the air flow will be reduced and the inlet temperature can be maintained. The result will be a flat *sfc* curve. The ICR gas turbine referred to in the previous section has, apart from an advanced thermodynamic cycle, also variable turbine geometry. This engine therefore can maintain the low specific fuel consumption it has at the nominal point down to 40% load; see Figure 8.31. The flatter air excess ratio that causes this is shown in Figure 8.32.

8.6.3   *Effect of ambient conditions and installation losses*

The brake power of a gas turbine is also influenced by environmental conditions and the losses in intake and exhaust ducts.

At higher ambient temperature the amount of fuel supplied to a gas turbine must be reduced in order to keep the turbine inlet temperature below the maximum allowable value. As a result the power output of a gas turbine is significantly reduced in (sub)tropical conditions; see Figure 8.33.

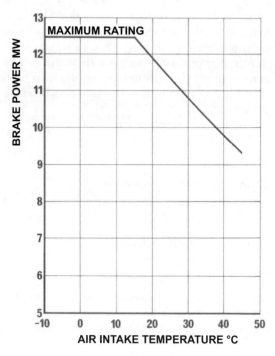

Figure 8.33   Power reduction of gas turbine at increasing ambient temperature.

The efficiency also decreases and specific fuel consumption increases. The physical reason for this tendency is two-fold:

- Due to a lower density at intake the density throughout the engine is lower and the mass flow decreases. If fuel flow is not reduced, the temperature in the combustion chamber would increase inversely, proportional to the density decrease.

- A higher inlet temperature causes all (absolute) temperatures to be higher (with the same factor if all other conditions would be the same). So fuel must be decreased also to compensate for this effect.

Ideally, fuel would be reduced in order to maintain the temperature constant at the inlet of the first turbine. This temperature normally cannot be measured however and the practical solution is to schedule fuel, based on the *power* turbine entry temperature, which is an observable quantity.

At lower ambient temperatures, power may be reduced in order to keep the gas generator speed within tolerable limits.

A gas turbine also is relatively sensitive to pressure at intake and exhaust. When the ambient pressure varies, the pressure at intake and exhaust vary in the same manner. The influence on power and specific fuel consumption is comparable to the effect of ambient temperature. Both a decrease of ambient pressure and an increase of ambient temperature cause the intake density to be lower than normal and a limitation of fuel is necessary to prevent the temperatures from being too high at the critical blading.

The pressure losses in intake and exhaust ducts are also important. Sometimes gas turbine performance is presented as 'no loss'. Then the values will be too optimistic and not representative for the conditions that the gas turbine will encounter when installed on board. It is good practice to compare gas turbines on the basis of their performance with assumed realistic intake and exhaust losses: for instance 1 kPa underpressure at the inlet and 1.5 kPa overpressure at the outlet.

Some typical data for installation losses are:

- at 1% intake loss (air filters, intake duct and silencer):
  - 2% decrease in power
  - 1% increase in specific fuel consumption.
- at 1% exhaust loss (exhaust duct, silencer and exit velocity loss):
  - 1% decrease in power
  - 1% increase in specific fuel consumption.

8.7   Installation on board

The radiated airborne noise of the core engine is very high with maximum levels lying in the higher frequency bands for which the human ear is very sensitive. A gas turbine on board a ship therefore requires an acoustical enclosure which, together with the bedplate, forms the total gas turbine module; see Figure 8.34.

The structure-borne noise of a gas turbine is low and a gas turbine for merchant navy application can be rigidly mounted in the ship. In case of more stringent requirements, such as for instance in naval ships, the bed plate is put on (rubber) mounts; these serve the double function of noise attenuation and shock protection.

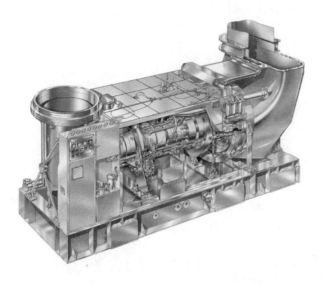

Figure 8.34   Rolls-Royce Spey SM1A gas turbine module suitable for installation on board ships. (Courtesy of Rolls-Royce).

Apart from its function as an acoustical enclosure the module also offers fire protection: it may be seen as an engine room within the engine room and have its own independent fire-fighting system. The module has its own ventilation, for which clean air is taken from the gas turbine intake air system. Ventilation air is normally discharged to the exhaust duct: the underpressure in the exhaust due to the high velocity makes a fan in the system superfluous.

High frequency noise from the compressor inlet is isolated from the deck area by a silencer in the inlet duct. Depending on the noise requirements the (low frequency) noise of the exhaust gas stream is often acceptable if a certain length of duct is present and the position of the outlet is high.

The required volume for the inlet and exhaust ducts ("up- and down-takes") of a gas turbine installation is quite large. Also the detailed flow design of bends and area changes requires careful engineering. In particular, the inlet duct is sensitive in this respect since the compressor cannot handle a distorted flow. Further, the selection of flow velocities in the inlet and exhaust ducts always is a compromise between small dimensions and low intake and exhaust losses.

A view of the up- and down-takes for a naval ship is given in Figure 8.35 An example of an installation of a fast ferry with waterjet propulsion is shown in Figure 8.37.

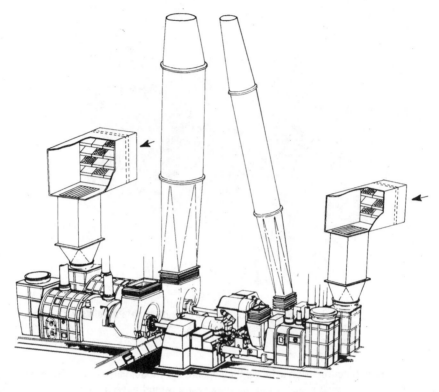

Figure 8.35   Up- and down-takes of a gas turbine driven frigate.

The air at the inlet of a gas turbine must be very clean. A gas turbine in particular is sensitive to salt ingress, because it will lead to fouling of the compressor blades and corrosion of the turbine blades. Normally, a three-stage filter system is installed in the superstructure or elsewhere in the ship. In the first stage of a so-called inertial filter, the air is forced to take a curved path. The water droplets cannot follow this and become attached to the wall where they are drained at the bottom. In the second stage, the remaining finer spray is forced to form greater droplets (coalescer). In the third stage, the droplets are removed. Since these filters operate at relatively low speeds they require a considerable cross sectional area to handle the large air flow of a gas turbine. Figure 8.36 gives a picture of a 3-stage air filter system.

The injected fuel must be free of water. To achieve this not only fuel centrifuges are used but normally filters and water separators are combined and put in series. Since fuel often is used as the hydraulic fluid in the gas turbine control system (inherited from its aeronautical past) the pressure at the inlet of the gas turbine sometimes has to be controlled within certain limits.

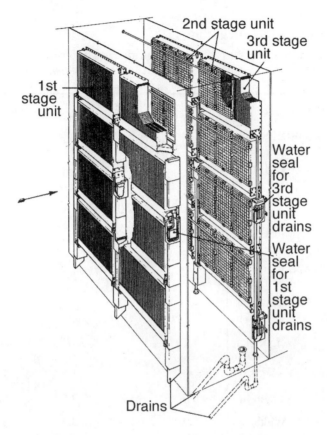

Figure 8.36   3-stage inlet air filter system for marine gas turbine.

Aero-derived gas turbines can only run on light distillate fuels:

- Light Diesel Fuel Oil, LDF (or sometimes LDO); ISO designation: DMA; density: 840 to 890 kg/m³; viscosity 1.5 to 5 cSt at 40°C. This fuel corresponds to NATO F 76.

Industrial or heavy-duty gas turbines sometimes are capable of burning somewhat heavier (and cheaper) grades of fuel, but they still need distillate fuels:

- Marine Diesel Oil, MDO; ISO designation DMB; density 860 to 900 kg/m³; viscosity 5 to 11 cSt at 40°C.

Some manufacturers claim that their gas turbines can handle Blended Marine Diesel Fuel, ISO designation DMC. These are distillate fuels blended with not more than 20% residual fuel.

8.8   Gas turbine technical data

The number of manufacturers for aero-derived marine gas turbines is limited: Rolls-Royce and General Electric. For an overview of some data see the following tables.

Rolls-Royce	*Allison 601 KF9*	*Allison 601 KF11*	*Spey SM1C*	*WR 21*
Brake power (no loss) [kW]	6500	7800	19500	25240 max rating
Output speed [rpm]			5500	3600
Spec. fuel cons. (no loss) [g/kWh]	≈ 250	≈ 250	230	200
Air mass flow [kg/s]			66	72
Specific power [kJ/kg]			295	350
Spec. Air Cons. [kg/kWh]			12.2	10.3
Weight [kg]			25700	46000
Specific mass [kg/kW]			1.4	1.8
Length [m]	≈ 5.0	≈ 5.0	7.5	8.0
Width [m]	≈ 1.9	≈ 1.9	2.3	2.7
Height [m]	≈ 2.5	≈ 2.5	3.1	4.8
Volume [m^3]	≈ 29	≈ 29	53.1	103.6
Specific volume [dm^3/kW]	≈ 4.5	≈ 4.5	2.7	4.1
Remarks	Allison engine	Allison engine		ICR

Table 8.2   Rolls-Royce aero-derived gas turbines for marine applications.

General Electric	*LM 500*	*LM 1600*	*LM 2500*	*LM 2500+*
Brake power (no loss) [kW]	4400	14900	24000	26000
Output speed [rpm]	7000	7000	3600	3600
Spec. fuel cons. (no loss) [g/kWh]	266	233	238	236
Air mass flow [kg/s]	16.3	47	68	78
Specific power [kJ/kg]	270	317	353	334
Spec. Air Cons. [kg/kWh]	13.3	11.4	10.2	10.8
Weight [kg]		15440	22000	
Specific mass [kg/kW]		1.04	0.92	
Length [m]		6.5	8.3	
Width [m]		2.3	2.7	
Height [m]		3.0	3.0	
Volume [m^3]		44.9	67.2	
Specific volume [dm^3/kW]		2.5	2.8	
Remarks			Workhorse of the USN	

Table 8.3   General Electric aero-derived gas turbines for marine applications.

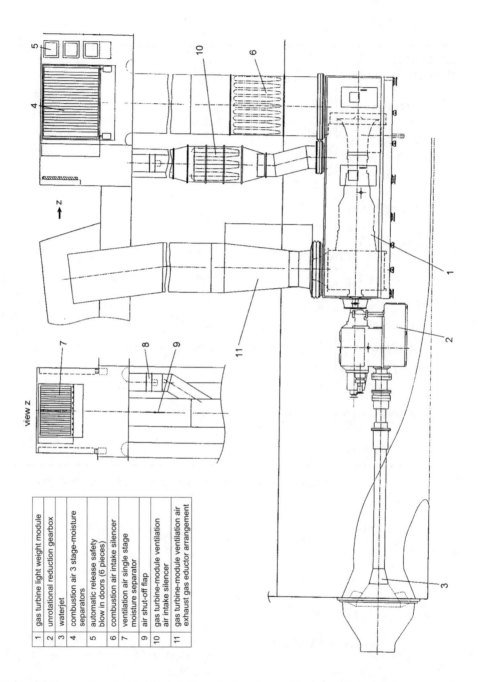

1	gas turbine light weight module
2	unrotational reduction gearbox
3	waterjet
4	combustion air 3 stage-moisture separators
5	automatic release safety blow in doors (6 pieces)
6	combustion air intake silencer
7	ventilation air single stage moisture separator
8	air shut-off flap
9	gas turbine-module ventilation air intake silencer
10	gas turbine-module ventilation air exhaust gas eductor arrangement

Figure 8.37   Gas turbine installation of a fast ferry with water jet propulsion.

8.9 Exercises

Exercise 1

A simple cycle gas turbine has a maximum turbine entry temperature of 1077 °C and a maximum pressure after the compressor of 20 bar. The ambient temperature and pressure are 27 °C and 1 bar respectively.

The gas constant of air is 0.287 kJ/kgK. The fuel is a light distillate diesel fuel with a lower heating value of 42700 kJ/kg.

One is interested in the order of magnitude of the specific fuel consumption in g/kWh and specific air consumption in kg/kWh. Also one wants to have an impression of the inlet duct size in case of an 18 MW gas turbine. Furthermore the question arises what these figures will be for a cycle with a maximum pressure of 10 bar instead of 20 bar. In order to arrive at a quick answer it is allowed to make use of the figures in this chapter.

Exercise 2

For a simple cycle gas turbine intended for a fast ship the following data are applicable:

- Ambient temperature   27°C
- Ambient pressure   1 bar
- Maximum turbine entry temperature   1077°C
- Maximum pressure in combustion chamber   5 bar
- Mass flow of air through engine   60 kg/s (neglect addition of fuel)
- Specific heat at constant pressure   1.0 kJ/kgK
                                                 (constant through engine)
- Lower heating value of fuel   42700 kJ/kg
- Isentropic index   1.4 (constant through engine)

The irreversible losses in the compressor and turbine are accounted for by the following assumptions for a polytropic index:

- $n_C = 1.5$ for compression
- $n_T = 1.333$ for expansion

Pressure losses in inlet and exhaust will be neglected.

Celsius versus absolute temperature: 0°C = 273 K

In order to improve the performance, two alternatives will be investigated on top of the base case:

- *Case II*: Increase maximum pressure to 16 bar while maintaining the simple cycle principle
- *Case III*: Addition of a recuperator with an effectiveness of 80% to the cycle while maintaining the low maximum pressure of 5 bar.

Base case I

A). Calculate the temperature after compression as well as the power required for compression. What is the polytropic efficiency of the compression process?

B). Calculate the temperature after expansion to ambient pressure as well as power delivered during expansion. What is the polytropic efficiency of the expansion process?

C). Calculate the amount of heat released in the combustion chamber that is required to attain the turbine entry temperature as specified. Also calculate the fuel mass flow.

D). What is the brake power of this gas turbine and what the efficiency? Also calculate specific fuel consumption.

E). For mechanical (geared) drive of a propeller or waterjet the expansion process of a marine gas turbine normally is split between a High Pressure turbine driving the compressor and a Low Pressure turbine driving the propeller or waterjet.
   What is the temperature between the two turbines? What is the power of the HP compressor turbine? What is the power of the LP power turbine? Is the latter the greater, the same or smaller than the brake power found under d. Explain!

Case II

F). Calculate the temperature after compression as well as the power required for compression.

G). Calculate the temperature after expansion to ambient pressure as well as power delivered during expansion.

H). Calculate the amount of heat released in the combustion chamber that is required to attain the turbine entry temperature as specified. Also calculate the fuel mass flow.

I). What is the brake power of this gas turbine and what the efficiency? Also calculate specific fuel consumption. Discuss the differences found when compared to the base case.

Case III

J). Have the temperature after compression en power required for compression changed relative to the base case under I?

K). Have the temperature after expansion in the turbine(s) and the power developed during expansion changed relative to the base case I?

L). Calculate the amount of heat released in the combustion chamber that is required to attain the turbine entry temperature as specified. Also calculate the fuel mass flow.

M). What is the brake power of this gas turbine and what the efficiency? Also calculate specific fuel consumption. Discuss the differences found when compared to the base case.

N). Does it make sense to apply a recuperator to case II (i.e. the cycle with pressure ratio 16)?

Solution Exercise 1

First calculate the maximum temperature ratio. Of course temperature must be in Kelvin:

$T_3 = 1077°C = 1077 + 273 = 1350$ K

$T_1 = 27°C = 27 + 273 = 300$ K

Then:

$$\tau = \frac{1350}{300} = 4.5$$

Also determine the maximum pressure ratio:

$p_3 = 20$ bar

$p_1 = 1$ bar

Then:

$$\pi = \frac{20}{1} = 20$$

Specific power can be read from Figure 8.8. The curves for the cycle with losses gives of course more realistic results then the ideal cycle. Read Figure 8.8 at $\pi = 20$ and interpolate between $\tau = 4$ en 5:

$\beta_m = 220$ *kJ/kg*

Specific air consumption is the inverse of this value. Moreover work in kJ and in kWh differ by a factor 3600:

$$sac = \frac{1}{220} \ kg/kJ = \frac{3600}{220} = 16.4 \ kg/kWh$$

For a 18000 kW gas turbine the mass flow would be :

$$\dot{m} = \frac{P}{\beta_m} = \frac{18000}{220} = 82 \ kg/s$$

Air density at ambient conditions is :

$$\rho = \frac{p}{R \cdot T} = \frac{1 \cdot 10^5}{0.287 \cdot 10^3 \cdot 300} = 1.16 \ kg/m^3$$

Then the volume flow is:

$$\dot{V} = \frac{\dot{m}}{\rho} = \frac{82}{1.16} = 71 \ m^3/s$$

An inlet duct area of 1 m^2 would imply an inlet duct velocity of 82 m/s, which of course is much too high and would result in unacceptable inlet losses. Depending on the chosen inlet duct velocity, which preferably would be in the order of 20 to 30 m/s, the inlet duct area is 2.4 to 3.5 m^2. At the inlet filters a much lower speed is necessary and their cross sectional area is very large.

Now the efficiency: read this from Figure 8.9 at $\pi = 20$ and again interpolate between $\tau = 4$ en 5. Again use the curves for the more realistic cycle with losses:

$\eta = 0.39$

This is still pretty high for a simple cycle gas turbine, but not all losses are included in Figure 8.9, in particular internal pressure losses are not taken into account as well as the intake and exhaust losses. The result for the specific fuel consumption therefore will be somewhat optimistic. To calculate the latter, consider that (lower) heat value is heat per kg fuel burnt.

$$42700 \ kJ/kg \ fuel = \frac{42700}{3600} = 11.86 \ kWh \ of \ heat/kg \ fuel \ burnt$$

After multiplication with efficiency one gets brake power per kg fuel burnt:

$$0.39 \cdot 11.86 = 4.62 \ kWh \ work/kg \ fuel \ burnt$$

The inverse of this is specific fuel consumption:

$$sfc = \frac{1}{4.62} = 0.216 \ kg/kWh = 216 \ g/kWh$$

Of course it is also possible to get an direct answer by using equation 7.33.

Now repeat the exercise for a maximum pressure of 10 bar.
The maximum temperature ratio remains $\tau = 4.5$, but the maximum pressure ratio becomes $\pi = 10$. Again, reading Figure 8.8:

$$\beta_m = 250 \ kJ/kg$$

and specific air consumption:

$$sac = \frac{1}{250} \ kg/kJ = \frac{3600}{250} = 14.4 \ kg/kWh$$

Air mass and volume flow for a 18000 kW gas turbine:

$$\dot{m} = \frac{P}{\beta_m} = \frac{18000}{250} = 72 \ kg/s$$

$$\dot{V} = \frac{\dot{m}}{\rho} = \frac{72}{1.16} = 62 \ m^3/s$$

These figures are 12 % lower than for the gas turbine with higher pressure ratio. Air intake (and exhaust) ducts as well as filters will be accordingly smaller.
Read again Figure 8.9 to obtain efficiency:

$$\eta = 0.35$$

This is lower than for the gas turbine with higher pressure ratio (but remember that it still is a somewhat optimistic figure)
Calculate specific fuel consumption with equation (7.33)

$$sfc = \frac{3600000}{\eta \cdot h^L} = \frac{3600000}{0.35 \cdot 42700} = 241 \ g/kWh$$

Although the figures are not quite precise (in particular for sfc) the observed trend is correct: the gas turbine with 20 bar maximum pressure is close to optimum efficiency but requires more air than the cycle with maximum pressure of 10 bar. The latter would need less volume for intake and exhaust ducts.

Solution Exercise 2

Base case I

A). Compression process

The inlet temperature is:

$$T_1 = 27 + 273 = 300 \ K$$

The end temperature after polytropic compression follows from:

$$\frac{T_2}{T_1} = \left(\frac{p_2}{p_1}\right)^{\frac{n_c - 1}{n_c}}$$

With the polytropic index for compression the exponent becomes:

$$\frac{n_c - 1}{n_c} = \frac{0.5}{1.5} = 0.333$$

Then:

$$T_2 = 300 \cdot \left(\frac{5}{1}\right)^{0.333} = 513 \ K = 240°C$$

Power required by compression is equal to increase of specific enthalpy (kJ/kg) times mass flow (kg/s):

$$P_C = \dot{m} \cdot \Delta h_{12} = \dot{m} \cdot c_p \cdot (T_2 - T_1) = 60 \cdot 1.0 \cdot (513 - 300) = 12780 \ kW$$

In the isentropic case the exponent would be:

$$\frac{\kappa - 1}{\kappa} = \frac{0.4}{1.4} = 0.286$$

The polytropic efficiency is the ratio between both exponents, i.e:

$$\eta_{p,C} = \frac{\kappa - 1}{\kappa} \cdot \frac{n_c}{n_c - 1} = \frac{0.286}{0.333} = 0.859$$

B). Expansion process

Maximum temperature after combustion chamber at the entry of the turbine is:

$$T_1 = 1077 + 273 = 1350 \ K$$

The end temperature after polytropic expansion follows from:

$$\frac{T_3}{T_4} = \left(\frac{p_3}{p_4}\right)^{\frac{n_T - 1}{n_T}}$$

With the polytropic index for expansion the exponent becomes:

$$\frac{n_T - 1}{n_T} = \frac{0.333}{1.333} = 0.25$$

The compression ratio over the turbine(s) is, neglecting pressure losses:

$$\frac{p_3}{p_4} = \frac{p_2}{p_1}$$

Then:

$$T_4 = 1350 \cdot \left(\frac{1}{5}\right)^{0.25} = 903 \ K = 630°C$$

Power delivered during expansion is equal to increase of specific enthalpy (kJ/kg) times mass flow (kg/s):

$$P_T = \dot{m} \cdot \Delta h_{34} = \dot{m} \cdot c_p \cdot (T_3 - T_4) = 60 \cdot 1.0 \cdot (1350 - 903) = 26820 \ kW$$

In the isentropic case the exponent would be the same as for the compression process (since specific heat is assumed to be constant through the engine):

$$\frac{\kappa - 1}{\kappa} = \frac{0.4}{1.4} = 0.286$$

The polytropic efficiency is the ratio between both exponents, i.e:

$$\eta_{p,T} = \frac{n_T - 1}{n_T} \cdot \frac{\kappa}{\kappa - 1} = \frac{0.25}{0.286} = 0.875$$

Note that the definition for the turbine needs to be reversed in comparison to the definition of the polytropic efficiency for the compressor in order to get a value <1 (as it should be for an efficiency).

C). Combustion process

The heat release during combustion must be sufficient for the enthalpy (and thus temperature) rise from compressor exit to turbine entry:

$$\dot{Q}_{in} = \dot{Q}_{23} = \dot{m} \cdot \Delta h_{23} = \dot{m} \cdot c_p \cdot (T_3 - T_2)$$

$$= 60 \cdot 1.0 \cdot (1350 - 513) = 50220 \ kW$$

With the lower heating value of the fuel the fuel consumption can be calculated:

$$\dot{m}_f = \frac{\dot{Q}_{in}}{h^L} = \frac{50220}{42700} = 1.176 \ kg/s = 4234 \ kg/hr$$

D). Performance

Brake power is net cycle power, i.e. the difference between power delivered by the turbine(s) and power required by the compressor:

$$P_B = P_T - P_C = 26820 - 12780 = 14040 \ kW$$

Efficiency is exactly this brake power divided by heat release flow in the combustion chamber as calculated under c:

$$\eta_e = \frac{P_B}{\dot{Q}_{in}} = \frac{14040}{50220} = 0.28$$

Specific fuel consumption is the fuel consumption calculated in C.) (in g/hr) divided by brake power (in kW):

$$sfc = \frac{\dot{m}_f}{P_B} = \frac{4234 \cdot 10^3}{14040} = 302 \ g/kWh$$

E). Power turbine

If the compressor is driven by its own (HP) turbine, the power of the latter is equal to mass flow times the enthalpy drop to the intermediate condition 'g'. It also must be equal to the power required by the compressor:

$$P_{CT} = \dot{m} \cdot \Delta h_{3g} = \dot{m} \cdot c_p \cdot \left(T_3 - T_g\right) = 60 \cdot 1.0 \cdot \left(1350 - T_g\right) = 12780 \ kW$$

From this equation the temperature between the turbine sections can be solved:

$$T_g = 1350 - \frac{12780}{60} = 1137 \ K = 864 \ C$$

This is the power turbine entry temperature (PTET) that normally is presented in the control and monitoring system. It is an indication of gas generator power.
Pressure after polytropic expansion in the HP turbine follows from:

$$\frac{p_3}{p_g} = \left(\frac{T_3}{T_g}\right)^{\frac{n_T}{n_T - 1}}$$

The (reversed) exponent for expansion now is:

$$\frac{n_T}{n_T - 1} = \frac{1.333}{0.333} = 4$$

Then:

$$p_g = p_3 \cdot \left(\frac{T_g}{T_3}\right)^{\frac{n_T}{n_T - 1}} = 5 \cdot \left(\frac{1137}{1350}\right)^4 = 2.51 \ bar$$

The temperature after the (LP) power turbine can be calculated from:

$$\frac{T_g}{T_4} = \left(\frac{p_g}{p_4}\right)^{\frac{n_T}{n_T - 1}}$$

With the exponent again:

$$\frac{n_T - 1}{n_T} = \frac{0.333}{1.333} = 0.25$$

The pressure ratio over the LP turbine is, when pressure losses are neglected:

$$\frac{p_g}{p_4} = \frac{2.51}{1} = 2.51$$

Then:

$$T_4 = 1137 \cdot \left(\frac{1}{2.51}\right)^{0.25} = 903 \ K = 630°C$$

Power delivered during expansion in the (LP) power turbine as always is equal to the decrease of specific enthalpy (kJ/kg) times mass flow (kg/s):

$$P_{PT} = \dot{m} \cdot \Delta h_{g4} = \dot{m} \cdot c_p \cdot (T_g - T_4)$$

$$= 60 \cdot 1.0 \cdot (1137 - 903) = 14040 \ kW$$

This of course is the brake power. Therefore both the exhaust temperature and brake power have not altered compared to case I: the split of the expansion process over two turbine sections does not alter the thermodynamic process, as long as the polytropic index over the complete expansion process remains the same.

Case II: maximum pressure 16 bar

F). Compression process

The begin temperature and the polytropic index are the same:

$$T_1 = 300 \ K$$

$$\frac{n_c - 1}{n_c} = 0.333$$

The temperature after the polytropic compression with the increased pressure ratio is:

$$T_2 = 300 \cdot \left(\frac{16}{1}\right)^{0.333} = 756 \ K = 483°C$$

Power required by compression is now:

$$P_C = \dot{m} \cdot \Delta h_{12} = \dot{m} \cdot c_p \cdot (T_2 - T_1)$$

$$= 60 \cdot 1.0 \cdot (756 - 300) = 27360 \ kW$$

This is considerably higher then for case I.

G). Expansion process

Maximum temperature at the turbine entry is kept the same as is the polytropic index during expansion:

$$T_3 = 1350 \ K$$

$$\frac{n_T - 1}{n_T} = 0.250$$

The temperature after polytropic expansion follows from:

$$T_4 = 1350 \cdot \left(\frac{1}{16}\right)^{0.25} = 675 \ K = 402°C$$

So the exhaust temperature is considerable lower than for case I. It may be expected that this is beneficial for efficiency (less heat lost in the exhaust)
Power delivered during expansion is now equal to:

$$P_T = \dot{m} \cdot \Delta h_{34} = \dot{m} \cdot c_p \cdot (T_3 - T_4) = 60 \cdot 1.0 \cdot (1350 - 675) = 40500 \ kW$$

As for compressor power this is significantly higher than for case I.

H). Combustion process

The heat release during combustion again must be sufficient for the enthalpy (and thus temperature) rise from compressor exit to turbine entry:

$$\dot{Q}_{in} = \dot{Q}_{23} = \dot{m} \cdot \Delta h_{23} = \dot{m} \cdot c_p \cdot (T_3 - T_2) = 60 \cdot 1.0 \cdot (1350 - 756) = 35640 \ kW$$

With the lower heating value of the fuel the fuel consumption can be calculated:

$$\dot{m}_f = \frac{\dot{Q}_{in}}{h^L} = \frac{35640}{42700} = 0.835 \ kg/s = 3005 \ kg/hr$$

This is considerable lower than for case I. Before jumping to conclusions with respect to specific fuel consumption, first calculate net brake power.

I). Performance

Brake power is net cycle power, i.e. the difference between power delivered by the turbine(s) and power required by the compressor:

$$P_B = P_T - P_C = 40500 - 27360 = 13140 \ kW$$

Efficiency is brake power divided by heat release flow:

$$\eta_e = \frac{P_B}{\dot{Q}_{in}} = \frac{13140}{35640} = 0.369$$

This is slightly less than for case I with pressure ratio 5. Probably the optimum power output is achieved for a pressure ratio somewhere between 5 and 16.

Specific fuel consumption is the fuel consumption calculated in h (in g/hr) divided by brake power (in kW):

$$sfc = \frac{\dot{m}_f}{P_B} = \frac{3005 \cdot 10^3}{13140} = 229 \ g/kWh$$

This is lower than for case I of course.

Case III: recuperated cycle

J). Compression process

The begin temperature and the polytropic index are the same:

$$T_1 = 300 \ K$$

$$\frac{n_c - 1}{n_c} = 0.333$$

Since pressure ratio is the same as for case I, the temperature after polytropic compression will also be the same:

$$T_2 = 300 \cdot \left(\frac{5}{1}\right)^{0.333} = 513 \ K = 240°C$$

Power required by compression is then also equal to case I:

$$P_C = \dot{m} \cdot \Delta h_{12} = \dot{m} \cdot c_p \cdot (T_2 - T_1)$$
$$= 60 \cdot 1.0 \cdot (513 - 300) = 12780 \ kW$$

K). Expansion process

Maximum temperature at the turbine entry is kept the same as is the polytropic index during expansion:

$$T_3 = 1350 \ K$$

$$\frac{n_T - 1}{n_T} = 0.250$$

Since pressure ratio is the same as for case I, the temperature after polytropic compression will also be the same:

$$T_4 = 1350 \cdot \left(\frac{1}{5}\right)^{0.25} = 903 \ K = 630°C$$

Power delivered during expansion then is also equal to case I:

$$P_T = \dot{m} \cdot \Delta h_{34} = \dot{m} \cdot c_p \cdot (T_3 - T_4)$$
$$= 60 \cdot 1.0 \cdot (1350 - 903) = 26820 \ kW$$

L). Combustion process

The air after the compressor has a temperature:

$$T_2 = 513 \ K = 240°C$$

In an ideal recuperator this would be heated up to the turbine exhaust temperature:

$$T_5 = T_4 = 903 \ K = 630°C$$

The recuperator however has an effectiveness of 80%. Then the temperature increase in practice will be lower:

$$T_5 = T_2 + \eta_{HE} \cdot (T_4 - T_2)$$
$$= 513 + 0.8 \cdot (903 - 513) = 825 \ K = 552°C$$

The heat release during combustion must be sufficient for the enthalpy (and thus temperature) rise from this temperature to turbine entry temperature:

$$\dot{Q}_{in} = \dot{Q}_{53} = \dot{m} \cdot \Delta h_{53} = \dot{m} \cdot c_p \cdot (T_3 - T_5)$$
$$= 60 \cdot 1.0 \cdot (1350 - 825) = 31500 \ kW$$

With the lower heating value of the fuel the fuel consumption can be calculated:

$$\dot{m}_f = \frac{\dot{Q}_{in}}{h^L} = \frac{31500}{42700} = 0.738 \ kg/s = 2656 \ kg/hr$$

This is lower than for case I and also lower than for case II.

M). Performance

Brake power is net cycle power, i.e. the difference between power delivered by the turbine(s) and power required by the compressor:

$$P_B = P_T - P_C = 26820 - 12780 = 14040 \ kW$$

i.e. the same as for the simple cycle of case I.

Efficiency is brake power divided by heat release flow as calculated under m:

$$\eta_e = \frac{P_B}{Q_{in}} = \frac{14040}{31500} = 0.446$$

This is much higher than for the simple cycle with low pressure ratio (case I) but also significantly better than the simple cycle with high pressure ratio (case II). This illustrates the enormous potential of the regenerative cycle, in particular for low pressure ratios.

Specific fuel consumption is the fuel consumption calculated in m (in g/hr) divided by brake power (in kW):

$$sfc = \frac{\dot{m}_f}{P_B} = \frac{2526 \cdot 10^3}{14040} = 189 \ g/kWh$$

This value is quite comparable to what the diesel engine can achieve. However the value as calculated is somewhat flattered since internal and external pressure losses were not taken into account and also because no allowance was made for the higher specific heat of the combustion gases.

N). Recuperator for case II?

The temperature at the compressor exit was (see F):

$$T_2 = 756 \ K = 483°C$$

while the temperature at the exit of the turbine is (see G):

$$T_4 = 675 \ K = 402°C$$

So, for the relatively high pressure ratio of case II, it is not possible to heat the air after the compressor with heat from the exhaust gases from the turbine since the latter have a lower temperature. This gas turbine simply is too good to benefit from recuperation.

8.10   References and further reading

Cohen, Rogers and Saravanamuttoo, 1996
   H. Cohen, G.F.C. Rogers and H.I.H. Saravanamuttoo: *"Gas Turbine Theory"*, Addison Wesley Longman Limited, 4th edition 1996

Gasparovic, 1970
   N. Gasparovic: *"On the theory of Brayton cycles"*, ASME paper 70-GT-130, 1970

Harrington, 1992
   R.L. Harrington, et al.: *"Marine Engineering"*, The society of Naval Architects and marine Engineers, 1992:
   Chapter IV *Gas turbines*, Dan A. Groghan
           - Section 1: Introduction
           - Section 2: Arrangement and structural details

Stapersma, 1999
   D. Stapersma: *"The potential of gas turbines with complex cycles"*, Advanced Marine Machinery Systems MARPOWER 99, Newcastle upon Tyne, March 1999

Wilson, 1984
   D. G. Wilson: "Design of High-Efficiency Turbomachinery and Gas Turbines", MIT Press, Cambridge, Massachusetts, 1984

For notes

For notes

Chapter 9

Electrical Components

9.0   Learning goals

After studying this chapter, the student should be able to:

-   *Describe the working principles and the drive characteristics of AC and DC electric motors.*

-   *Describe the possibilities to limit the starting current and speed control methods of electric motors.*

-   *Describe the working principle of AC generators.*

-   *Describe methods for frequency control, voltage control, power sharing and reactive current sharing.*

-   *Describe the methods of short circuit protection, selectivity and the functions of fuses and circuit breakers.*

-   *Describe the main characteristics of diodes, transistors and thyristors.*

-   *Describe the main characteristics and their fields of application of rectifiers, choppers, synchro-converters, pwm converters and cyclo-converters.*

9.1   Introduction

In this chapter the electrical components, introduced in section 6.5, are discussed in more detail. The description of electric motors and converters is mainly based on [Hughes, 1993]. Non electrical engineers who wish to understand the operational principles of electric motors and power electronic converters are advised to read this book. For a profound discussion of electric drives, reference is also made to [Mohan, 2001] and [Hamels, 1992, in Dutch].

9.2   Electric motors

Electric motors convert electrical energy to mechanical energy based on the Lorentz principle (see section 2.3.5): a force will act on a current-carrying conductor when placed in a magnetic field. In an electric motor, current-carrying conductors are located on the rotor. The rotor is placed in a magnetic field which is created on the stator; see Figure 9.1.

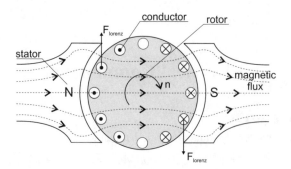

Figure 9.1   A rotor with current-carrying conductors in the magnetic field of a stator.

The magnetic flux is created on the *stator* by field windings and an iron package. So, in general, we can distinguish two sets of windings in an electric motor:

- field windings to create a magnetic field,
- armature windings to provide current-carrying conductors.

(Note that permanent magnet motors (motors without field windings) have their field magnet on the *rotor*.)

In a DC motor both the stator and the rotor are excited by direct current. In a synchronous AC motor, AC is fed to the armature on the stator and DC to the field winding, which is almost invariably placed on the rotor. In an induction motor, AC is supplied to the stator and by induction to the rotor. DC motors and AC motors will be discussed in more detail in this section. First, the basic theory on electric motors will be reviewed.

If the magnetic flux density is assumed perpendicular to the direction of the current in a conductor, the Lorentz force F_L on a conductor is:

$$F_L = B \cdot I \cdot l \qquad\qquad \text{ref (2.92)}$$

where,

   $B = $ *flux density of the magnetic field [T]*

   $I = $ *electric current in the conductor [A]*

   $l = $ *length of the conductor [m]*

As the conductors on opposite sides of the rotor carry currents in opposite directions all Lorentz forces contribute to the output torque *M* of the motor. In section 2.3.5, a general expression for output torque of a motor has been introduced. The output torque is proportional to the magnetic flux of the field magnet and to the current in the armature windings:

$$M = K_M \cdot \Phi \cdot I \qquad\qquad \text{(ref. 2.93) (9.1)}$$

where,

K_M = *constant for given motor*

Φ = *magnetic flux [Wb]*

I = *current in the conductors (rotor current) [A]*

As the rotor is rotating, the conductors are moving relative to the magnetic field. So, according to Faraday's law (section 2.3.5) a motional electromotive force (*EMF*) is generated, which counteracts the external voltage U applied to the conductors. As shown in section 2.3.2, the induced EMF is proportional to the magnetic flux Φ and the rotational speed of the rotor n:

$$E = K_E \cdot \Phi \cdot n \qquad \text{(ref. 2.96) (9.2)}$$

where,

K_E = *constant for given motor*

Φ = *magnetic flux [Wb]*

n = *speed [s^{-1}]*

Figure 9.2 shows a simple electric circuit for the rotor system. In this figure U is the voltage applied to the rotor, R represents the resistance of the rotor and E is the EMF induced in the rotor.

The resulting current is I. With the second law of Kirchhoff, a relation can be found for the voltages:

$$U = E + I \cdot R \qquad (9.3)$$

Consequently, the following expression holds for power:

$$P = U \cdot I = E \cdot I + I^2 \cdot R \qquad (9.4)$$

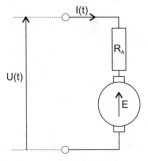

Figure 9.2   Equivalent circuit of the rotor of an electric motor.

In words, this energy conservation relation tells: input power $U \times I$ is equal to the sum of the mechanical output power $E \times I$ and the resistance losses $I^2 \times R$. The resistance losses are frequently called *copper losses*. They represent the heat which is generated in the windings on the rotor. Cooling of the windings is, in most cases, achieved by ventilation air. The allowed temperature rise in the windings is determined by the type of insulation of the conductors. To keep the temperature within limits, the current to the rotor should remain below its rated maximum current. Above this limit, overheating and burning of the insulation may occur.

The current I can be calculated with equation (9.3)

$$I = \frac{U - E}{R}$$ ref. (9.3)

As voltage U and electromotive force E are, for normal operation, of the same order of magnitude, the current I strongly depends on the induced EMF. As EMF is proportional to rotational speed n (refer to equation (9.2)) it can be concluded that a relatively small reduction of rotational speed, which will reduce the EMF, will result in a considerable increase of the current. And with equation 9.1 it then follows that a reduction of speed results in an increase of torque.

Although the above relations were derived for an electric motor, they also hold for a generator. If voltage U is greater than the induced EMF, the electrical machine acts as a motor and delivers mechanical power. On the other hand, if the induced EMF is greater than the voltage U, the direction of the current is reversed and the mechanical power becomes negative: the machine has to be driven. The electrical machine now generates electrical power UI and acts as a generator. Generators will be discussed in more detail in section 9.3.

9.2.1   DC motors

Figure 9.3 shows the principal layout of a DC motor. The main components are the stator and the armature or rotor. The stator houses the field magnet, which may be a permanent magnet but in the majority of machines is an electromagnet powered by field windings. Both the stator and the rotor are excited by a direct current. As explained in the previous section, the Lorentz forces acting on the armature windings generate the desired torque.

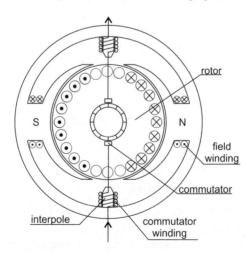

Figure 9.3   Principal layout of a DC motor.

The current to the rotor conductors is supplied through the commutator brushes. The commutator has to reverse the direction of the current such that current always flows as shown in Figure 9.3. The principle of these commutator brushes is shown for one winding in Figure 9.4. The current flows through the brush, through the rotor conductors, to the other brush. During half a revolution the current in a coil has to flow in one direction, while the other half revolution the current has to flow in opposite direction through the same coil.

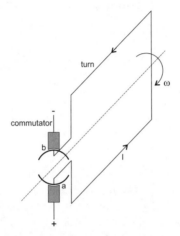

Figure 9.4   The working principle of commutator brushes.

The reversal of current is resisted by the self-induction of the rotor coils. This would lead to sparks when a brush leaves a commutator segment. To minimise sparking, interpoles are provided halfway between the main poles. These interpoles with their windings induce an EMF in the rotor coils in the direction in which the current has to flow the next half revolution.

Figure 9.5 shows the equivalent circuit of a DC motor consisting of a rotor and an externally excited field.

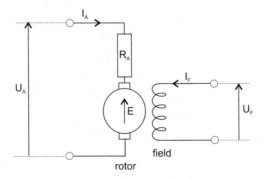

Figure 9.5   Equivalent circuit of a DC motor with separate excitation for armature and field windings.

The steady-state characteristics of a DC motor can be derived with the voltage, EMF and torque relationships:

$$U_A = E + I_A \cdot R_A \qquad\qquad \text{ref (9.3)}$$

$$E = K_E \cdot \Phi \cdot n \qquad\qquad \text{ref (9.2)}$$

$$M = K_M \cdot \Phi \cdot I_A \qquad\qquad \text{ref (9.1)}$$

For the motor speed the following relationship can be derived:

$$n = \frac{U}{K_E \cdot \Phi} - \frac{M \cdot R_A}{K_E \cdot K_M \cdot \Phi^2} \qquad\qquad (9.5)$$

This equation reveals that, if the motor is running without load, i.e. torque M is almost zero, the motor speed is proportional to voltage U:

$$n \approx \frac{U}{K_E \cdot \Phi} \qquad\qquad (9.6)$$

In practice, the influence of a load (torque M) proves to be rather small. If the magnetic flux is kept at its rated maximum value, this leads to a torque–speed diagram as shown in Figure 9.6. In this operational envelope, four lines are shown for different supply voltages at maximum flux.

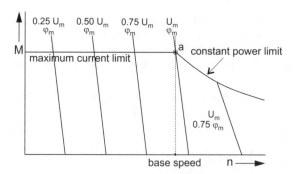

Figure 9.6   Torque–speed characteristic of a DC motor with externally excited field.

To prevent overheating of the rotor windings the armature current I_A has an upper limit. As torque is proportional to the armature current, refer to equation (9.1), the torque is limited to a maximum value. Point *a*, at maximum torque and maximum voltage, defines the maximum speed of the motor in the full magnetic flux area. This speed is called *base speed*. At speeds lower than base speed, the DC motor could be called a constant torque motor. In this region, the desired torque-speed relation is achieved by a proper choice of the armature voltage.

If it is required that the motor operates at a speed higher than base speed, this is only possible by reduction of the magnetic flux, known as *field weakening*. If the flux is reduced, the no-load speed is increased inversely proportional to the flux according to equation (9.6). At the same time, the output torque at maximum armature current is reduced proportional with the flux (equation 9.1). The result is a constant power limit above base speed, whereas there is a constant torque limit below base speed.

The operational envelope in terms of output power versus speed is shown in Figure 9.7.

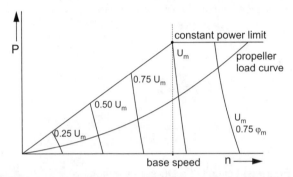

Figure 9.7   Power–speed characteristic of a DC motor with externally excited field.

The operational envelopes show that a DC motor is very suited to drive a propeller for ship propulsion. A propeller load curve is indicated in Figure 9.7. There is ample margin for acceleration.

The operating envelopes in Figure 9.6 and Figure 9.7 are valid for DC motors with separate excitation of the rotor and stator windings. With modern power electronics, speed control can be achieved by means of voltage control of the main armature and, for higher speeds, by means of field weakening. In the past however, without power electronics, it was customary to connect the armature windings and the field windings to the same (main) voltage supply. This resulted in two basic types of DC motor:

- A shunt motor with the field winding in parallel with the armature winding. See Figure 9.8.

- A series motor with the field winding in series with the armature winding. See Figure 9.9.

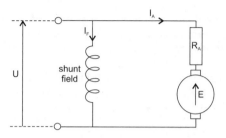

Figure 9.8   Equivalent circuit of a DC shunt motor.

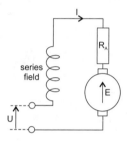

Figure 9.9   Equivalent circuit of a DC series motor.

The operational envelope of a shunt motor is the same as that of a motor with externally excited field windings. (See Figure 9.6 and Figure 9.7). Field weakening can be achieved by adjustable resistors in the field winding circuit.

The operational envelope of a series motor is different. In a series motor, the current through the field windings and armature windings is the same. For voltage, induced EMF and developed torque, the same relationships apply as for the shunt or externally excited motor:

$$U = E + I \cdot R_A \qquad \text{ref (9.3)}$$

$$E = K_E \cdot \Phi \cdot n \qquad \text{ref (9.2)}$$

$$M = K_M \cdot \Phi \cdot I \qquad \text{ref (9.1)}$$

For the flux can be written:

$$\Phi = K_F \cdot I \qquad (9.7)$$

Where K_F is a constant for a given motor. For the developed torque follows:

$$M = K_M \cdot K_F \cdot I^2$$

And after elimination of *I*:

$$M = \frac{K_M \cdot K_F \cdot U^2}{\left(R + K_E \cdot K_F \cdot n\right)^2} \qquad (9.8)$$

The torque–speed relation at constant voltage U is shown in Figure 9.10. The series DC motor is suited for traction purposes.

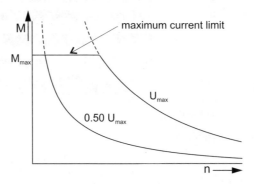

Figure 9.10   Torque–speed curves of a series DC motor at different exciter voltages.

A compound motor combines two field windings: one shunt winding and one series winding. They are connected in such a way that they amplify each other. The operational torque–speed relation is a mix of the characteristics of the shunt and of the series motor.

9.2.2   Induction motors (AC)

The induction motor is by far the most widely used type of electric motor because of its simple construction. As in almost every electric motor, it consists of a rotor, on which the current-carrying conductors are provided and a stator, which houses field windings. The field windings are powered by AC, thus creating a rotating magnetic field. The magnetic field will be treated in more detail later in this section.

In an induction motor, the rotor winding current is generated by *induction* due to relative speed of the rotor in the rotating magnetic field. Because the rotor is not powered externally, there is no need for slip-rings as for a DC motor. The induction motor is sometimes referred to as an asynchronous motor.

The induction motor exists in two main types:

- (squirrel) cage rotor motor.

- wound rotor motor.

The rotor of a squirrel cage motor consists of a number of conductor bars, which, at their ends, are short-circuited by end rings. The conductors are integrated within an iron package which is necessary for the magnetization. See Figure 9.11.

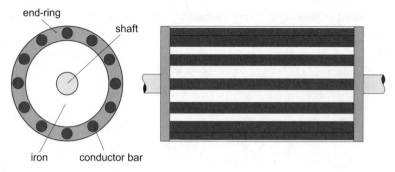

Figure 9.11   Sketch of cage rotor.

The rotor of a wound rotor motor has armature windings. They are three phase-windings connected in star. The ends of the three phases are brought out to slip-rings. Externally these windings are closed through adjustable resistors. The principle of a wound motor is shown Figure 9.12.

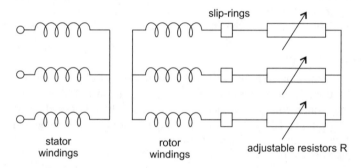

Figure 9.12   Equivalent circuit of a wound rotor asynchronous induction motor.

The rotating magnetic field

Consider a two-pole machine: one rotating magnetic field with one north pole and one south pole. The rotating magnetic field in the stator is created by three phase-windings a, b and c. The phase windings are connected to a three-phase AC supply. Assume that the three phases have equal amplitude and differ an angle of $120°$ with each other. The phase currents may be written as:

$$I_a(t) = I_F \cdot \cos \omega t$$

$$I_b(t) = I_F \cdot \cos\left(\omega t - \tfrac{2\pi}{3}\right)$$

$$I_c(t) = I_F \cdot \cos\left(\omega t - \tfrac{4\pi}{3}\right)$$

(9.9)

First it will be shown that the three phase-windings cause a total magnetic field that rotates with the frequency of the alternating current. Figure 9.13 shows the magnetic field in the stator as it changes in time. Figure 9.13-A shows the situation when $\omega t = 0$ and Figure 9.13-B when $\omega t = \frac{1}{3}\pi$.

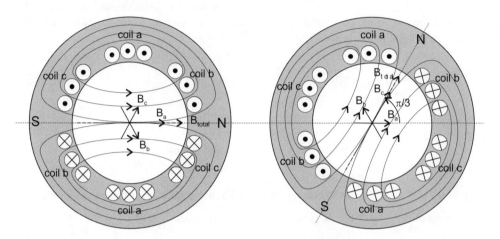

A) Magnetic field in stator at $\omega t = 0$ B) Magnetic field in stator at $\omega t = \pi/3$

Figure 9.13   The rotating magnetic field of a stator.

At $\omega t = 0$, the currents in the windings are:

$$I_a = I_F \quad and \quad I_b = -0.5I_F \quad and \quad I_c = -0.5I_F$$

Each winding will generate a magnetic field with a flux density B_n. The arrows in the centre of the stator indicate the direction and the relative magnitudes of the magnetic flux density:

$$B_a = B \quad and \quad B_b = -0.5B \quad and \quad B_c = -0.5B$$

The resultant magnetic flux density is the vector sum of B_a, B_b and B_c. With basic trigonometry, the relative magnitude of the total flux density can be determined as 1.5B. In Figure 9.13-A the magnetic field lines of the resulting magnetic field are indicated.

Figure 9.13-B shows the situation when $\omega t = \frac{1}{3}\pi$. The currents in the windings are:

$$I_a = 0.5I_F \quad and \quad I_b = 0.5I_F \quad and \quad I_c = -I_F$$

Consequently the relative magnitudes of the flux density are:

$$B_a = 0.5B \quad and \quad B_b = 0.5B \quad and \quad B_c = -B$$

The vectors that indicate the flux density are given in the figure. Again the vector sum gives the relative magnitude of the total flux density: 1.5B, and the direction: a rotation over an angle of $\frac{1}{3}\pi$ with respect to the situation in Figure 9.13-A. Also indicated is the resulting magnetic field.

From this explanation it is clear that the total magnetic flux Φ has a constant magnitude. The magnetic field has a close to sinusoidal radial distribution around the stator, as shown in Figure 9.14 for a two-pole stator. To achieve this sinusoidal flux pattern the phase windings should be distributed in the stator accordingly. The distribution of the phase windings is beyond the scope of this book.

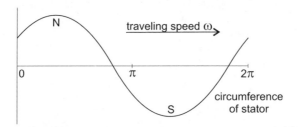

Figure 9.14   The sinusoidal flux pattern on the two-pole stator of an induction motor.

The speed of rotation of the magnetic field n_s is equal to the frequency of the AC:

$$n_s = f = \frac{\omega}{2\pi}$$

Note that, in this example, a stator with three phase-windings has been assumed that produce a rotating magnetic field with two poles: a north and a south pole. If two sets of phase-windings are distributed over the stator, i.e. three phase-windings over one half and the next three phase-windings over the second half of the stator, a magnetic field with four poles would be created (two north and two south poles). The speed of rotation of the complete four-pole magnetic field would be half the AC frequency.

In general, the rotation rate of the magnetic field can be expressed as:

$$n_s = \frac{2 \cdot f}{p} \tag{9.10}$$

where,

n_s = *synchronous (rotational) speed* [s^{-1}]

f = *the frequency of the AC supply [Hz]*

p = *number of poles*

So, the following synchronous speeds can be reached with 2, 4, 6, 8 or 10 poles respectively:

- 50 Hz supply: 3000, 1500, 1000, 750 and 600 rev/min
- 60 Hz supply: 3600, 1800, 1200, 900 and 720 rev/min

To determine the magnitude of the magnetic flux, the equivalent circuit of one stator winding will be considered. See Figure 9.15.

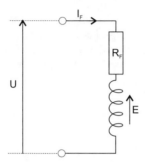

Figure 9.15   Equivalent circuit of a field winding of an AC induction motor.

The influence of the rotor is neglected. The applied voltage U causes a current I_F which generates the magnetic field. Due to the self-inductance of the winding an EMF is induced in each winding.

The induced EMF in an N-turn coil is equal to the rate of change of the flux:

$$E = -N \cdot \frac{d\Phi}{dt} \qquad \text{ref. (2.95)}$$

The rate of change of the magnetic flux, as felt by the coil (or a group of coils; a winding), is proportional to the total magnetic flux of the field and the frequency f. The EMF in the stator can be written as the product of a constant and two variables:

$$E = constant \cdot \Phi \cdot f \qquad (9.11)$$

The voltage relation for the stator winding as shown in Figure 9.15 is:

$$U = I_F \cdot R + E \qquad (9.12)$$

The winding's resistance is, in practice, very low. So, the voltage and the induced EMF are almost equal:

$$U \approx E$$

With equation (9.11), the following can be concluded:

$$\Phi = K_F \cdot \frac{U}{f} \qquad (9.13)$$

where,

K_F = *constant for a given motor*

This is a surprising conclusion. Fundamentally, the magnetic flux is proportional to current I_F, but in the case of stator phase-windings, it has been shown that the magnetic flux is proportional to the externally applied voltage U and inversely proportional to the frequency of that voltage.

The flux generated by the stator windings is, once it has been built up, of a constant magnitude. That means that the energy input to maintain this magnetic field is low. Only the resistance losses (copper losses) in the windings and the iron losses in the iron cores of the stator and rotor have to be supplied. As stated before, the resistance of the stator winding is low and inductance plays an important role. Consequently, the magnetising current I_F has a phase lag of almost $\pi/2$, see Figure 9.16. There is a substantial apparent power and also a substantial blind power, but almost no real power (because the power factor $\cos\varphi \approx 0$).

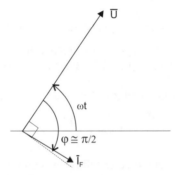

Figure 9.16   Vector diagram of the stator of the AC motor.

Torque generation

If the rotor has a speed relative to the magnetic field, an EMF will be induced in the rotor conductors. So, if both are running at synchronous speed, i.e. the speed of the rotor and the rotational speed of the magnetic field are the same, no induction takes place. On the other hand, if the rotor is stationary, the change of magnetic flux on the rotor conductors is maximally and large rotor currents will be induced.

The current induced in the rotor conductors and the generated torque strongly depend on the difference of the rotational speed of the magnetic field n_s, i.e. the synchronous speed, and the rotor speed n. The difference in speed is quantified with the slip s of an electric motor:

$$s = \frac{n_s - n}{n_s} \tag{9.14}$$

If the rotor is standing still, the slip is 1 and if it runs at the same speed as the magnetic field the slip is zero. When an induction motor is running at its rated load (torque) the slip normally is in the order of one to eight percent. The larger the motor, the smaller the nominal slip will be.

The induced EMF in the rotor conductor is proportional to the magnetic flux (which is constant but rotating) and the velocity of the conductors relative to the magnetic field. This means that the amplitude of the induced EMF is proportional to the slip s. The frequency of the rotor EMF is equal to the product of slip and synchronous motor speed, or, which is the same, the synchronous speed minus the rotor speed:

$$f_{R,EMF} = s \cdot n_s = n_s - n \tag{9.15}$$

The EMF in the different rotor bars will be of different magnitude, depending on the position of the rotor bar relative to the rotating (sinusoidal) flux pattern. The EMF in the rotor bars will cause a current which can flow from bar to bar through the end rings that connect the rotor bars.

At low slip (0-10%) the rotor inductive reactance (X_L) hardly plays a role, because the frequency of the rotor EMF is low (X_L="ωL"= $2\pi\ f_{R,EMF} \times L$; see section 2.3.4). In that case the rotor (or armature) current I_A almost only depends on the rotor resistance R_A. Consequently, the current in the rotor bars is in phase with the EMF, which is in phase with the flux pattern. As a result, the Lorentz forces that act on the rotor bars (BIl) are all working in the correct direction to contribute to the torque: under the north pole positive current, under the south pole negative current, thus resulting in forces in the same direction.

As shown, the flux pattern has a constant magnitude. Also, the induced rotor EMF and with that the induced current I_A are proportional to slip. For low slip of an electric motor, this results in a torque proportional to slip:

$$M = K \cdot s \tag{9.16}$$

At a slip value of zero, the torque is zero but with increasing slip torque rises sharply almost linearly. The characteristic is comparable to the characteristic of a DC motor. As the induction motor normally operates in the low slip region, the motor is suitable to drive loads which are more or less constant. See Figure 9.17.

At higher slip values, the rotor EMF frequency increases and rotor inductance starts to play a role. The rotor inductance has two effects. First, the rotor current I_A gets a phase lag with respect to EMF and to the flux pattern. Consequently, the rotor current no longer has its maximum value when the EMF in the rotor bar reaches its maximum value. Second, the current no longer increases proportionally.

For the developed torque this means that torque no longer increases linearly with slip but it falls. Due to the importance of the phase lag, there proves to be a maximum in the torque–speed relation. This peak torque is called the *pull-out* torque. Figure 9.18 shows a typical torque–speed curve for an induction motor.

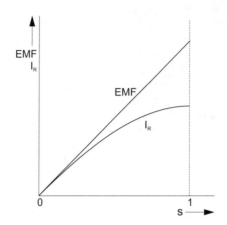

Figure 9.17   Rotor EMF and current as a function of slip.

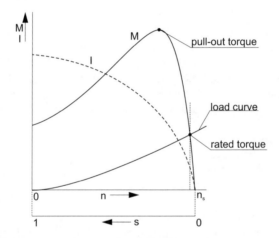

Figure 9.18   Torque –speed curve of an induction motor.

The diagram also shows a typical square load curve (as for instance of a propeller), with its rated nominal operational point. As said before, the motor operates at low slip. If the motor operates at higher slip, much higher currents are flowing which would result in rotor and stator overheating when operating continuously in those regions.

The figure also shows the current that is supplied to the stator. As the current on the rotor increases with increasing slip, the real power for this has to be delivered by a load component of the current to the stator. The current to the stator consists of two parts: a magnetising current I_F, necessary for maintaining the magnetic flux, and a load component. The magnetising current has a phase lag of almost $\pi/2$ and the load current has almost no phase lag. This leads to the vector diagrams as shown in Figure 9.19.

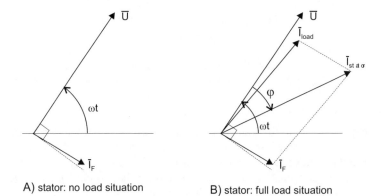

A) stator: no load situation   B) stator: full load situation

Figure 9.19   Vector diagrams of the stator for A) no load and B) full load situations.

In the situation of large slip, the current on both the rotor and the stator is further increasing. At zero speed there is a high current (a number of times higher than the full load current) again with a large phase lag relative to the voltage U.

Influence of rotor resistance

The *pull-out* torque is reached at a speed where rotor resistance is equal to rotor inductance. This means that the motor designer can influence the shape of the torque–speed curve. By increasing the resistance of the rotor, the induced current is reduced and consequently the torque rise is less sharp.

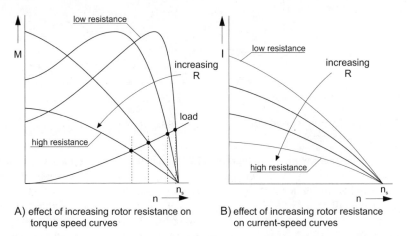

A) effect of increasing rotor resistance on   B) effect of increasing rotor resistance
   torque speed curves   on current-speed curves

Figure 9.20   Torque–speed curves for different rotor resistances.

In Figure 9.20-A four different torque–speed curves are shown for different rotor resistances. Figure 9.20-B shows the relation between current and motor speed and the effect of increasing resistance. With higher resistance, the rotor currents will be lower and consequently the stator currents are lower as well. This is the idea behind the wound rotor motor, see Figure 9.12. By increasing the external resistance in series with the rotor windings, it is possible to adapt the torque–speed curve to match a load. With this arrangement, limited speed control of an induction motor is possible. It should be noted however, that this type of control results in low motor efficiency at higher rotor resistance.

Influence of supply voltage

When the supply voltage to the induction motor is decreased and the supply frequency is maintained it will be clear, from equation (9.13), that the magnetic flux is reduced proportional to the voltage. Then also the induced EMF on the rotor and the rotor current will be reduced proportional to the supply voltage. The Lorentz forces and thus the generated torque are proportional to both flux and current. Consequently, torque is proportional to the square of the supply voltage.

This offers a second possibility for limited speed control of an induction motor. Figure 9.21 shows the torque–speed relation for a high resistance rotor with varying supply voltage.

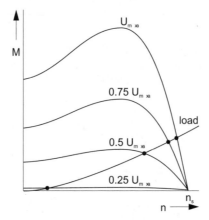

Figure 9.21   Torque–speed curves of a high- resistance rotor with varying supply voltage.

A load curve is also drawn in the diagram. The intersection with the torque–speed curves of the motor demonstrates the limited speed control by means of supply voltage.

When an induction motor operates at its rated output, a voltage reduction may occur unnoticed. This will result in a slight, most probably unnoticed, speed reduction, but also in an unwanted significant current increase which is necessary to maintain the required torque at a higher slip. This increased current might lead to overheating of the motor.

Starting induction motors; limiting the starting current

When an induction motor is started, the slip value is one and the current will initially be a number of times higher than the rated current at nominal load (Figure 9.18): I_{start} is 5 to 10 times I_{rated}. This means a temporary increase of the load of the generator(s) that supply the AC and their prime movers. A significant voltage and frequency dip may be the result.

Only if the started motor is of limited size in relation to the generator capacity (as a rule of thumb a rated motor power of less than 15-20% of the generator power), direct on-line starting may be acceptable. A number of measures can be taken to prevent unacceptable voltage and frequency dips, when starting large induction motors:

■ *Star–delta starting*

During normal operation, the stator field windings are connected in delta (Δ) to the supplied AC. In case of star–delta starting the field windings will initially be connected in star. The star connection will be maintained until the motor has almost reached its rated speed and then the connection of the field windings will be changed to delta.

During normal operation, with the field windings in delta, the voltage applied to one phase winding will be equal to the supply line voltage:

$$U_{P,\Delta} = U_L \qquad\qquad \text{ref. (2.86)}$$

During the starting time with the windings connected in star the voltage applied to one phase winding reduces with a factor √3 (See also section 2.3.4):

$$U_{P,star} = \frac{U_L}{\sqrt{3}} \qquad\qquad \text{ref. (2.85)}$$

This also results in a reduction of the phase winding current with a factor √3:

$$I_{P,star} = \frac{I_{P,\Delta}}{\sqrt{3}}$$

The line current in the rated situation and the starting situation are respectively:

$$I_{L,\Delta} = I_{P,\Delta} \cdot \sqrt{3}$$

$$I_{L,star} = I_{P,star}$$

The line current during starting (star) can now be expressed in the phase current during operation and next in the line current in operation (delta):

$$I_{L,star} = \frac{I_{P,\Delta}}{\sqrt{3}} = \frac{I_{L,\Delta}}{\sqrt{3}\cdot\sqrt{3}} = \frac{I_{L,\Delta}}{3}$$

So, with star–delta starting, the starting current can be reduced with a factor 3. It requires that all the stator phases are brought out and that two main switches are provided for control.

- *Use of a wound rotor motor*

  As shown Figure 9.20 the torque–speed characteristic and also the currents can be influenced by the rotor resistance. When during starting additional resistors are switched on, which are later left out the circuit, it is possible to reduce the starting current significantly.

- *Use of an auto-transformer starter*

  In this case a three-phase transformer is used to reduce the supply voltage during starting. During the starting process, the transformer is increasing its output voltage until the rated situation is almost achieved. Then the transformer is left out the circuit. With an auto-transformer, larger reductions in starting current may be achieved than with star–delta starting.

- *Soft starting*

  This method uses a power electronics converter with six thyristors: two thyristors per phase. Each thyristor supplies during part of half a cycle. This way the average supply voltage and current to the motor can be increased from zero to the rated value, giving a very smooth behaviour. The drawback of a soft starter is the distortion of the electrical net.

- *Use of a variable frequency inverter*

  Where a frequency inverter is used to control the speed of the motor, soft starting can be used at the same time.

Four quadrant characteristics of an induction motor

The motor may run with negative speed, i.e. a speed with an opposite direction to the rotating magnetic field. In that case the slip will be greater than one:

$$s = \frac{n_s - n}{n_s} \qquad \text{ref. (9.14)}$$

The motor still supplies a positive torque as shown in Figure 9.22 and operates in the second quadrant.

When the motor would run with a speed larger than synchronous speed, the slip and also the torque become negative. This means that the motor no longer operates as a *motor* but as a *generator*. Torque is supplied to the motor and electric power is generated and is fed back into the electrical mains. The motor now operates in the fourth quadrant.

Figure 9.22 also shows a typical load curve. It will be clear that the difference between supplied motor torque and the required load torque in every quadrant leads to an acceleration or deceleration in the direction of the stationary operational point.

The induction motor can only operate as a generator if the stator is connected to a three-phase AC supply. If that is not the case no magnetic field will be generated and consequently the rotor would be free to rotate without torque generation.

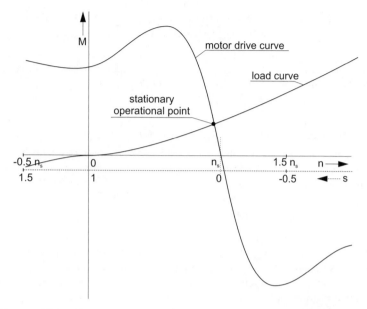

Figure 9.22   Torque–speed curve of an induction motor in four-quadrant plane.

Speed control

As long as an induction motor is supplied with a constant frequency the speed control possibilities are limited. The most flexible speed control is obtained by variation of the supply frequency. For an AC supply with constant frequency this requires a frequency converter. These power electronic devices will be treated in the next section.

With a constant-frequency supply to the motor limited speed control is possible in the following ways:

- *Pole-changing motors*

  As shown earlier the synchronous speed of an induction motor is depending on the number of poles:

$$n_s = \frac{2 \cdot f}{p} \qquad \text{ref. (9.10)}$$

If the stator is provided with two systems of field windings with different numbers of poles, the motor can run on two discrete speeds. For instance, a motor with one field winding system with four poles and a second system with six poles is capable to run at two different synchronous speeds. With a 60 Hz AC-supply the motor can run either at 1800 rpm or at 1200 rpm synchronous speed, depending on which field winding system is activated. So a speed ratio of 3 to 2 is achieved.

It is pretty easy to realize a speed ratio of 2 to 1 by pole changing. For example: a four-pole machine with 6 field windings could be made to operate as a two-pole machine by reversing the power supply to three of the field windings. The original pole pattern N-S-N-S would then become S-N-N-S, which is effectively a two-pole machine.

Pole-changing is only a good solution if the driven machine has two operational modes. An example is a motor driving a cooling water pump. The pump runs at full speed in case the cooling system is fully loaded and runs at 67% speed at low thermal load.

- *Rotor resistance variation of a wound rotor motor*

   Earlier the speed control capability of a wound rotor motor is shown by variation of the rotor resistance. This limited form of speed control results in low motor efficiencies at reduced speed. It is hardly used on board ships nowadays.

9.2.3   Synchronous motors (AC)

The main difference between the synchronous motor and the induction or asynchronous motor is the working principle of the rotor. In a synchronous motor, the rotor is excited by DC. The stator is the same as the stator in the induction motor: a number of field windings are provided, which are connected to a three-phase AC, so they create a rotating flux pattern with two or more poles.

The windings on the rotor are supplied with DC via slip-rings on the shaft. A magnet is created on the rotor with the same number of poles as produced by stator. Figure 9.23 shows the diagram of the stator and rotor. It is also possible to have a rotor with permanent magnets instead of DC-excited magnets.

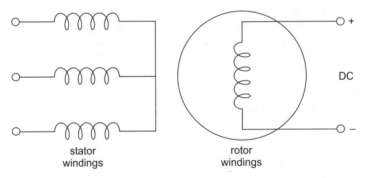

Figure 9.23   Layout of a synchronous motor.

The magnets on the rotor lock onto the rotating magnetic field produced by the stator windings. This way the rotor runs at synchronous speed, hence the name of the motor. The torque–speed characteristic of the synchronous motor is consequently a vertical line as shown in Figure 9.24.

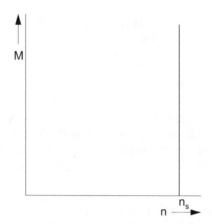

Figure 9.24   Torque–speed curve of a synchronous AC motor.

The pull-out torque, i.e. the maximum torque that the synchronous motor is able to produce is approximately 150% of the rated torque. In cases where higher torques are required, the synchronisation will be lost and no torque will be transferred at all because the produced torque will vary between positive and negative values and will be zero in average.

It will be clear that at zero torque the magnetic fields of the rotor and the stator are at exactly the same circumferential location: the N-pole on the stator is opposite to the S-pole of the rotor. If the torque increases, the rotor magnetic field will be lagging behind the stator magnetic field.

At pull-out torque, identical poles on stator and rotor are opposite. The phase lag between stator magnetic field and rotor magnetic field is called the *load-angle*. As the load of the synchronous motor increases, the load angle also increases, but eventually the rotor will run at synchronous speed again.

The power supplied to the rotor for the excitation of the rotor magnetic field is small. The mechanical output power is supplied to the motor via the stator windings. The synchronous machine can also be used as a generator: in that case it operates in the fourth quadrant. In fact almost all generators are synchronous machines as will be described in section 9.3.

Start-up

It is not possible to start a synchronous motor by applying an AC supply with constant frequency to the field windings. With a non-rotating rotor the rotating magnetic field of the stator will produce a varying torque between positive and negative values, with an average value of zero.

To start the synchronous motor an induction cage is provided on the rotor, so the motor is started as an induction motor. When synchronous speed is nearly reached, the rotor field windings are excited by DC. Consequently, the rotor speed will synchronise with the rotating magnetic field of the stator.

To reduce the starting currents, supply voltage control will be required in most cases. If the synchronous motor is supplied with a variable frequency supply, starting of the motor is possible through frequency control.

Influence of excitation current

An interesting aspect of synchronous motors is that, for the same torque, the excitation current to the rotor can be varied. A stronger magnet will be generated when a higher DC is supplied to the rotor windings, and consequently the load angle will be reduced. Also, the phase lag between the supply voltage to the stator and the stator current can be influenced. A high rotor excitation results in a low phase lag (a low power factor) on the stator side.

It is even possible to run a synchronous motor with a phase lead of current relative to voltage. This gives the opportunity to use a large synchronous motor to compensate for the phase lag introduced by the inductive loads in the net.

9.3   AC generators

A generator converts mechanical energy, delivered by a diesel engine, gas turbine or steam turbine into electrical energy. This conversion is based on the principle of Faraday, see Chapter 2: an induction voltage is generated in a conductor when it encounters a change of flux, i.e. when it is moving in a magnetic field or when it is in a moving magnetic field:

$$E = -B \cdot l \cdot v = -\frac{d\Phi}{dt} \qquad\qquad \text{ref. (2.94 \& 2.95)}$$

The total induced EMF in a generator is proportional to the flux and the speed of rotation:

$$E = K_G \cdot \Phi \cdot n \qquad\qquad \text{ref. (2.96)}$$

where K_G is a constant for a given generator that captures the construction of the generator.

In general terms, a generator requires:

- A winding or a group of coils in which the desired voltage is to be induced. This is the armature winding and the structure containing this winding is the armature.

- A magnetic field which for small motors may be produced by permanent magnets, but for the majority of machines the flux will be created by a separate winding: the field winding.

- Rotation, which causes continuous change in the amount of flux linking the armature coils. This can be achieved either by rotating the armature through a magnetic field or by rotating a magnetic field past an armature. In a DC generator the armature rotates. In AC generators, however, the field is rotating and the armature is stationary; so the field winding is on the rotor and the armature winding on the stator.

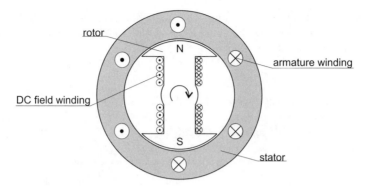

Figure 9.25   Diagram of a two-pole three-phase AC generator.

In most cases synchronous AC generators are used. As DC generators are hardly ever found onboard vessels they will not be discussed here. (If DC is required it will be obtained with an AC generator in combination with a rectifier.)

Figure 9.25 shows a two-pole three-phase generator (or a synchronous AC motor with DC-excited rotor windings). The armature windings of the generator are usually connected in star.

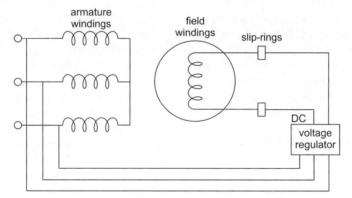

Figure 9.26   Equivalent circuit of a three phase AC-generator with slip-rings for field excitation.

In a synchronous AC generator, the field winding is excited by direct current. This can be achieved in two ways:

- The field current can be conducted to the winding through carbon brushes bearing on slip-rings. (see Figure 9.26)

- The field winding is connected to an excitation system which rotates with the main rotor. This system also consists of a field and an armature. The field winding of this system is on the stator and the direct current induces an alternating current in the armature on the rotor. (See Figure 9.27). On the rotor, the AC will be converted to DC and connected to the field winding. The main advantage of this solution is that no brushes and slip-rings are required to feed the rotor. This type of generator is therefore called a brushless generator.

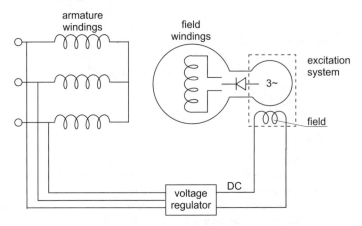

Figure 9.27   Equivalent circuit of a three-phase brushless AC-generator.

By turning the rotor at a constant speed the distribution of flux around the air gap is a sine wave. Therefore, the voltage induced in any armature coil varies sinusoidally with time. For each revolution of the rotor, the voltage passes through a complete range of values. It can be concluded that the frequency of the voltage in Hertz is the same as the mechanical speed of the rotor in revolutions per minute. In other words, the speeds are synchronised, hence synchronous generator.

It is now clear that a two-pole machine must revolve at 3600 rpm to produce a 60 Hz voltage. This may be achieved by a steam or gas turbine-driven generator. Many generators, however, have more than two poles so a prime mover with lower nominal speed, such as a diesel engine, can be used. The frequency of the voltage is:

$$f = \frac{p}{2} \cdot n \qquad (9.17)$$

(Which basically is the same relationship as equation (9.10))

If a synchronous AC generator is excited by a constant field current, the voltage–load characteristic would look like the curves in Figure 9.28.

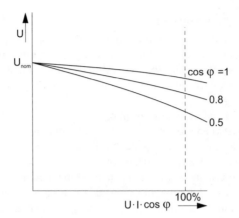

Figure 9.28   Nominal output voltage of a synchronous AC generator as a function of load; speed and field current are constant.

Voltage control

In order to maintain a constant output voltage for all load conditions between zero and full load rating of the generator, a voltage regulator is necessary. If no voltage control is applied, the output voltage of the generator decreases with increasing generator load, as shown in Figure 9.28. The purpose of the regulator is to maintain a constant output voltage in stationary conditions and also to keep voltage fluctuation within limits after load disturbances. Figure 9.29 shows the voltage fluctuation after a load has been switched on.

In a voltage regulator, a power electronic system controls the field current of the field winding on the rotor or the field winding of the excitation system. The voltage regulators have already been shown in Figure 9.26 and Figure 9.27.

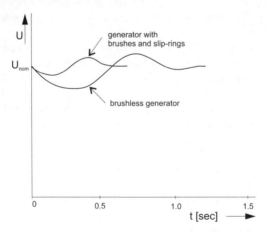

Figure 9.29   Effect of voltage regulation after a load disturbance for an AC generator with slip-rings and for a brushless AC generator.

Frequency control and power sharing

The output frequency of the generator is controlled by the speed of the driving prime mover. The speed governor of the driving engine controls engine speed, by regulating the engine fuel input. As engine speed and generator speed are identical or proportional, in case of a geared drive, it follows that the engine speed governor controls the AC frequency.

In case a number of generating sets are in parallel operation, it is desirable to share the (real or active) power between the sets evenly. The diesel engines (or gas turbines) should be equally loaded. This power sharing is done through set point control of the governors. In case the set point (desired engine speed) of one of the engines is increased, the fuel input will increase and consequently the load share of that engine will increase.

The voltage regulator of the generator controls the output voltage of the generator. In case of parallel operation of a number of generating sets, it is also desirable that the reactive power (or said in other words: the reactive current) is shared evenly. This reactive current sharing is done through set point control of the voltage regulators. In case the set point (desired generator voltage) of one of the generators is increased the reactive power share of that generator will increase.

Short circuit protection

When two or three phases come into direct contact (e.g. due to an accident or bad cable isolation) a short circuit is created. The currents will increase to very high values, resulting in heat dissipation much larger than acceptable for cables and machinery. To protect the power supply system against the damage, resulting from these high overcurrents, protection devices have to be included. During the design phase of the power supply system *short circuit calculations* have to be made. The short circuit currents are calculated as a function of time. The short circuit current is depending on the reactance (self-inductance) in the system and the remaining resistance between generator(s) and short circuit location. The generator stator reactance is the main characteristic determining the short circuit current.

In case of a short circuit it is necessary to isolate the short circuit from the power supply as quickly as possible. To prevent that the complete or large parts of the power supply system are lost, it is also of importance that the protection devices are *selective*. Selectivity means that only that part of the system is disconnected, where the overcurrent situation is caused. To give an example: If a short circuit arises in the cable between an electric motor and its control switch, only the supply to that motor should be switched off. The circuit breakers upstream, e.g. the switch connecting the main switchboard to the distribution panel (see Figures 3.4 and 3.5) and the switches connecting the generators to the main switchboard, may not be disconnected. Otherwise much more consumers would be disconnected from their power supply unnecessarily.

The protection devices to safeguard against short circuits and overloads are fuses and circuit breakers. Fuses are melting devices, as also used in electric systems in houses. Fuses are available from small (6 A) up to very large (thousands of Amperes). Circuit breakers exist in different sizes: small (up to 63 A), medium: *moulded case circuit breakers* (up to 1000 A) and large: *air circuit breakers* (up to 6300 A). Use of circuit breakers as protection has the advantage that the switch and protection device are integrated. In the medium and large size circuit breakers it is furthermore possible to adjust the protection characteristics, with regard to selectivity. The advantage of fuses is that these are relatively cheap devices and have well-defined short circuit characteristics. A disadvantage of fuses is that after operation they need to be replaced and spare fuses should be available.

It will be clear that the cable between the generator and its circuit breaker, which is located in the main switchboard, should be kept as short as possible and mechanically protected, because that cable cannot be protected against a short circuit. The only possible protection in such a case is stopping the generator.

9.4 Power electronics and converters

9.4.1 Power electronic components

Modern electric drive systems in which speed control of the electric motor is required use power supply converters. These converters adapt the voltage and frequency of the power supply to the electric motor as required for the desired motor speed. The basic components of the converters are diodes, transistors and thyristors.

Diodes

A diode is a component which allows a flow of current in one direction only; from anode to cathode. If a current tries to flow in the opposite direction, because the voltage on the output side is higher than the voltage on the input side, the diode will block as long as the voltage difference between the cathode and the anode remains below the breakdown voltage. The symbol of a diode is shown in Figure 9.30. A current is only possible in the indicated direction.

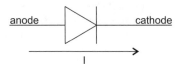

Figure 9.30   Symbol for a diode.

As the voltage drop over a diode is in the order of 1 to 2 volts, the power loss in diodes cannot be ignored. This means that effective cooling by means of natural or forced ventilation is required.

Diodes are used in uncontrolled rectifiers as will be discussed in section 9.4.2 Rectifiers (AC–DC).

Transistors

A transistor is a component with three connections: a collector, an emitter and a base connection. A transistor is a variable resistor: the resistance between collector and emitter can be controlled by a very small base-emitter current. The symbol of the transistor is shown in Figure 9.31.

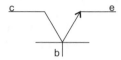

Figure 9.31   Symbol for a transistor.

A transistor can be used as a switch. It has a high resistance in the *off*-mode and it has a very low resistance in the *on*-mode. In other words, a transistor is *on* if it conducts a current: i.e, if the base current is sufficiently high. An important characteristic of a transistor is that it remains *on* as long as there is sufficient base current. It returns to the *off*-mode when the base-current is made zero.

The base current and the base-emitter voltage difference are small. This means that the control circuit of the transistor needs limited power compared to the transmitted power.

As the voltage drop over the transistor in the on-mode is in the order of 1 volt, some energy will always be dissipated in the transistor. Consequently, cooling by natural or forced air ventilation is required. If the switching rate is relatively high, there are switching losses to consider. The transition from off to on takes a few microseconds during which the current will increase and the resistance will decrease. At high switching rates, i.e. when the time it takes to switch the transistor on is comparable with the time it is on, the switching loss may become significant. For this reason the switching rate in electric drives is limited to approximately 20 kHz.

It is important to keep the current through a transistor below its safe maximum current, otherwise the transistor will be destroyed by overheating. Also it should be ensured that the voltage across the collector-emitter in the off-mode remains below the safe maximum voltage otherwise the transistor will break down and permanently be in the on-mode.

There are a number of different types of transistors, such as BJT, MOSFET, IGBT and IGCT. Each type has its individual characteristics with advantages and disadvantages. It lies outside the scope of this book to discuss these different types of transistor.

Transistors are used in choppers (see section 9.4.3) and inverters (see section 9.4.4).

Thyristors

A thyristor is a component with three connections: an anode, a cathode and a gate. As in a diode, the current can flow only from anode to cathode. A thyristor however will not conduct until a current pulse has been applied to the gate-cathode circuit. This is called firing of the thyristor. After the start of the gate pulse, the main current through anode and cathode builds up very quickly. After the current has reached a certain value, the thyristor will remain in the on-state, also after removal of the gate pulse. It is not possible to stop the on-state by an action on the gate. It is only possible to return to the off-state by means of reducing the anode current to zero and to remain zero during a turn-off time of some 100 microseconds. The symbol of a thyristor is shown in Figure 9.32.

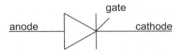

Figure 9.32   Symbol for a thyristor: a current will flow only from anode to cathode after a current pulse has been applied to the gate.

In the on-state, the voltage drop across the thyristor is very low (a single volt) over the complete range of currents. Nevertheless heat is dissipated in the thyristor and cooling, frequently forced with a fan, needs to be provided.

The voltage difference over the thyristor in the off-mode should, as for the transistor and the diode, remain below the safe voltage otherwise the device will break down. The current also should remain below the safe value. An overcurrent of a factor two during a few seconds might destroy the thyristor. To protect thyristors against high overcurrents they have to be safeguarded by fuses.

The thyristor basically does the same as a transistor: it conducts a current during the on-time. A thyristor, however, cannot be switched off, unless the anode-current is made zero. For applications in which there is no need to interrupt the current through the thyristor, it is not a disadvantage to be unable to do so. The advantages of the thyristor over the transistor are that thyristors are cheaper and suitable for higher power.

Thyristors can be used in controlled rectifiers (see section 9.4.2) and they can also be used as the switching device in drive systems for synchronous motors.

Gate turn-off (GTO) thyristors

The gate turn-off thyristor, like the ordinary thyristor, is a component with three connections: an anode, a cathode and a gate. The working principle of the GTO thyristor is the same as of a thyristor: it conducts current only from the anode to the cathode after a current pulse on the gate. Contrary to the thyristor, the GTO thyristor can return to the off-state by an action on the gate: a negative current pulse, i.e. a current flow from cathode to gate.

The GTO thyristor is indicated by the thyristor-symbol, which has two arrows to indicate the gate, as shown in Figure 9.33.

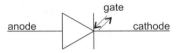

Figure 9.33   Symbol for a gate turn-off thyristor (GTO).

The voltage drop over a GTO thyristor is typically twice the voltage drop over an ordinary thyristor. GTO thyristors can be made to suit high voltages and currents.

Commutation

Commutation is the process of switching a thyristor from the on-state to the off-state. Transistors and GTO thyristors switch off by turning off the base current or by applying a negative current pulse on the gate. On the other hand, an ordinary thyristor in the on-state will not react to gate actions; it will only return to the off-mode when the anode-cathode current is reduced to zero.

This can be achieved in a natural way when the thyristor is connected to an active AC supply. In that case the thyristor current naturally reduces to zero. At that moment the thyristor is turned off. Due to the phase difference between voltage and current the moment of voltage reversal is not equal to the moment of current reversal. This means that commutation in an inductive system (a phase lag of current relative to voltage) takes place at the moment of current reversal. Such a commutation process is called *natural commutation*.

When the thyristor is connected to a passive load, such as an induction motor, there is no natural reversal of current. In this case, commutation of the thyristor requires a special electrical circuit. This method of commutation is called forced commutation. Such a forced commutating circuit is complex, bulky and expensive. In the past, the forced commutating circuits were the only suitable solution in the passive circuits of an induction motor. Nowadays, power transistors and GTO thyristors have made thyristors with forced commutation superfluous.

9.4.2   Rectifiers (AC–DC)

Rectifiers are used to convert single or three-phase alternating current to direct current.

Uncontrolled rectifiers

Uncontrolled rectifiers generate a DC with a fixed output voltage. The output voltage only depends on the supplied AC. In uncontrolled rectifiers, diodes are the active elements and a capacitor smoothes the output DC voltage. Figure 9.34 and Figure 9.35 show rectifier bridges for single- and three-phase AC, respectively. A rectifier bridge for a single-phase current needs four diodes, whereas the rectifier for a three-phase AC needs six diodes.

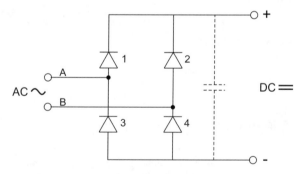

Figure 9.34   Rectifier bridges for single-phase AC.

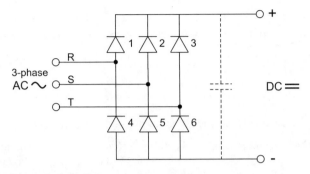

Figure 9.35   Rectifier bridges for three-phase AC.

If the input voltage is sinusoidal, the output voltage of the single-phase and the three-phase AC-supply are as in Figure 9.36 and Figure 9.37 respectively. These figures also show which diodes are conducting and which phases of the AC source are connected to the DC side.

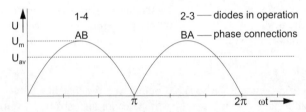

Figure 9.36   Output voltage wave of single-phase rectifier bridge.

For the single-phase rectifier, the diodes 1 and 4 conduct simultaneously during half a period, whereas the diodes 2 and 3 conduct during the other half period.

Per AC period two pulses are transmitted. It is therefore called a two-pulse system. The average output voltage of a single-phase uncontrolled rectifier is:

$$U_{av} = \frac{2}{\pi} \cdot U_m = \frac{2}{\pi} \cdot \sqrt{2} \cdot U_e \cong 0.9 \cdot U_e$$

where,

         U_m = *voltage amplitude of single phase supply*
         U_e = *effective voltage of single phase supply*

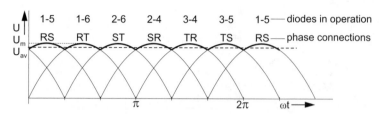

Figure 9.37   Output voltage wave of three-phase rectifier bridge.

For the three-phase rectifier bridge, six pulses are transmitted per period of AC. It is therefore called a six-pulse system. In Figure 9.37, the conducting diodes are shown as well as the connected phase legs (R, S, T). The average output voltage of a three-phase rectifier is:

$$U_{av} = \frac{3}{\pi} \cdot U_m = \frac{3}{\pi} \cdot \sqrt{2} \cdot U_e \cong 1.35 \cdot U_e$$

Note that the DC-output voltage is higher than the effective voltage of the three-phase supply. From the figures, it will be clear that the output voltage of a three-phase rectifier is much closer to the desired DC, than the output of a single-phase rectifier. Consequently, the capacitor to smooth the voltage in a six-pulse system may be smaller.

Controlled rectifiers

A controlled rectifier generates a variable output voltage that lies between zero and the maximum output voltage (i.e. the output voltage of an uncontrolled rectifier). Controlled rectifiers use ordinary thyristors as active elements. They have natural commutation. Controlled rectifiers can be used to control the speed of DC motors, but also as the DC-link in an AC–DC–AC converter (see sections 9.4.5 and 9.4.6) for speed control of AC motors. The controlled rectifier may be connected to a resistive load or an inductive load. Figure 9.38 shows the output voltage of a single-phase rectifier with resistive load with a firing angle α of the thyristor. The circuit diagram of the controlled rectifier is as the uncontrolled rectifier in Figure 9.34 provided the diodes are replaced by thyristors.

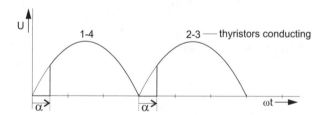

Figure 9.38   The output voltage waveform of a single-phase controlled rectifier with resistive load.

The thyristors 1 and 4 are fired simultaneously as well as thyristors 2 and 3. At the moment of firing, the thyristors start to conduct and they commutate naturally as the current reverses. Current reversal coincides with voltage reversal because there is only a resistive load. The output voltage of the rectifier bridge (connected to a resistive load) is:

$$U_{av} = \frac{1}{2} \cdot (1 + \cos\alpha) \cdot \frac{2}{\pi} \cdot \sqrt{2} \cdot U_e \cong 0.45 \cdot (1 + \cos\alpha) \cdot U_e$$

So, at a firing angle $\alpha=0$ the output voltage is the same as for the uncontrolled rectifier, at $\alpha=\pi/2$ the voltage is halved and at and $\alpha=\pi$ the output voltage is zero.

When the rectifier is connected to an inductive load, such as a DC motor, current reversal will not occur at the moment of voltage reversal. So, commutation will happen at a later moment than it would with a resistive load. The output voltage of the rectifier is depending on the magnitude of the resistance and inductance of the load. However, most motor circuits have such a high inductance that there is a continuous flow of current and current reversal will not happen. The result will be that once a pair of thyristors have been fired, they will not commutate due to current reversal. These thyristors will now commutate at the moment the other pair of thyristors are fired and another leg takes over the current supply. This is shown in Figure 9.39.

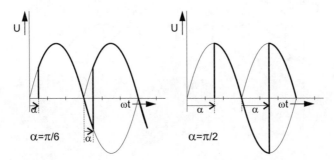

Figure 9.39   Output voltage waveform of a single-phase controlled rectifier with inductive load (continuous current condition).

The result is that also portions of negative voltage are connected to the output side. With a firing angle $\alpha=\pi/2$, half a period is transmitted of which half is a positive voltage and half is a negative voltage. The resulting output voltage is 0.

With firing angles greater than $\alpha=\pi/2$, it is even possible to have a negative output voltage. This can be used to run the motor in the fourth quadrant during deceleration (regenerative braking). The output voltage of the single-phase rectifier in this continuous current condition (with a significant inductive load) is:

$$U_{av} = \cos\alpha \cdot \frac{2}{\pi} \cdot \sqrt{2} \cdot U_e \cong 0.9 \cdot \cos\alpha \cdot U_e$$

The circuit diagram of a fully controlled three-phase rectifier is shown in Figure 9.40.

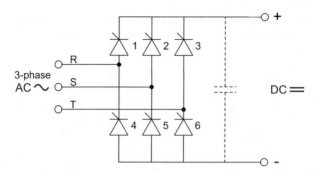

Figure 9.40   Circuit diagram of a three-phase, fully controlled rectifier.

The output voltage waveforms (for inductive loads with a continuous current condition) for $\alpha=\pi/6$ and $\alpha=\pi/3$ are shown in Figure 9.41 and Figure 9.42 respectively. The firing angle is measured from the moment that the phase voltages are equal.

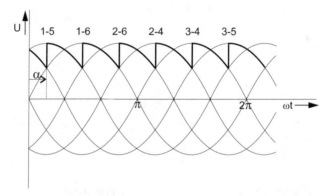

Figure 9.41   The output voltage of a three-phase, fully controlled rectifier for $\alpha=\pi/6$.

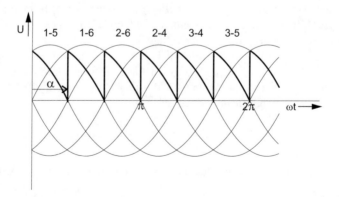

Figure 9.42   The output voltage of a three-phase, fully controlled rectifier for $\alpha=\pi/3$.

The output voltage is, due to the six pulses per period, much smoother than for a single-phase rectifier. The output voltage is:

$$U_{av} = \cos\alpha \cdot \frac{3}{\pi} \cdot \sqrt{2} \cdot U_e \cong 1.35 \cdot \cos\alpha \cdot U_e$$

If the output voltage is not smooth enough with a six-pulse system, a 12-pulse system rectifier may be used. In that case, the three-phase AC supply is converted to two three-phase AC supplies by means of a phase shifting transformer. The phase shifts in the second AC supply is 30°. Figure 9.43 shows the layout of a 12-pulse rectifier.

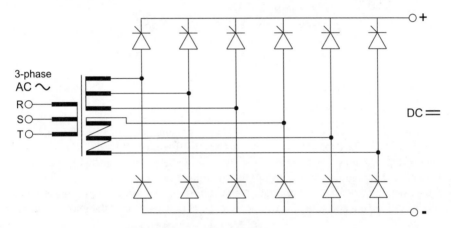

Figure 9.43   Layout of a 12-pulse rectifier bridge.

9.4.3   Choppers (DC–DC)

Choppers are used to provide a varying DC output voltage from a DC source with more or less constant voltage. They are used to control the speed of a DC motor for which a DC-supply is available. A diesel electric submarine is a good example. The electric power generated by the diesel generator sets is stored in large batteries. The propulsion of the submarine, but also other large consumers use DC motors which are fed from the main batteries of the submarine.

A chopper uses transistors (or GTO thyristors) as switching elements. Figure 9.44 shows the circuit of a chopper and the voltage and current output.

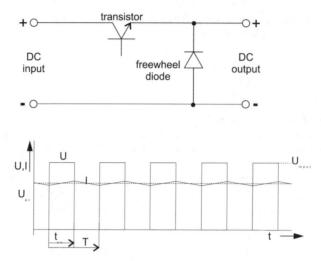

Figure 9.44   Circuit of a chopper and its voltage and current output.

The transistor switches on and off and supplies rectangular blocks of voltage to the output side. As the load of the chopper has an inductive character (the armature or field winding of the DC motor) the current does not follow the rectangular blocks but increases during the on-time and decreases during the off-time of the transistor.

If the switching rate is high enough, the variation of the current will be small and the DC motor will have a constant speed. The average output voltage of the chopper will be:

$$U_{av} = \frac{t_{on}}{T} \cdot U_{input}$$

where,

t_{on} = *the on-time of the transistor*

T = *total period*

To enable the current flow during the off-period of the transistor, a freewheel diode is necessary in the chopper circuit. It also prevents the transistor from breaking down. If the transistor would be turned off without a freewheel diode, the inductive load would try to keep the current flowing, which is impossible in such a case. It would result in a very high voltage difference over the transistor and break down of the transistor.

To control the output, two switching strategies can be used:

▪ Pulse width modulation (PWM) uses a constant switching frequency of the transistor but varies the on-time (the width of the pulse), so ton varies but T is constant.

▪ Pulse frequency modulation (PFM) uses a constant pulse width but varies the number of pulse in time, so ton is constant but T varies.

9.4.4 Inverters (DC–AC)

Inverters are used to generate AC with varying frequency and are fed with DC. As DC-AC conversion is the inverse process of rectifying, this type of converter is called *inverter*. Inverters are used to supply electric power to, and to control the speed of, both asynchronous induction motors and synchronous AC motors.

The most simple form of inverter supplies a rectangular block of voltage equal to the DC supply voltage. For one third of the period T a positive voltage block is transmitted and for one third of the period a negative voltage block. Between those blocks, two times one sixth of a cycle no voltage is transmitted. By variation of the period T, the frequency can be controlled. Figure 9.45 shows the situation at a low frequency and a higher frequency. It is clear that the transmitted voltage is far from the desired sine wave, but for the current the situation is better due to the inductance of the load. The output voltage for this type of inverter is fully depending on the voltage of the DC source.

In section 9.2.2, it has been shown that when a constant magnetic flux is desired in an AC motor, the applied voltage and the frequency should be proportional:

$$\Phi = K_F \cdot \frac{U}{f} \qquad\qquad \text{ref. (9.13)}$$

This leads to the conclusion that when the output frequency of the inverter is varied, the output voltage should also be varied in proportion. It will be clear that such a situation, for this simple type of inverter, is only possible by variation of the DC voltage supply. It requires a controlled rectifier to supply a DC with a varying output voltage as required.

With an inverter using PWM, as principally shown in Figure 9.46 it is possible to control the frequency and voltage of the output at the same time. This means that with a PWM-converter a simple uncontrolled rectifier (with diode bridges) suffices.

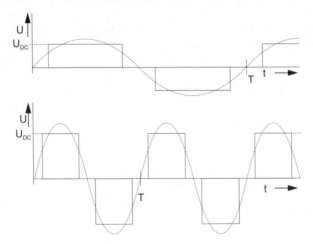

Figure 9.45   Inverter voltage blocks, as a very crude form of the desired fundamental sine wave.

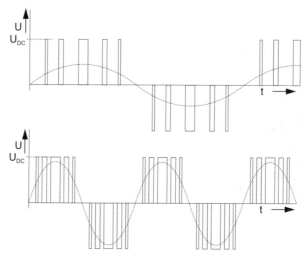

Figure 9.46   Inverter with Pulse Width Modulation (PWM) by proper variation of the
pulse width it is possible to control the output frequency and voltage.

9.4.5   *Synchro-converters (AC–DC–AC)*

In most drive systems, it is necessary to convert three-phase AC with constant frequency
and voltage to a three-phase AC with varying frequency and voltage. In most cases this is
achieved by rectifying the input AC to DC and subsequently by inverting DC to AC with
controlled variable frequency. These types of converter are said to have a DC link. In this
section the synchro-converter will be discussed and in the next the PWM converter.

The synchro-converter is used to power and to control the speed of synchronous AC
motors. It consists of a controlled rectifier (see section 9.4.2) and a simple type of
inverter. The inverter is built up with thyristors which have natural commutation; see
Figure 9.47. As synchro-converters use ordinary thyristors there is almost no power limit.

The power supplied by the rectifier to the DC link should be equal to the power
absorbed by the inverter. As there are small disturbances during switching, some energy
accumulation in the DC link should be possible. This is done by the inductors L in the DC
link. The inductors smooth the current. The link is therefore called a *current source DC
link* and the inverter a *current source inverter*.

The thyristors on the rectifier side are naturally commutated by the input AC. The
thyristors on the inverter side are also naturally commutated now by the synchronous AC
motor. This natural commutation is only possible when there is a phase advance of current
relative to voltage (a leading power factor). With a synchronous motor this can be
achieved by over-excitation. Consequently, a synchro-converter can only be used in
combination with a synchronous motor.

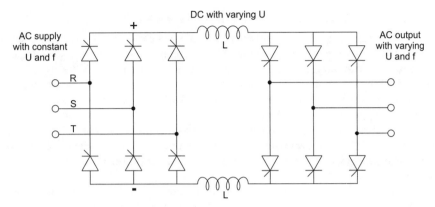

Figure 9.47   Synchro-converter consisting of a controlled rectifier a current source DC link and a thyristor inverter.

The switching-on actions of the thyristor are determined by shaft encoders. This ensures that the supply frequency of the inverter always matches with motor speed. The motor always runs in step with the supplied AC. This way, the synchronous motor behaves like a DC motor. A drive which consists of a synchro-converter and a synchronous motor is therefore sometimes called a *brushless* DC motor. This name is understandable if the diagram in Figure 9.48 is used. In a real DC motor, commutation takes place by a mechanical commutator which reverses the current through the rotor coils, whereas in the synchronous motor electronic commutation reverses the current in the stator coils.

The speed of the synchro-converter–synchronous motor combination is controlled by the voltage in the DC link. So, speed control is effected by voltage control of the rectifier. The combination has the major advantage that full four-quadrant operation is possible: the combination can run ahead (first quadrant) and backward (third quadrant) but also regenerative braking (second and fourth quadrant) is possible.

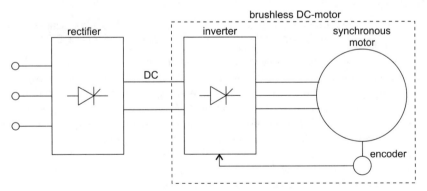

Figure 9.48   Synchro-converter plus synchronous motor, seen as a brushless DC motor.

9.4.6   *Pulse width modulation converters (AC-DC-AC)*

Pulse width modulation (PWM) converters are, like synchro-converters, inverters with a DC link. They also convert three-phase AC with constant frequency and voltage to a three-phase AC with varying frequency and voltage. PWM converters are used to power and to control the speed of asynchronous induction motors. They can also be used to drive synchronous motors but that is hardly ever done, because the synchro-converter is cheaper than a PWM converter.

The combination of a PWM converter and an asynchronous motor is becoming more popular because it uses a cheap simple electric motor. Also, due to the developments in power transistors and GTO thyristors, the possible output power of a PWM converter is increasing.

A PWM converter consists of an uncontrolled diode rectifier, a voltage source DC-link and a PWM inverter as shown in Figure 9.49. It needs transistors or GTO thyristors as the switching elements, because natural commutation is impossible. Both the switching to the on-state and to the off-state is achieved by control of the base current to the transistor or by positive and negative current pulses to the GTO gate.

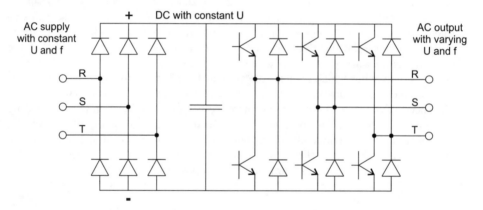

Figure 9.49   PWM converter consisting of an uncontrolled (diode) rectifier, a voltage source DC link and a PWM inverter (using transistors or GTO thyristors).

By PWM, rectangular voltage blocks are transmitted to the output side of the converter (as principally shown in Figure 9.46. This way both the output frequency and the output voltage are controlled. Because the current flows have to be continuous it is necessary to have freewheel diodes parallel to the transistors or GTO thyristors. These freewheel diodes also prevent breakdown of the thyristors. See also section 9.4.3 in which the need for freewheel diodes is explained for a chopper.

In a PWM converter a voltage source DC link is used. This means that some energy is accumulated in a capacitor, which smoothes the DC voltage. With a PWM converter it is possible to run in the first and third quadrant (forward and astern drive) but it cannot be used for regenerative braking in the second and fourth quadrant, because it is impossible to generate a negative voltage with the uncontrolled rectifier.

Present-day technology (power transistors and GTO thyristors) enables PWM converters up to powers of 10 MW.

9.4.7   Cyclo-converters (AC–AC)

Cyclo-converters convert AC with a constant frequency directly, i.e. without a DC link to AC with a controlled variable frequency. They can be used to power and control the speed of both synchronous and asynchronous induction motors.

The output frequency of a cyclo-converter can vary between 0 and 35 % of the frequency of the input AC. So, with an AC-supply frequency of 50 or 60 Hz, the maximum output frequency is of the order of 15 or 20 Hz. With high pole numbers (e.g. 20 poles) it then becomes possible to have large slow running motors (e.g. 120 rpm) which can be used to drive a propeller without a gearbox.

Cyclo-converters use ordinary thyristors which are naturally commutated. The output voltage of a cyclo-converter is constructed by switching the motor winding directly to one of the three phases of the supplied AC which comes closest to the desired voltage at that moment. For each of the three motor windings, two controlled converters (each having six thyristors) are used: one to supply positive current and one to supply negative current to the motor winding (controlled converters are in fact the same as controlled rectifiers). Figure 9.50 shows the arrangement of these two converters for one motor winding.

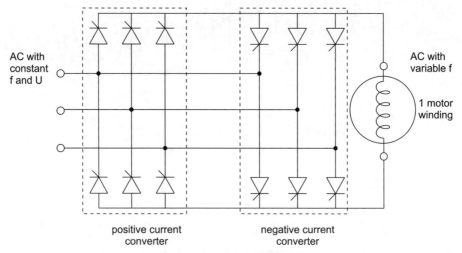

Figure 9.50   One section of a cyclo-converter for one motor winding (a complete cyclo-converter consists of 3*12 = 36 thyristors).

Figure 9.51 shows the three phase-voltage waveforms of the AC supply and the parts of the waves that are used to construct the voltage wave with a frequency of one third of the supply frequency. The figure also shows the current, which has a phase lag relative to voltage. In the figure is indicated when the positive current converter and when the negative current converter supplies. The converter acts partly as rectifier and partly as inverter.

In a cyclo-converter, the inputs and outputs of the three converter sections must be isolated, otherwise short circuit will occur. This can be achieved in two ways:

- Feed each motor winding through a cyclo-converter section (consisting of 12 thyristors) as shown in Figure 9.50. This means that the motor windings are not connected.

- Feed the two cyclo-converter sections separately, i.e. by independent AC supplies through a transformer, as shown in Figure 9.52, while connecting the motor windings, as is normal, in delta. The advantage of this arrangement is that the transformer can bring the supply voltage at the desired level independent of the voltage in the main circuit.

The cyclo-converter can be used for full four-quadrant operation and can be used for very high powers as the building blocks are ordinary thyristors.

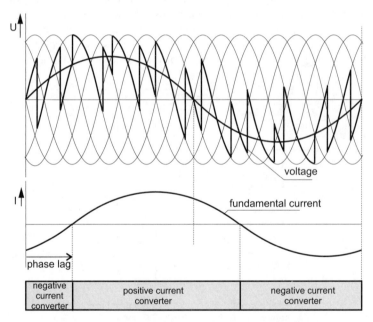

Figure 9.51   The three phase output voltage waveforms of the cyclo-converter.

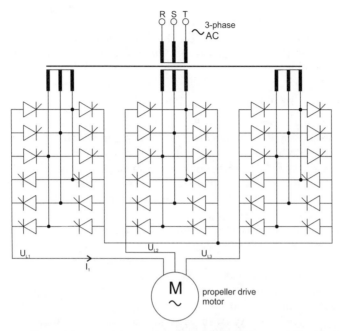

Figure 9.52   Motor drive supplying each motor winding with a 12-pulse cyclo-converter.

9.4.8   *Harmonic distortion*

In an AC-power supply system without power converter, the voltage and current wave forms are, in principle, pure harmonic with a frequency equal to the frequency of the supply (50 or 60 Hz). If a power electronic converter is included, the current is taken in non-harmonic blocks.

This will result in a current wave form with primarily the frequency of the supply and components of second, sixth or twelfth order (depending on whether the converter is of the 2, 6 or 12 pulse type respectively) and multiples of the higher orders. Due to the impedance of the supply system, the voltage wave form will also show these higher harmonics.

This harmonic distortion of the supply does not create problems for the drive of electric motors, but it does lead to some increase of the resistance losses (I^2R) due to the fluctuation of the currents. For sensitive equipment such as radio, radar and computer systems the harmonic distortion of the supply may be a problem. For this reason requirements for the maximum allowable harmonic distortion has to be regarded.

To reduce harmonic distortion the following measures can be taken:

- limitation of converter power relative to the total generator power.

- limitation of impedance in the supply net. It has to be recognised however, that low impedance may result in high short circuit currents.

- use of 12 pulse systems in stead of 2 or 6 pulse systems.

- application of harmonic filters.
- sometimes the supply system for the electronic drives will be separated from the supply for other systems. This can be achieved by the use of rotating converters (motor-generator units).

9.5 Examples of electric propulsion drives

This section gives an overview of some electric drives for ship propulsion. It is assumed that the electric power is supplied by three-phase AC-generators with constant output voltage and frequency. Even for DC power systems, rectifier systems using diodes or thyristors have made DC generators with their high-maintenance commutator brushes obsolete.

In this section, a constant-speed drive and a simple variable-speed drive will be introduced. In sections 9.5.1 and 9.5.2 the more common variable-speed DC and AC drives with power electronics will be discussed.

A constant-speed electric-propulsion drive is not frequently applied. It may for example be used to drive a steerable thruster. A constant-speed drive uses an asynchronous induction motor. The motor may have pole-changing capacity in order to provide two fixed speeds. The motor is fed with a constant frequency AC and has direct on-line starting. Ship speed control is ensured by pitch control of a CP propeller.

A very simple variable-speed drive is possible in combination with variable-speed generators, which supply an AC with variable frequency and voltage. The propulsion motor speed is then directly proportional to generator speed. The ship speed is controlled by controlling the prime mover speed.

This drive is sometimes referred to as an *electric shaft*. It has only a few of the advantages of the electrical concepts as described in the previous chapter (see section 5.3) and is seldom used. It may, however, be an interesting option if a mechanical transmission (gears and shafts) between prime mover (diesel engine or gas turbine) and propeller becomes too complicated, for instance due to a large distance between the components.

The more frequently used variable-speed electric-propulsion drives include power electronics. They will be described next.

9.5.1   DC-motor drive

Figure 9.53 shows a DC-motor drive which is suitable for ship propulsion. It includes a controlled rectifier connected to the armature and two back-to-back rectifiers connected to the field.

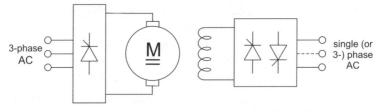

Figure 9.53   Variable speed DC-motor drive with a controlled rectifier for the
                   armature current and two back-to-back rectifiers for the field current.

The controlled rectifier supplies the armature with a variable DC voltage. This ensures good speed control up to base speed. It also enables regenerative braking because although the rectifier can only transmit current in one direction, it can transmit a negative voltage (see section 9.4.2).

The two back-to-back rectifiers supply positive and negative DC current to the field winding. The reversal of the field current enables motor reversal. By means of field weakening it is possible to run the motor above base speed.

This drive is very flexible: it is suitable for full four-quadrant operation and it has excellent transient capabilities. Nevertheless, DC–drives of this type are seldom used nowadays. An important disadvantage of the DC-drive is that because of the commutation brushes a DC-motor requires more maintenance than an AC motor. And although, modern AC drives may have less flexibility in operation, they are sufficiently suited for ship propulsion in which transients are not that important: motor reversal is not required in 2 to 3 seconds, but may take 10-15 seconds as can be achieved with a modern AC-drive.

However, application of a DC-drive may still be attractive on warships for which the low vibration level of the DC-motor is beneficial for the low underwater signature.

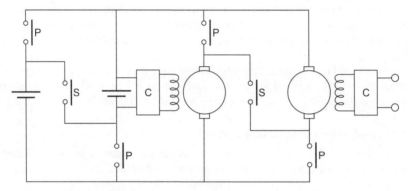

Figure 9.54   DC-propulsion drive of a submarine: 2 batteries and 2 motors may be connected in series and parallel.

As an example a brief description will be given of a DC propulsion system of a submarine, in which besides DC-motors, a DC power supply system is available due to the battery systems. In the example, it is assumed that the drive system consists of two main batteries connected to two DC motors which drive one propeller. Both the battery systems and the DC motors may be connected in series or in parallel. Figure 9.54 shows the layout of the system.

To get a variable supply voltage, choppers (see section 9.4.3) could be used for the armature and the field windings. However, as it is of utmost importance to minimise vibrations and noise, no choppers are used in the armature circuit, where large currents would have to be chopped. Choppers are used only for the field supplies in which much smaller currents are chopped.

Three different output speeds can be achieved by switching the batteries and the DC-motors, because the voltage supplied to the motor armatures is then varied in fixed steps that are in the proportion of 1 to 2 to 4:

- The batteries are in parallel by using the P-switches and the motor armatures are connected in series by using the S-switch: each armature is connected to half the battery voltage.

- The batteries and motors are in parallel, or both are in series: each armature is connected to the battery voltage.

- The batteries are in series and the armatures parallel: each armature is connected to twice the battery voltage.

Depending on the battery charging state, the motors can now run on three different base speeds. Further control is achieved by field weakening with the field choppers, as indicated in Figure 9.54. The choppers can supply both negative and positive currents to the field windings so motor reversal becomes possible. Regenerative braking is also possible.

To prevent too large starting currents, resistors are provided in the armature circuits: current passes through them during start up and will be switched off when the motor has almost reached the desired speed. The starting resistors are not shown Figure 9.54.

9.5.2   Variable-speed AC-motor drive

Most variable speed drives of AC motors use power electronics converters, because for most applications, an electric shaft solution, as described in the introduction of this section is not attractive.

For high-power, slow-running propulsion drives, the synchronous motor is most widely used. The motor then drives a FP propeller without a geared transmission. The synchronous motor can be fed through a synchro-converter (see section 9.4.5) or a cyclo-converter (see section 9.4.7). As both types of converter use ordinary thyristors, there is almost no power limit. The maximum (variable) frequency delivered at the machine side of the converter is for a synchro-converter 100 Hz, and for a cyclo-converter in the order of 20 Hz. Both types of converter enable full four-quadrant operation.

Motor reversal from full ahead to astern is achieved as follows. The power to the motor is reduced to zero in a synchro-converter by reducing the voltage in the DC-link. The propeller speed will fall almost immediately to approximately 60 % of full-power speed. The propeller will now act as a water turbine and is driven by the water that flows through the propeller disc. The ship speed is still close to the original speed. This situation might continue for a long period of time, unless a negative torque is applied to the propeller. This means that the motor has to operate as a generator in the fourth quadrant.

The motor will operate as a generator if the voltage in the DC link is reduced below the motor EMF by the controlled rectifier at the supply side. During the end phase of the braking process the controlled rectifier will even transmit negative voltages. The direction of the power flow through the synchro-converter will reverse: power will now flow from machine to supply instead of from supply to machine. Consequently, the machine-side converter (in normal operation an inverter) will operate as a rectifier and the supply-side converter (in normal operation a controlled rectifier) operates as an inverter. When the motor reaches zero speed, the switching sequence of the thyristors in the machine-side converter is changed, so that ultimately the direction of rotation of the motor will reverse. The supply side rectifier resumes the normal rectifying process and again supplies a positive voltage to the DC-link. The motor now operates as a motor in reverse direction in the third quadrant.

When a drive includes power electronic devices, pulses are transmitted to the motor. Consequently, not only harmonic distortion has to be regarded, but also torque pulsation. The torque pulsation needs to be evaluated with a thorough torsional vibration analysis. To reduce the torque pulsation (and the harmonic distortion), it is common to apply a 12-pulse synchro-converter arrangement. This requires six phase-windings in the motor, each set of three phase-windings being supplied by two six-pulse converters with a phase difference of 30 degrees. See Figure 9.55.

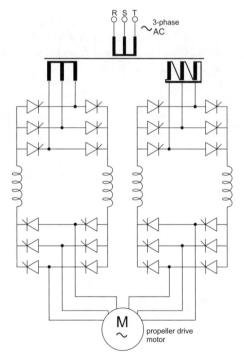

Figure 9.55   AC propulsion drive with 12-pulse synchro-converter and synchronous motor.

For lower power, high-speed propulsion drives, a PWM converter (see section 9.4.6) with an asynchronous induction motor becomes more and more attractive. The induction motor is of a simple construction and is small. It drives the propeller indirectly through a gearbox transmission. The power limit of a PWM converter with GTO thyristors as switching elements in the machine side inverter is approximately 10 MW.

Because the PWM converter uses an uncontrolled diode bridge rectifier, it supplies a constant DC-link voltage and it cannot operate in the second and fourth quadrant, i.e. regenerative braking is impossible.

Motor reversal will take place in the same manner as described earlier for the synchronous motor with synchro-converter drive, but the braking cannot be achieved by power reversal back to the supply side. During braking, the reverse energy supplied by the motor to the converter has to be absorbed by resistors in the DC link. The braking energy is converted to heat. Third quadrant operation can be achieved by changing the switching sequence of thyristors in the machine side converter.

9.6   References and further reading

Borman and Sharman, 1996

>   J. B. Borman and B. P. Sharman: *"Electric propulsion –A view from a classification society"*, 1st International Conference on Diesel Electric Propulsion, Norwegian Society of Chartered Engineers and The Royal Institution of Naval Architects, Norway 1996.

Hamels, 1991 –in Dutch

>   ir. D. Hamels: *"Elektrische Aandrijftechniek"*, Stenfert Koese Uitgevers, Leiden/ Antwerpen 1991.

Hughes, 1993

>   A. Hughes: *"Electric motors and drives"*, Second edition, Newness, Great Britain 1993 (reprinted 2001).

Mohan, 2000

>   N. Mohan: *"Electric Drives –An integrative approach"*, MNPERE, USA 2000.

Nordgård, 1996

>   D. E. Nordgård: *"Diesel Electric Propulsion –Definition of Electroctechnical terms"*, 1st International Conference on Diesel Electric Propulsion, Norwegian Society of Chartered Engineers and The Royal Institution of Naval Architects, Norway 1996

Chapter 10

Propellers

10.0 Learning goals

After studying this chapter, the student should be able to:

- *Describe and use the non-dimensional propeller parameters: thrust coefficient, torque coefficient and advance ratio,*

- *Describe and sketch open water propeller diagrams for FP propeller and CP propeller: K_T, K_Q and J*

- *Describe and use four-quadrant open water propeller diagram, C_T^*, C_Q^* and β*

- *Determine optimal propeller speed or propeller diameter for given ship.*

10.1 Introduction

Although the propeller of the ship is often regarded as the naval architect's concern, its main characteristics are important to the marine engineer: the propeller has to fulfil its task within the propulsion system in a satisfactory manner.

In this chapter, the working principles of the screw type propeller are discussed. Some basic knowledge of resistance and propulsion is assumed. The propeller performance parameters, the advance ratio, the thrust coefficient and the torque coefficient, are introduced, as well as the common methods to visualise them: the open water and the four quadrant diagrams. These diagrams will prove to be useful for the design of a propeller for a given ship and the matching of the propeller with a prime mover.

10.2 Working principle

The advance velocity v_A together with the propeller circumferential speed $2\pi r n_p$ form a resultant velocity v_R that meets the propeller at a certain angle of attack: see Figure 10.1. The angle of attack α is the difference between the pitch angle θ of the propeller blade and the resultant flow angle β, which is called the hydrodynamic pitch angle.

As a result of the oblique flow to the propeller, a circulation is created around the propeller blade causing hydrodynamic forces on the blade: a lift force L acting perpendicular to the direction of the resultant velocity and a drag force D opposing the motion of the blade and acting along the line of the resultant velocity. The resulting force can be resolved into an axial and a tangential direction; the first contributing to the thrust T on the blade, and the latter to the torque Q.

The speeds shown in Figure 10.1 are *water* speeds, so they are drawn as if the blade is stationary. Note that in order to simplify, the induced velocities resulting from the circulation around the propeller blade are not shown, so the velocities as drawn actually occur at some distance of the blade.

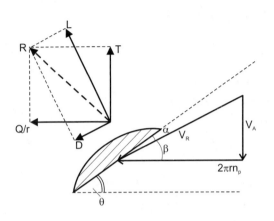

α   angle of attack
β   hydrodynamic pitch angle
θ   pitch angle
r   propeller radius

Speeds shown are the water speeds as experienced by a cross section of the blade as it rotates at speed n_p:
$2\pi r n_p$ circumferential speed
v_A velocity of advance
v_R relative water velocity

Forces on the blade:
D   drag force
L   lift force
R   resultant force of drag and lift
Q   torque
T   thrust

Figure 10.1   Propeller flow velocities and forces on the blade.

Figure 10.2 is used to explain slip. A screw propeller would, based on the position of the blades, advance a distance equal to the pitch during one revolution (see also Figure 6.38). However, due to the fluidity of water the propeller advances a distance less than the pitch. The difference between those distances is the slip.

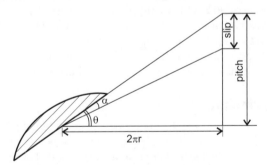

Figure 10.2   Propeller blade terminology: pitch and slip.

10.3 Performance

In this book, performance of a propeller will be described by the open water propeller efficiency as defined in Chapter 3.

$$\eta_O \overset{def}{=} \frac{P_T}{P_O} = \frac{1}{2\pi} \cdot \frac{T \cdot v_A}{Q \cdot n_p} \qquad\qquad \text{ref. (3.21)}$$

The ideal efficiency of a propeller, i.e. the maximum efficiency that is theoretically possible will be determined with the momentum theory for a propeller.

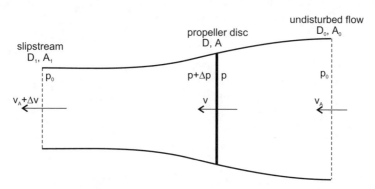

Figure 10.3   The propeller as actuator disc: the momentum theory.

Assume that the propeller is an actuator disc, i.e. a disc with diameter D and area A, causing a sudden increase in pressure Δp. The propeller acts on a circular column of fluid. Upstream, the flow is undisturbed and has a velocity of advance v_A while passing through area A_0 with diameter D_0. Downstream, the flow has contracted; the diameter has decreased to D_1 and the speed has increased to $v_A+\Delta v$. The pressure in the slipstream is the same as the pressure in the undisturbed flow.

In front of the propeller, the pressure is p and the speed at the propeller disc is v. Assume that the thrust T exerted by the propeller on the fluid is uniformly distributed so the pressure increase at the disc is the same in every position.

$$T = A \cdot \Delta p \tag{10.1}$$

A streamline is chosen as the boundary, so there will be no accumulation of mass in the region considered. The principle of conservation of mass, or the continuity equation, states that the mass flow through the different areas is constant:

$$\rho \cdot v \cdot A = constant$$

Apply this principle to mass flow at the undisturbed flow, the propeller disc and the slipstream:

$$\frac{\dot{m}}{\rho} = v_A \cdot A_0 = v \cdot A = (v_A + \Delta v) \cdot A_1 \tag{10.2}$$

Or, expressed in terms of the propeller diameter:

$$v_A \cdot D_0^2 = v \cdot D^2 = (v_A + \Delta v) \cdot D_1^2 \rightarrow$$

$$D_0^2 = \frac{v}{v_A} \cdot D^2 \quad and \quad D_1^2 = \frac{v}{(v_A + \Delta v)} \cdot D^2 \tag{10.3}$$

From the momentum theory it follows that the force exerted on the fluid equals the net outflow of momentum. Momentum is the product of mass flow and speed. For a propeller without a nozzle, thrust is the only force exerted on the fluid (ambient pressure on the outer boundary cancels), so:

$$T = \dot{m}_{out} \cdot (v_A + \Delta v) - \dot{m}_{in} \cdot v_A \rightarrow$$
$$T = \rho \cdot A_1 \cdot (v_A + \Delta v)^2 - \rho \cdot A_0 \cdot v_A^{\,2}$$

$$(10.4)$$

Use equation (10.3) to eliminate A_1 and A_0 from this expression, the expression for thrust becomes:

$$T = \frac{\pi}{4} \cdot D^2 \cdot \rho \cdot v \cdot \Delta v \qquad (10.5)$$

In which one will recognise equation (6.11): thrust results from giving a mass of water a velocity.

The next physical principle used here is Bernoulli's law, which is valid if no force is applied on the fluid and the flow is frictionless.

$$p + \tfrac{1}{2} \cdot \rho \cdot v^2 = constant$$

Force is exerted on the fluid at the propeller disc, but not ahead and aft of the propeller disc. Therefore, Bernoulli's law may be applied:

$$\textit{Aft of propeller:} \;\; p + \Delta p + \tfrac{1}{2} \cdot \rho \cdot v^2 = p_0 + \tfrac{1}{2} \cdot \rho \cdot (v_A + \Delta v)^2$$
$$\textit{Ahead of propeller:} \;\; p + \tfrac{1}{2} \cdot \rho \cdot v^2 = p_0 + \tfrac{1}{2} \cdot \rho \cdot v_A^{\,2}$$

$$(10.6)$$

If the second equation is subtracted from the first, the pressure rise over the propeller disc can be solved:

$$\Delta p = \tfrac{1}{2} \cdot \rho \cdot \Delta v (2 \cdot v_A + \Delta v) \qquad (10.7)$$

By combining equations (10.5) and (10.7), the velocity at the propeller disc can be related to the total speed difference over the control volume and the undisturbed speed of advance:

$$T = A \cdot \Delta p = \frac{\pi}{8} \cdot D^2 \cdot \rho \cdot \Delta v \cdot (2 \cdot v_A + \Delta v) = \frac{\pi}{4} \cdot D^2 \cdot \rho \cdot v \cdot \Delta v \qquad (10.8)$$

From which v can be solved:

$$v = v_A + \tfrac{1}{2} \Delta v$$

So,

$$T = \frac{\pi}{4} \cdot D^2 \cdot \rho \cdot (v_A + \tfrac{1}{2} \Delta v) \cdot \Delta v \qquad (10.9)$$

Define the non-dimensional thrust loading coefficient as:

$$C_T \overset{def}{=} \frac{T}{\frac{1}{2} \cdot \rho \cdot v_A^{\,2} \cdot \frac{\pi}{4} \cdot D^2} \tag{10.10}$$

With equation (10.9), this can be written as:

$$C_T = \frac{\left(v_A + \frac{1}{2}\Delta v\right) \cdot \Delta v}{\frac{1}{2} \cdot v_A^{\,2}} = 2 \cdot \frac{\Delta v}{v_A} + \left(\frac{\Delta v}{v_A}\right)^2 \tag{10.11}$$

From this quadratic equation, the relative speed increase can be determined in relation to thrust loading:

$$\frac{\Delta v}{v_A} = \frac{-2 \pm \sqrt{4 + 4 \cdot C_T}}{2} = -1 \pm \sqrt{1 + C_T} \tag{10.12}$$

(Note that only one solution has physical significance)

The ideal axial disc efficiency can be defined as:

$$\eta_i \overset{def}{=} \frac{P_T}{P_{added}} \tag{10.13}$$

In this equation the power added is caused by the increase in kinetic energy over the axial disc:

$$\begin{aligned} P_{added} &= \frac{1}{2} \cdot \dot{m} \cdot \left\{ \left(v_A + \Delta v\right)^2 - v_A^{\,2} \right\} \\ &= \frac{1}{2} \cdot \dot{m} \cdot \left(2 \cdot v_A \cdot \Delta v + \Delta v^2\right) = \dot{m} \cdot \Delta v \cdot \left(v_A + \frac{1}{2} \cdot \Delta v\right) \end{aligned} \tag{10.14}$$

or with (10.4):

$$P_{added} = T \cdot \left(v_A + \frac{1}{2} \cdot \Delta v\right) \tag{10.15}$$

Thrust power is defined as:

$$P_T \overset{def}{=} T \cdot v_A \qquad \text{ref. (3.15)}$$

Then the ideal axial disc efficiency becomes, making use of the relation between velocity increase and the thrust loading coefficient, equation (10.12):

$$\eta_i = \frac{v_A}{v_A + \frac{1}{2} \cdot \Delta v} = \frac{2}{2 + \frac{\Delta v}{v_A}} = \frac{2}{1 + \sqrt{1 + C_T}} \qquad (10.16)$$

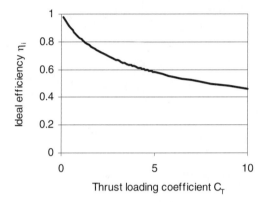

Figure 10.4   The ideal efficiency as a function of the thrust loading coefficient C_T:
                   Equation (10.16).

The Quality Index is the ratio of ideal axial efficiency and open water efficiency:

$$\text{Quality Index} = \frac{\eta_o}{\eta_i} \qquad (10.17)$$

It can be used to indicate the quality of the energy conversion over the propeller. The Quality Index will prove useful in the remainder of this chapter, because it can be a measure of performance in extreme off-design conditions.

10.4 Open water diagram

Propeller performance can be expressed in three non-dimensional parameters:

- The advance ratio J.
- The thrust coefficient K_T.
- The torque coefficient K_Q.

In the advance ratio J, the advance velocity v_A is made non-dimensional with the circumferential speed n_pD, which is the propeller tip speed:

$$J = \frac{v_A}{n_p \cdot D} \qquad (10.18)$$

Where v_A is the advance velocity relative to the water [m/s], D is the propeller diameter in [m] and n_p is the rotation rate or speed of the propeller in [rev/s]. Note that the physical importance of J is that it is proportional to the tangent of the angle between the advance velocity v_A and the circumferential speed of the propeller. In Figure 10.1 this angle has already been defined as the hydrodynamic pitch angle β. Note how the slip, as indicated in Figure 10.2, would increase if this angle decreases.

Thrust and torque can be made non-dimensional with the speed n_p, diameter D and the density of the sea water. This results in the thrust coefficient (10.19) and the torque coefficient (10.20):

$$K_T = \frac{T}{\rho \cdot n_p^{\,2} \cdot D^4} \qquad (10.19)$$

$$K_Q = \frac{Q}{\rho \cdot n_p^{\,2} \cdot D^5} \qquad (10.20)$$

The open water propeller efficiency has been defined by equation (3.21), and can be expressed in terms of the three parameters J, K_T and K_Q:

$$\eta_0 = \frac{1}{2\pi} \cdot \frac{T \cdot v_A}{Q \cdot n_p} = \frac{K_T \cdot \rho \cdot n_p^{\,2} \cdot D^4 \cdot v_A}{2\pi \cdot K_Q \cdot \rho \cdot n_p^{\,2} \cdot D^5 \cdot n_p} = \frac{1}{2\pi} \cdot \frac{K_T \cdot J}{K_Q} \qquad (10.21)$$

Figure 10.5 shows an open water propeller diagram of fixed pitch propellers from the Wageningen B systematic series, as published in [van Lammeren, 1969]. In the propeller diagram the thrust K_T and torque K_Q coefficients are a function of the advance ratio J. Note that it is an open water diagram, so the interaction with the hull is not included. It is common practice to also include the open water efficiency η_O as a function of the advance ratio. Note that K_Q is usually multiplied by ten in order to represent the curves in one diagram.

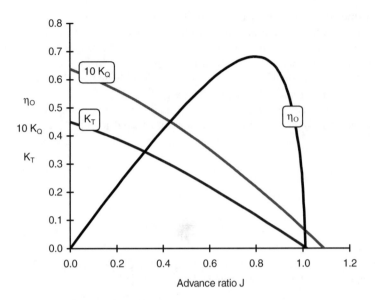

Figure 10.5   Propeller characteristic: Wageningen B 5 75 pitch ratio P/D = 0.96.

From equation (10.21) it is clear that the open water efficiency must drop to zero if either the thrust coefficient K_T or the advance ratio J is zero. Continuity requires a maximum in between.

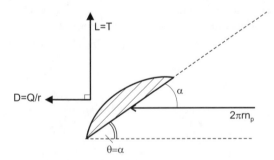

Figure 10.6   Bollard condition for propeller.

It can be observed that both the torque and the thrust coefficient increase with decreasing advance ratio, i.e. thrust and torque increase with increasing slip. The maximum value for the coefficients occurs for an advance ratio of zero, which implies that the velocity of advance is also zero. This is referred to as the *bollard* condition, see Figure 10.6. It is an important design condition for tugs.

At zero advance ratio however, the open water efficiency according to equation (10.21) is also zero, so efficiency can not be used as a quality measure in the bollard condition. This is the reason that the Quality Index was introduced in the foregoing section. The Quality Index can be expressed in terms of advance ratio and thrust and torque coefficients by using the propeller load coefficient as given by equation (10.10):

$$C_T = \frac{T}{\frac{\pi}{2} \cdot D^2 \cdot \frac{1}{2} \cdot \rho \cdot v_A^2} = \frac{K_T \cdot \rho \cdot n_p^2 \cdot D^4}{\frac{\pi}{2} \cdot D^2 \cdot \frac{1}{2} \cdot \rho \cdot v_A^2} = \frac{8 \cdot K_T}{\pi \cdot J^2} \qquad (10.22)$$

With the ideal axial efficiency:

$$\eta_i = \frac{2}{1 + \sqrt{1 + C_T}} \qquad \text{ref. (10.16)}$$

The Quality Index can be written as:

$$Quality\ Index = \frac{\eta_O}{\eta_i} = \frac{1}{2\pi} \cdot \frac{K_T \cdot J}{K_Q} \cdot \frac{1 + \sqrt{1 + \dfrac{8 \cdot K_T}{\pi \cdot J^2}}}{2} \qquad (10.23)$$

$$= \frac{1}{4\pi} \cdot \frac{K_T}{K_Q} \cdot \left(J + \sqrt{J^2 + \frac{8}{\pi} \cdot K_T} \right)$$

So, when advance ratio is zero the Quality Index still has a value that can be used to evaluate the quality of the propeller in the bollard pull condition:

$$Quality\ Index\ (J = 0) = \frac{1}{4\pi} \cdot \frac{K_T}{K_Q} \cdot \sqrt{\frac{8}{\pi} \cdot K_T} = \frac{1}{\pi\sqrt{2\pi}} \cdot \frac{K_T^{1.5}}{K_Q} \qquad (10.24)$$

Other extremes in the open water diagram are zero torque and zero thrust. Note that the thrust and the torque coefficient are zero for different values of the advance ratio.

The relative velocity of the water may also approach the blade in such a manner that the generated lift and drag forces contribute only to the torque and not to the thrust. This is the *zero thrust condition*; the torque is small but still positive, see Figure 10.7.

Zero torque is associated with a trailing shaft, i.e. a shaft that is not driven by the propelling machinery, so torque is approximately zero. The thrust is negative and is felt as added resistance of the ship: see Figure 10.8. This negative thrust for a trailing shaft may even be more negative when the torque is not zero but also negative. This is not unlikely because a considerable part of the shaft and gearbox system is rotating and driven by the milling propeller. (As the coupling is in the gearbox, usually at the input side most of the gearbox of a trailing shaft is running.)

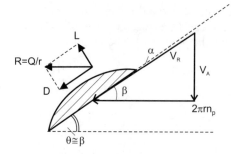

Figure 10.7   Zero thrust condition for propeller.

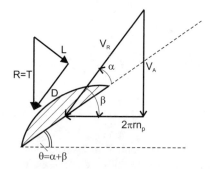

Figure 10.8   Zero torque condition for propeller.

10.5 Four quadrants diagrams

Open water diagrams represent the condition for stationary forward sailing only. Insight into the whole field of operation for the propeller, including running astern and dynamic behaviour like stopping and acceleration, is obtained by the four quadrants diagram (Figure 10.9).

Quadrant		Ship speed v_S	Propeller speed n_p	
1st	0 – 90	+	+	normal forward operation
2nd	90–180	-	+	forward thrust at negative speed (manoeuvring)
3rd	180–270	+	-	reversing propeller during stopping manoeuvre
4th	270–360	-	-	normal astern operation

Table 10.1   Four quadrant operation of the propeller.

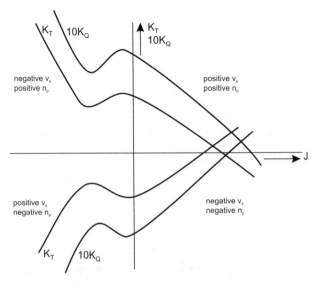

Figure 10.9   Four quadrants diagram.

The open water diagram as shown in Figure 10.5 provides information for part of the first quadrant: positive ship speed and positive propeller speed. Even if open water diagrams were expanded to cover four quadrants as shown in Figure 10.9 they do not provide all information for all the combinations of velocity of advance and propeller speed. For instance when propeller speed approaches zero, the advance ratio approaches infinity and so do the thrust and torque coefficients.

The Maritime Research Institute Netherlands (MARIN) developed C_T^*, C_Q^* versus β diagrams to describe these conditions so the entire four quadrant operation of a propeller can be described. The thrust and torque coefficient are based on the resulting velocity V_R. See Figure 10.10 and equations (10.25), (10.26) and (10.27).

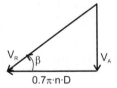

Figure 10.10   Water velocities at blade section at diameter of nominal pitch, i.e. *0.7 D*.

$$\beta = \arctan\left(\frac{v_A}{0.7\pi \cdot n_p \cdot D}\right) \qquad (10.25)$$

$$C_T^* = \frac{T}{\frac{1}{2}\rho \cdot \left(v_A^2 + \left(0.7\pi \cdot n_p \cdot D\right)^2\right)\frac{\pi}{4} \cdot D^2} \tag{10.26}$$

$$C_Q^* = \frac{Q}{\frac{1}{2}\rho \cdot \left(v_A^2 + \left(0.7\pi \cdot n_p \cdot D\right)^2\right)\frac{\pi}{4} \cdot D^3} \tag{10.27}$$

The four quadrant diagram, Figure 10.11, shows the coefficients as a function of the hydrodynamic pitch angle β for the Wageningen B4-70 propeller series.

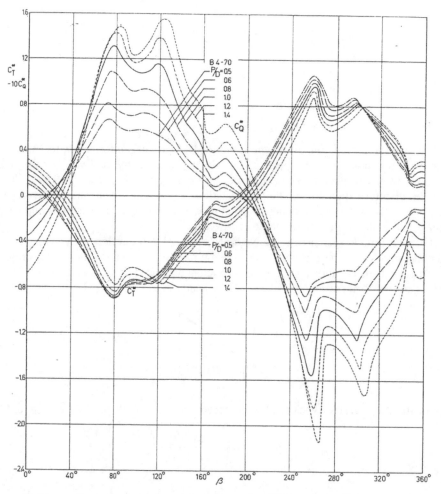

Figure 10.11   Four quadrant measurement results of Wageningen B4-70 propellers. (Courtesy of MARIN).

10.6 CP propellers

The lift generated by an element decreases when the angle of attack of the flow decreases. Consider a CP propeller which design condition is the same as the condition given in Figure 10.12. Due to adverse conditions like heavy seas or towing another ship, the velocity of advance decreases. This is shown in Figure 10.13: the velocity of advance decreases, the propeller speed stays the same, so the relative water velocity decreases slightly and the angle of attack increases.

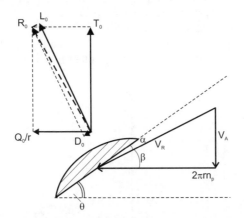

Figure 10.12   Design condition of a propeller.

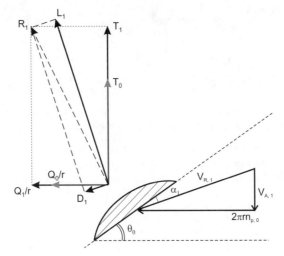

Figure 10.13   Forces on a propeller blade if velocity of advance would reduce and pitch would not change: higher engine torque required at constant engine speed.

As a result of the increased angle of attack, the lift force generated by the blade will increase. This will increase the thrust. The increase of lift and drag is likely to increase to the situation as shown, in which not only thrust but also the engine torque will increase relative to the design condition. This causes an unfavourable situation for the engine as it has to develop a higher torque at the same (propeller) speed.

To bring the engine torque back to its original design value (see Figure 10.12) the lift needs to decrease. With a CP propeller this is achieved by reducing the pitch, which will reduce the angle of attack. At reduced pitch angle the engine can operate at the torque of the design point ($Q_2/r = Q_0/r$) and will not be overloaded. The thrust generated by the propeller has increased to T_2 as shown in Figure 10.14.

Note that the arrows in Figure 10.12, Figure 10.13 and Figure 10.14 give a qualitative impression only. Their relative magnitude to each other may not be representative.

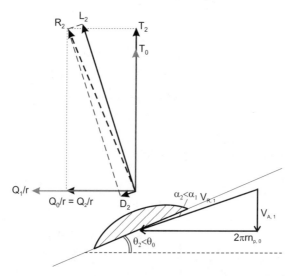

Figure 10.14   Change of pitch to prevent the engine from overload: T_o is the thrust in Figure 10.12 and Q_1 is to the engine torque in Figure 10.13.

At every pitch–diameter ratio, the delivered thrust and required torque will be different. Therefore, the open water propeller diagram of a CP propeller consists of series of lines at different pitch ratios as does the diagram of FP propellers. (But in the diagram of a FP propeller the lines represent a series of propellers.) An open water diagram for a CP propeller is given in Figure 10.15.

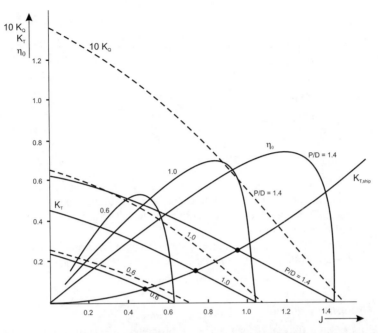

Figure 10.15   Open water propeller diagram for CP propeller with different pitch ratios P/D.

10.7 Propeller design using open water diagram

Open water diagrams may be used to specify the propeller design, if ship resistance and design speed are known and wake and thrust deduction can be estimated. Design parameters such as the number of blades, blade shape and expanded blade area ratio lie outside the scope of this book. For these considerations reference in made to [Kuiper, 1994] and [Carlton, 1994].

In this book, propeller design is restricted to finding the optimum propeller diameter or optimum speed when the criterion is maximum propeller efficiency. Obviously restrictions may be encountered:

- limited propeller diameter dictated by aftship design or draft restrictions.
- choice of engines is limited which, especially for direct drive, influences both speed and delivered power.

For a given design condition, the thrust as required by the ship can be determined. The design parameters are indexed *0*. The resistance, ship speed, thrust deduction factor and wake factor have been determined in the design condition.

$$T_0 = \frac{R_0}{k_0 \cdot (1 - t_0)} = \frac{P_{E,0}}{k_0 \cdot (1 - t_0) \cdot v_{S,0}} \tag{10.28}$$

$$v_{A,0} = (1 - w_0) \cdot v_{S,0} \tag{10.29}$$

With these relations, the thrust coefficient and the advance ratio as required by the ship in the design condition can be determined:

$$K_{T,\text{ship},0} = \frac{T_0}{\rho \cdot n_{p,0}^2 \cdot D^4} = \frac{R_0}{k_0 \cdot (1 - t_0) \cdot \rho \cdot n_{p,0}^2 \cdot D^4} \tag{10.30}$$

$$J_0 = \frac{v_{A,0}}{n_{p,0} \cdot D} = \frac{(1 - w_0) \cdot v_{S,0}}{n_{p,0} \cdot D} \tag{10.31}$$

With these two relations and the open water diagrams for a series of propellers, either (1) the optimum propeller speed $n_{p,0}$ can be determined if the diameter D is known, or (2) the optimum diameter D can be determined if the propeller speed $n_{p,0}$ is known. This will be shown in the following sections.

The single-shaft ship that is used in this chapter to explain propeller selection methods is described by the following design variables: Δ_0 = 15000 tonnes, $P_{E,0} = 8000$ kW, $v_{s,0} = 20$ knots = 10.29 m/s, $w_0 = 0.2$, $t_0 = 0.12$ and $\eta_{R,0} = 0.99$.

10.7.1 Optimum propeller diameter

When the open water diagrams for a series of propellers are known, they can be used to determine the optimum diameter and corresponding pitch ratio for a given ship. The propeller is directly driven by a given engine, so propeller speed is a known variable.

The thrust as required by the ship at design conditions is found by transforming the ship resistance into a thrust coefficient as a function of the advance ratio. By combining equations (10.30) and (10.31), the unknown propeller diameter is eliminated:

$$\left(\frac{K_T}{J^4} \right)_0 = \frac{T_0}{\rho \cdot n_0^2 \cdot D^4} \cdot \frac{n_0^4 \cdot D^4}{v_{A,0}^4} = \frac{T_0 \cdot n_0^2}{\rho \cdot v_{A,0}^4} = c_6 \tag{10.32}$$

$$\rightarrow K_{T,\text{ship},0} = c_6 \cdot J_0^4$$

This fourth power curve, the demand curve, can be drawn in the open water diagram. As shown in Figure 10.16 this curve intersects the different propeller K_T–curves, which refer to the thrust delivered by the propellers.

The points of intersection determine the advance ratio of each propeller and its efficiency. The advance ratio resulting in the maximum efficiency determines the optimum diameter for this demand curve:

$$J_{\text{opt}} = \frac{v_{A,0}}{n_0 \cdot D_{\text{opt}}} \tag{10.33}$$

In Figure 10.16 the advance ratio for which the efficiency is best can be determined for the ship as introduced in the beginning of section 10.7. The design speed of the propeller has been taken 125 rpm. The propeller with pitch ratio P/D = 0.96 has the maximum efficiency (η_0= 64.6 %) at the required thrust; the optimum advance ratio J is 0.683. By using equation (10.33), it follows that the optimum propeller diameter is 5.8 metres:

$$D_{opt} = \frac{(1-w_0) \cdot v_{s,0}}{n_{p,0} \cdot J_{opt}} = 5.8m$$

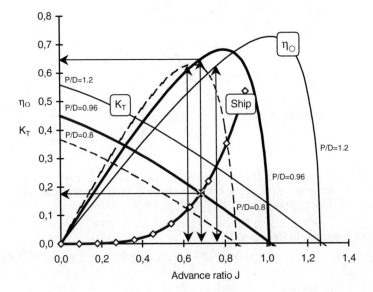

Figure 10.16   Determining the maximum efficiency and optimum propeller diameter for a given design condition and propeller speed of 125 rpm.

Figure 10.17 shows an alternative diagram. The open water efficiency is represented by lines of constant efficiency. The maximum value of the efficiency can easily be determined as the tangent of the demand curve and the lines of constant efficiency. Note that it is the demand curve that restricts the attainable efficiency.

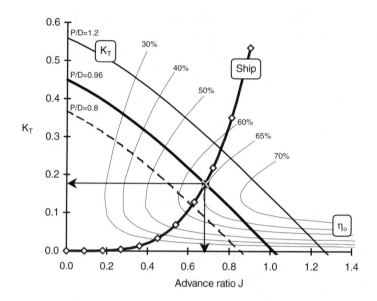

Figure 10.17   Evaluation of intersection of $K_{T,ship}$ and $K_{T,propeller}$ by means of lines of
constant open water efficiency to determine optimum diameter
(n_p=125rpm).

10.7.2 Optimum propeller speed

In a geared drive, the propeller speed can be matched to the prime mover by means of the
gearbox, so the optimum speed and the corresponding pitch ratio have to be determined.
The diameter of the propeller will be chosen as large as possible to provide lowest blade
loading and highest efficiency. Assume that the diameter of the propeller is limited by the
hull design. This is often the case: for a single-screw ship the propeller diameter is
restricted by the aftship draught, and for twin-screw ships the propellers are allowed to
protrude underneath the keel to a practical limit.

To solve this problem, again it is necessary to transform ship resistance into a thrust
coefficient as a function of the ratio of advance. Equations (10.30) and (10.31) should be
combined, so the unknown propeller speed is eliminated as follows:

$$\left(\frac{K_T}{J^2}\right)_0 = \frac{T_0}{\rho \cdot n_{p,0}^2 \cdot D_{max}^4} \cdot \frac{n_{p,0}^2 \cdot D_{max}^2}{v_{A,0}^2} = \frac{T_0}{\rho \cdot v_{A,0}^2 \cdot D_{max}^2} = c_7 \qquad (10.34)$$

Constant c_7 only depends on the design condition and the limiting propeller diameter;
assume for instance D = 5.5 m. Equation (10.34) results in a parabola in the propeller
characteristic; see Figure 10.18.

$$K_{T,ship,0} = c_7 \cdot J_0^2 \qquad (10.35)$$

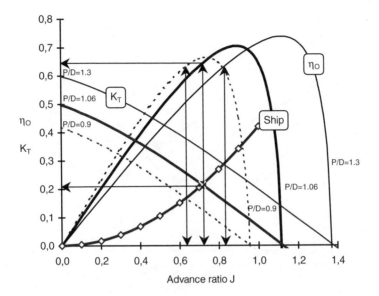

Figure 10.18   Determination of optimum shaft speed and propeller pitch for propeller diameter limitation of D = 5.5 m.

By intersecting the parabola with the K_T-curves for propellers with different pitch–diameter ratio P/D, the values of J and consequently η_O can be determined for each pitch. The optimum shaft speed is found from the advance ratio at optimum efficiency:

$$n_{opt} = \frac{v_{A,0}}{J_{opt} \cdot D_{max}} \qquad (10.36)$$

The advance ratio at maximum efficiency is 0.715, where the efficiency is 64.0 % and the pitch ratio is 1.06. Using Equation (10.36), it follows that the optimum speed is 126 rpm:

$$n_{opt} = \frac{v_{A,0}}{J_{opt} \cdot D_{max}} = \frac{(1 - w_0) \cdot v_{S,0}}{J_{opt} \cdot D_{max}} = 2.09 \ s^{-1} = 126 \ rpm$$

Figure 10.19 contains the same information as the foregoing figure. Instead of the traditional representation of open water efficiency it contains lines of constant open water efficiency. With this figure, it becomes clear that it is important to select the largest propeller diameter possible. A large diameter would result in a lower c_7-value and thus a 'low' demand curve, which tends towards the area of high propeller efficiency. In theory, it is possible to select a propeller diameter that is too large (i.e. demand curve is in the bottom part of Figure 10.19). However, in practice the diameter at which this will occur is unrealistically large.

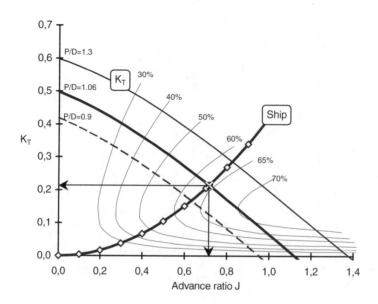

Figure 10.19   Evaluation of intersection of $K_{T,ship}$ and $K_{T,propeller}$ by means of lines of
                  constant open water efficiency to determine optimum speed (D=5.5m).

10.8 Exercises

Exercise 1

A single shaft ship is propelled by a fixed pitch propeller, which is driven by a diesel
engine through a reduction gearbox. For the design condition the following data apply:

- ship displacement $\Delta = 15000$ tonnes
- ship speed $v_s = 20\ knots = 10.29\ m/s$
- ship resistance $R = 777.5\ kN$
- effective power $P_E = 8000\ kW$
- wake fraction $w = 0.2$
- thrust deduction $t = 0.12$
- relative rotative efficiency $\eta_R = 0.99$
- maximum possible propeller diameter $D = 5.8\ m$
- sea water density $\rho = 1025\ kg/m^3$
- engine speed of diesel engine $n_e = 600\ rpm$
- transmission efficiency $\eta_{TR} = 0.95$

The transmission efficiency may be assumed to be constant.

It has been decided to use a fixed pitch propeller of the Wageningen B-series with 5 blades and a blade area ratio of 0.75 (the B5-75 series), see Figure 10.20 for the open water diagram of this series.

Determine the following:

- *the optimal pitch ratio of the propeller $(P/D)_{opt}$*
- *the corresponding optimal propeller speed $n_{p,opt}$ and the required gearbox ratio*
- *the corresponding open water propeller efficiency η_O*
- *the propulsive efficiency η_D*
- *the required propeller power $P_P (= P_D/k_P)$*
- *the required engine brake power P_B*
- *the advance ratio J and the hydrodynamic pitch angle β*
- *the thrust and torque coefficients K_T, C_T^*, K_Q and C_Q^**

Note: This exercise concerns the same case ship as in section 10.7. However, the optimum propeller diameter of 5.8 m resulting from the calculations in section 10.7.1 is now used as input of the problem.

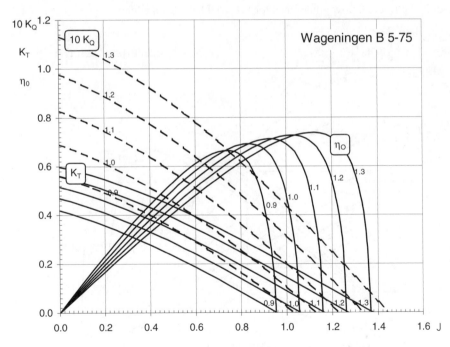

Figure 10.20   The open water propeller diagram of the Wageningen B 5-75 series for several P/D ratios.

Solution Exercise 1

First, the ship resistance is transformed to the dimensionless thrust coefficient $K_{T,ship}$ as a function of the advance coefficient J (refer to Equations (10.30), (10.31), (10.34) and (10.35)).

$$- \quad K_T = \frac{T}{\rho \cdot n^2 \cdot D^4} = \frac{R}{(1-t) \cdot \rho \cdot n^2 \cdot D^4}$$

$$- \quad J = \frac{v_A}{n \cdot D} = \frac{(1-w) \cdot v_s}{n \cdot D}$$

$$- \quad \frac{K_T}{J^2} = c_7 = \frac{R}{(1-t) \cdot \rho \cdot n^2 \cdot D^4} \cdot \frac{n^2 \cdot D^2}{v_s^2 \cdot (1-w)^2}$$

$$- \quad \frac{K_T}{J^2} = c_7 = \frac{R}{(1-t) \cdot (1-w)^2 \cdot \rho \cdot v_s^2 \cdot D^2} = 0.3781$$

$$- \quad K_T = 0.3781 \cdot J^2$$

This relation needs to be drawn into Figure 10.20. The intersections of the ship K_T-curve with the propeller K_T-curves can be determined and values for J, K_T, K_Q and η_0 can be read. In the figure below guide lines for P/D=0.9 have been added.

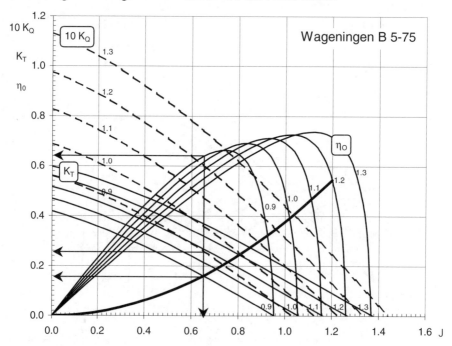

This results in:

P/D	J	K_T	K_Q	η_o
0.9	0.651	0.160	0.0259	0.639
1.0	0.706	0.188	0.0326	0.650
1.1	0.756	0.216	0.0399	0.652
1.2	0.804	0.245	0.0482	0.649
1.3	0.851	0.274	0.0575	0.644

The open water propeller efficiency is plotted as function of P/D. This gives the following result:

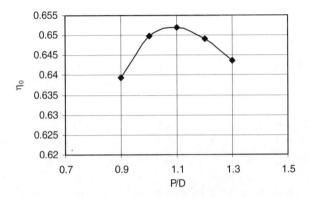

The *optimal P/D ratio* is now found as $(P/D)_{opt}$ = 1.10 for $\eta_{o,max}$ = 0.652. The other parameters for the optimal situation can also be determined:

$$K_{T,opt} = 0.216, \; K_{Q,opt} = 0.0399 \; \text{and} \; J_{opt} = 0.756$$

The *optimal propeller speed* is:

$$- \quad \left(n_p\right)_{opt} = \frac{v_A}{J_{opt} \cdot D} = \frac{v_s \cdot (1-w)}{J_{opt} \cdot D} = 1.877 \; s^{-1} = 112.6 \; rpm$$

(Note that this is lower than the propeller speed of 125 rpm as chosen for the case in section 10.7.1. Also note that the efficiency is higher than 64.6% found in section 10.7.1 for a propeller of the same diameter. It is left to the reader to compare the results with the optimum speed problem in section 10.7.2 in which the propeller diameter was limited to 5.5 m)

The *gearbox ratio i* should be chosen as:

$$- \quad i = \frac{n_e}{n_{p,opt}} = \frac{600}{112.6} = 5.33$$

The *propulsive efficiency* is:

$$- \quad \eta_D = \eta_o \cdot \eta_H \cdot \eta_R = \eta_o \cdot \frac{1-t}{1-w} \cdot \eta_R = 0.652 \cdot \frac{0.88}{0.80} \cdot 0.99 = 0.710$$

The *required propeller power* and *brake power* P_B are:

$$- \quad P_P = \frac{P_D}{k_P} = \frac{P_E}{k_P \cdot \eta_D} = \frac{8000}{1 \cdot 0.710} = 11267 \ kW$$

$$- \quad P_B = \frac{P_P}{k_e \cdot \eta_{TR}} = \frac{11267}{1 \cdot 0.95} = 11860 \ kW$$

The *hydrodynamic pitch angle*, C_T^*, and C_Q^* :

$$- \quad \beta = \arctan\left(\frac{v_A}{0.7 \cdot \pi \cdot n_P \cdot D}\right) = 18.98 \ ^\circ$$

$$- \quad C_T^* = \frac{T}{\frac{1}{2} \cdot \rho \cdot \left(v_A^2 + (0.7 \cdot \pi \cdot n_P \cdot D)^2\right) \frac{\pi}{4} \cdot D^2} = 0.1018$$

$$- \quad C_Q^* = \frac{Q}{\frac{1}{2} \cdot \rho \cdot \left(v_A^2 + (0.7 \cdot \pi \cdot n_P \cdot D)^2\right) \cdot \frac{\pi}{4} \cdot D^3} = 0.01877$$

10.9 References and further reading

Carlton, 1994

J.S. Carlton: *"Marine propellers and propulsion"*, Butterworth-Heinemann, UK 1994.

Kuiper, 1994

Prof. dr. ir. G. Kuiper: *"Resistance and Propulsion of Ships"*, (Lecture-notes for the course Resistance and Propulsion), Delft University of Technology, 1994

van Lammeren, 1969

W. P. A. van Lammeren, J. D. van Manen, M. W. C. Oosterveld: *"The Wageningen B-screw Series"*, SNAME. 1969.

Rawson and Tupper, 2001

K. J. Rawson and E. C. Tupper: *"Basic Ship Theory"* (Chapter 11 Powering of Ships: Application), Butterworth-Heinemann, UK 2001

Chapter 11

Matching Propulsion Engine to Propeller

11.0 Learning goals

After studying this chapter, the student should be able to:

- *Define MCR, CSR, service margin and engine margin*

- *Obtain $P_{D,load}$-n curve from ship characteristics and open water propeller diagrams*

- *Determine a suitable prime mover when propeller and ship curves are known (matching propeller and prime mover)*

- *Determine load and drive characteristics for off-design conditions when design condition curves are known*

- *Evaluate whether the load of a prime mover is acceptable in different operating conditions.*

11.1 Introduction

The matching of load and drive characteristics has been mentioned in previous chapters. In this chapter the process of matching the propulsor, the ship and the prime mover are dealt with in detail. Matching is the process in which the operating envelope of the driving machinery and the load as experienced by the driving machinery are tuned to each other. The load may be due to the propeller load and possible other loads. Before studying this chapter the student should be familiar with the following:

- The ship load curve; resistance or effective power versus ship speed, as introduced in Chapter 3.

- The propeller curve; the required delivered power versus propeller speed, as introduced in Chapter 3.

- The operating envelope of a diesel engine: brake power versus engine speed, as discussed in Chapter 7.

- The operating envelope of a gas turbine: brake power versus engine speed, as discussed in Chapter 8.

In this chapter the diagrams concerned will be matched in order to design a well-integrated propulsion plant. The open water diagrams as introduced in the previous chapter will turn out to be crucial in the discussion.

The operating condition for which the propulsion plant is optimised is the design condition. All operating conditions that differ from this condition are referred to as off-design conditions. The propeller load at the design condition is usually the load of a moderately fouled hull at maximum draft operating in calm seas. In due time, however, the hull is bound to become more severely fouled, encounter heavy seas, or sail at another draught or in shallow water. These circumstances are among the off-design conditions. In those conditions the propulsion plant should also function satisfactorily. Figure 11.1 shows that this is not that obvious.

In Figure 11.1 the operating envelope of a diesel engine and three load curves of a fixed pitch propeller are shown. Curve 1 represents the propeller load curve that is valid for the design condition. The engine and the propeller are tuned in such a way that maximum available power of the engine coincides with the required delivered power curve of the propeller: in other words, maximum engine power can be utilised in this situation.

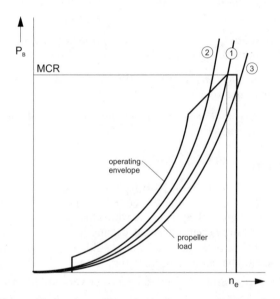

Figure 11.1   Three ship load conditions in engine operating envelope.

Curves 2 and 3 show the effect of increased and decreased resistance resulting from off-design conditions. On the one hand, the propeller curve may shift upward (Curve 2), compared to the design curve due to increased ship resistance. In the new condition, the maximum engine power cannot be delivered because the engine envelope limits the power, and the ship is no longer able to sail its design speed. On the other hand, the propeller curve may shift downward due to decreased ship resistance (Curve 3). Again the engine is not able to deliver the maximum power; this time because of the maximum engine speed limit. The power may, however, still be high enough to meet the ship's design speed (as we will see later on). Other off-design conditions that might need to be considered are: towing a load, driving a power take off and connecting or disconnecting of propeller shafts or prime movers in multi-shaft configurations.

As all the components in the propulsion chain contribute to the shifting of operational points, their effects have to be studied. When matching propulsion plant components it is important to realise that the process of matching is an iterative process. Fixing either end of the propulsion chain beforehand may lead to 'sub-optimised' solutions. The matching process is successful when:

1) The engine is able to develop full power, or nearly full power, at the design condition.
2) The propulsion plant functions satisfactorily in off-design conditions, i.e. delivers required speed or thrust without exceeding any limits imposed by the envelope of the driving machinery.

In this chapter, the main focus will be on the process of matching a ship, a propeller and a diesel engine. Both a FP propeller and a CP propeller will be considered.

11.2 Basic matching of propeller and engine

Assume that ship and propeller are given, and that the relations between the ship resistance and speed, and between effective power and speed, are known. To successfully match the propeller–ship combination to an engine, choose a condition under which to optimise the operational point of propeller and engine, i.e. the design condition. A well-chosen design condition is such that the corresponding displacement, the fouling, the sea state and the water depth are realistic and representative for the mean service conditions that the ship will encounter during its operational life. Good practice is to assume full design displacement, two years of fouling, sea state 2 or 3 and deep water.

The service condition is related to the sea trial condition by the service margin (SM):

$$SM = \frac{P_{E,Service}}{P_{E,Trial}} > 1 \qquad (11.1)$$

where $P_{E,service}$ is the effective power in service conditions and $P_{E,trial}$ is the effective power at sea trial. Often the trial condition is the same as the towing tank condition: the ship is clean and usually unloaded, and calm seas and deep water are assumed. Values for the service margin, taking into account the sea state and fouling, lie between 1.1 and 1.25. For merchant vessels this margin will be higher to account for the difference in displacement in service and trial condition.

Since propulsion efficiency will hardly be different under trial and service condition (as we will see later on) the service margin is also approximately equal to the ratio of the engine power under the two conditions:

$$SM \cong \frac{P_{B,Service}}{P_{B,Trial}} \qquad (11.2)$$

Note that the service margin is equal to the multiplier y as introduced in section 3.4.1:

$$P_E = c_1 \cdot v_S^3 \qquad ref. (3.3)$$

where

$$c_1 = y \cdot c_0 (v_S) \qquad\qquad\qquad \text{ref. (3.4)}$$

and

$$y = f(fouling,\ displacement,\ sea\ state,\ water\ depth) \qquad \text{ref. (3.5)}$$

The factor *y* could also be split up, to show how the service margin is built up:

$$SM = y = y_1\,(fouling) \cdot y_2\,(hull\ form) \cdot \left(\frac{\Delta}{\Delta_{nom}}\right)^{\!2/3} \cdot y_3\,(sea\ state) \cdot y_4\,(water\ depth) \qquad (11.3)$$

The following is an example containing values for a naval vessel.

For a naval vessel, the factors that are included in the service margin to describe the effects of fouling, displacement, sea state and water depth relative to the trial (or towing tank) condition are:
Fouling:

$$y_1\,(fouling) = 1.06$$

This is based on a 2-year docking period and 3% increase of resistance per year due to fouling.
Displacement:

$$y_{displ} = y_2\,(hull\ form) \cdot \left(\frac{\Delta}{\Delta_{nom}}\right)^{\!2/3} \cong 1.0 \cdot \left(\frac{3500}{3300}\right)^{\!2/3} = 1.04$$

This factor could be higher in the case of a merchant ship where the trial condition often is unloaded.
Sea state:

$$y_3\,(sea\ state) = 1.10$$

This value is approximately valid for sea state = 3.
Water depth:

$$y_4\,(water\ depth) = 1.0$$

Normally the service condition is assumed to be in deep water.

The total service margin with these values amounts to:

$$SM = y = 1.22$$

The service margin imposed on the ship resistance curve under trial condition gives the resistance under design conditions. After transformation of the ship resistance into a propeller load curve, as will be studied in section 11.3.1, and translation of the propeller load curve to brake power, as will be studied in section 11.3.3, the propeller load curve can be compared with the operating envelope of the engine (see Figure 11.2). Later it is shown that for the same ship's speed the heavier design condition requires more shaft speed than trial condition.

The operating envelope of a diesel engine has been discussed at length in Chapter 7. Some additional terminology will have to be introduced in light of the matching process. The rating of an engine states the ability of an engine to perform reliably at that level under specified circumstances. The level is usually expressed as a continuous power at a certain speed, i.e. the rated engine speed. As such, the maximum continuous rating (MCR), is the point in the operating envelope indicated by maximum (hundred percent) power at maximum (hundred percent) speed.

For merchant vessels, a lower rating is defined, at which the engine develops the power required for design speed under service conditions: the continuous service rating (CSR). The matching should be such that the engine is operated at this rating for the majority of the time. So, in normal operation the engine will have a margin relative to the MCR. This is called the engine margin (EM) and often lies between 0.80 and 0.90.

$$EM = \frac{CSR}{MCR} = \frac{P_{B,Service}}{P_{B,Max}} < 1 \qquad (11.4)$$

Engines intended for warships have a maximum speed requirement but normally not a required engine margin since maximum speed is seldom required. The engine may have a high-performance rating that allows for operation under conditions of overload for limited periods of time. This high rating is not beneficial for the engine's condition, and will reduce component lives and maintenance intervals.

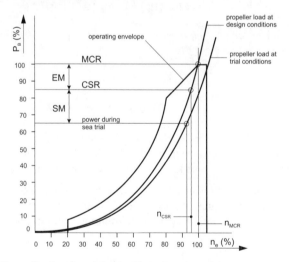

Figure 11.2   Propeller load matched with a diesel engine.

Figure 11.2 shows how the basic matching of a FP propeller and an engine is usually done for a merchant vessel. It shows the operating envelope of a diesel engine and the propeller load curves for the trial condition and for the service condition. The MCR, the CSR, the engine margin and the service margin are indicated.

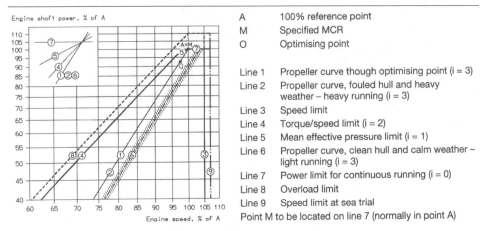

A	100% reference point
M	Specified MCR
O	Optimising point
Line 1	Propeller curve though optimising point (i = 3)
Line 2	Propeller curve, fouled hull and heavy weather – heavy running (i = 3)
Line 3	Speed limit
Line 4	Torque/speed limit (i = 2)
Line 5	Mean effective pressure limit (i = 1)
Line 6	Propeller curve, clean hull and calm weather – light running (i = 3)
Line 7	Power limit for continuous running (i = 0)
Line 8	Overload limit
Line 9	Speed limit at sea trial
Point M to be located on line 7 (normally in point A)	

Figure 11.3   Matching process (Courtesy of MAN B&W: Project guide K98MC, 1998).

Figure 11.3 has been taken from a MAN B&W project guide. It defines the powers and speed limits for continuous operation and overload of an installed 2-stroke engine of type K98MC. In the diagram logarithmic scales are used so the power functions are linear:

$$P_B = c \times n^i \Rightarrow \log(P_B) = i \times \log(n) + \log(c)$$

For example the engine power required for propulsion, if it is assumed that it may be expressed according to the propeller law, is:

$$P_B = c \times n_p^{\ 3}$$

$$\log(P_B) = 3\log(n_p) + \log(c)$$

In the diagram the engine margin can be distinguished as the ratio between the power developed in point O and the power in point M. With a FP propeller continuous operation would be allowed without limitations within the area limited by the lines 4, 5, 7 and 3.

Some engine manufacturers also define a light running margin (LRM) as shown in Figure 11.4. The LRM relates the engine speed difference between the service propeller curve and the propeller curve for trial or light running condition at CSR power to the speed at MCR. It is defined as:

$$LRM = \frac{n_{LRM} - n_{CSR}}{n_M}$$

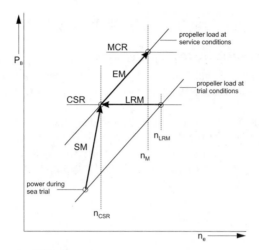

Figure 11.4   The EM, SM and LRM.

The LRM should have a value of 5 to 6 %. It is supposed to offer sufficient engine speed margin to maintain constant engine power when the ship deteriorates from trial condition to service condition. Either the sea margin SM or the light running margin LRM can be chosen. The other will be the result of the margin chosen.

If the propulsion engine also has to drive a shaft generator in the design condition, the power for the PTO should be included in the MCR power. See Figure 11.5. In this figure, the PTO is assumed to be constant and independent of ship speed. Note that the PTO power has not been included in the sea margin.

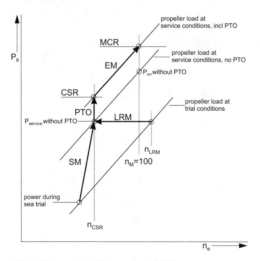

Figure 11.5   The EM, SM and LRM including PTO.

11.3 Transformation of ship resistance to engine brake power

11.3.1 From ship resistance to propeller load

The load of a propeller depends on the ship it has to propel and the conditions under which the ship operates. Open water diagrams describe the performance of propellers in open water.

In Chapter 10, the thrust coefficient as required by the ship has been introduced. In that chapter it was defined for the design condition. If the R–v_S relationship is known, the required thrust coefficient can be determined for every ship speed. Consider a ship's speed v_S with a corresponding ship resistance R and the relationship between them:

$$R = c_1 \cdot v_s^{\,2} \qquad\qquad \text{ref. (3.1)}$$

Using the wake factor resistance can also be written as:

$$R = c_1 \cdot \left(\frac{V_A}{1-w} \right)^2 \qquad\qquad (11.5)$$

With thrust deduction and number of shafts k_p, required thrust is equal to:

$$T = \frac{R}{k_p \cdot (1-t)} = \frac{c_1 \cdot v_A^2}{k_p \cdot (1-t) \cdot (1-w)^2} = c_8 \cdot v_A^2 \qquad\qquad (11.6)$$

where

$$c_8 = \frac{c_1}{k_p \cdot (1-t) \cdot (1-w)^2} \qquad\qquad (11.7)$$

Then the thrust coefficient required for this ship at speed v_S is

$$K_{T,ship} = \frac{c_8 \cdot v_A^{\,2}}{\rho \cdot n^2 \cdot D^4} = \frac{c_8}{\rho \cdot D^2} \cdot \frac{v_A^{\,2}}{n^2 \cdot D^2} = \frac{c_8}{\rho \cdot D^2} \cdot J^2 \qquad\qquad (11.8)$$

or

$$K_{T,ship} = c_7 \cdot J^2 \qquad\qquad (11.9)$$

where

$$c_7 = \frac{1}{\rho \cdot D^2} \cdot \frac{c_1}{k_p \cdot (1-t) \cdot (1-w)^2} \qquad\qquad (11.10)$$

Equation (11.9) implies that the ship curve for a certain speed is a parabola in the open water propeller diagram: see Figure 11.6. The intersection of the K_T-curve as required by the ship ($K_{T,ship}$) and the K_T-curve as delivered by the propeller leads to the operational point of the propeller. At this point the advance ratio and the thrust coefficient can be determined. By using the advance ratio, the torque coefficient and the open water propeller efficiency can also be found.

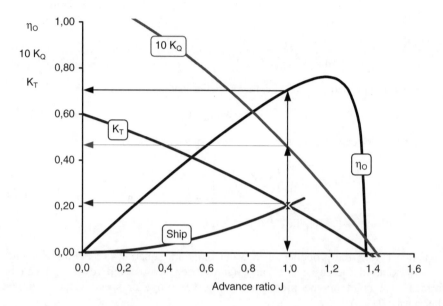

Figure 11.6   Ship curve intersecting with the thrust coefficient curve of a propeller.

The propeller load $P_{P,load}$ and the propeller speed can be determined at the operational point of the propeller. The propeller speed can be determined by using the wake factor and the advance ratio as found at the operational point:

$$\left. \begin{array}{l} J = \dfrac{v_A}{n_p \cdot D} \\[2mm] v_A = v_s \cdot (1-w) \end{array} \right\} \Rightarrow n_p = \dfrac{v_A}{J \cdot D} = \dfrac{(1-w)}{J \cdot D} \cdot v_s \qquad (11.11)$$

Or

$$n_p = c_3 \cdot v_s \qquad (11.12)$$

Where

$$c_3 = \dfrac{(1-w)}{J \cdot D} \qquad (11.13)$$

With the torque coefficient that has been found in Figure 11.6, the load of the propeller can be determined as a function of propeller speed. The open water torque Q as used to define the torque coefficient, and the real propeller torque M_p on the propeller behind the ship are related:

$$Q = \eta_R \cdot M_p \qquad \text{ref. (3.23)}$$

Therefore:

$$K_Q = \frac{Q}{\rho \cdot n_p^2 \cdot D^5} = \frac{\eta_R \cdot M_p}{\rho \cdot n_p^2 \cdot D^5} \rightarrow M_p = \frac{\rho \cdot D^5}{\eta_R} \cdot K_Q \cdot n_p^2 \qquad (11.14)$$

Hence, the required propeller power, i.e. the propeller load, is:

$$P_{p,load} = 2\pi \cdot M_{p,load} \cdot n_p \qquad \text{ref. (3.22)}$$

Then propeller power can be expressed in the shaft speed as follows:

$$\left. \begin{array}{c} P_{p,load} = \dfrac{2\pi \cdot \rho \cdot D^5}{\eta_R} \cdot K_Q \cdot n_p^3 \\[4mm] c_4 = \dfrac{2\pi \cdot \rho \cdot D^5}{\eta_R} \cdot K_Q \end{array} \right\} \rightarrow P_{p,load} = c_4 \cdot n_p^3 \qquad (11.15)$$

With equation (11.9), the propeller open water diagram, equation (11.11) and equation (11.15) any point of the resistance curve (ship speed versus ship resistance) can be transformed to a point on the propeller load curve (propeller speed versus required propeller power $P_{p,\,load}$).

11.3.2 Special case: propeller load follows propeller law

If we consider a special case – a ship with a squared resistance – speed curve, i.e. c_1 is a constant – it can be shown that under certain assumptions ship speed has no effect on the operational point of the propeller.

Consider a ship, which has a squared resistance–speed curve, and assume that the wake factor and the thrust deduction factor may be regarded as constants. The resistance curve will be transformed into the same ship curve $K_{T,ship}$ as in Figure 11.6 for every ship speed, because the influencing factor c_7 (equation (11.10)) does not change. If the pitch ratio of the propeller does not change, the propeller diagram does not change, so the operational point of the propeller remains unaltered. Consequently the advance ratio of the operational point does not change and thus c_3 (equation (11.13) is also a constant.

As we assumed a constant pitch, the torque coefficient of the operational point does not change either when the advance ratio is constant. Consider coefficient c_4: if the relative rotative efficiency is also assumed to be a constant, c_4 is a constant. So in effect:

$$R = c_1 \cdot v_s^2 \text{ where } c_1 \text{ is a constant.} \qquad (11.16)$$

$$n_p = c_3 \cdot v_s \text{ where } c_3 \text{ is a constant.} \qquad (11.17)$$

$$P_p = c_4 \cdot n_p^3 \ \text{where } c_4 \text{ is a constant.} \tag{11.18}$$

We came across the linear relationship between propeller speed and ship speed in section 3.4.2:

$$n_p = c_3 \cdot v_S \hspace{3cm} \text{ref. (3.33)}$$

In section 3.4.2, it has already been mentioned that it is caused by the fact that the propeller velocity triangles tend to preserve their shape when becoming smaller. Here we see that it is true indeed: if the intersection point does not change, the advance coefficient J remains constant and thus the ratio of the velocities v_A and n.

The propeller law, equation (11.18) has also been introduced in section 3.4.2. There it was derived under the assumption that the propulsion efficiency remains constant:

$$\eta_D = \eta_H \cdot \eta_0 \cdot \eta_R \hspace{3cm} \text{ref. (3.25)}$$

The main contribution is from the open water propeller efficiency η_O which, like the torque coefficient K_Q remains constant as long as J does not change. So if the hull efficiency is assumed constant (which it is when the wake factor and the thrust deduction factor are constant) and the relative rotative efficiency is also assumed constant, then the overall propulsion efficiency must be constant.

Assuming that Figure 11.6 shows the ship curve for a twin shaft ship which is described by the parameters in Table 11.1, it can be used to determine the constants c_3 and c_4 as shown in Table 11.2.

Parameters	Design condition
P_E	16000 kW
v_s	28 knots (1 knot =1.852 km/h)
R	1111 kN
k_p	2
w	0.04
t	0.06
η_R	0.99
D	3.8 m
ρ	1025 kg/m^3

Table 11.1   The parameters that describe the design condition for a twin-shaft CODAD configuration.

Parameters	Design condition
J	0.992
K_T	0.206
K_Q	0.0457
η_O	0.710
$c_1 = \dfrac{R}{v_s^{\,2}}$	5.35×10^3
$c_3 = \dfrac{1-w}{J \cdot D} = \dfrac{n_p}{v_s}$	0.255
$c_4 = \dfrac{2\pi \cdot \rho \cdot D^5}{\eta_R} \cdot K_Q = \dfrac{P_p}{n^3}$	236×10^3
$P_{p,load}$	11624 kW
$n_{p,0}$	220 rpm (=3.67 s^{-1})

Parameters	Design condition
$P_{B,o}$	6115 kW
$n_{e,o}$	979 rpm
MCR	6500 kW
n_{MCR}	1000 rpm
EM	0.94
k_e	2
η_{TR}	0.95
i	4.45

Table 11.2   Calculation tables for design condition: (left) propeller data; and (right) engine and transmission data

11.3.3 *From propeller load to brake engine power*

In the previous section, we determined the power that is required by the propeller to deliver the thrust required by the ship. Comparing the propeller load with the operating envelope of an engine requires a few more steps.

The propulsion chain as introduced in section 3.4.3 needs to be continued from propeller flange to engine flange. Transmission efficiency, gearbox ratio and power-take-off need to be considered. The power necessary for the power-take-off, if any, is assumed to be known either as a function of propeller speed or engine speed, or as a constant value and should be added to the propeller load.

First consider a direct drive without PTO (one engine, one propeller). For a 2-stroke, low-speed diesel, the propeller speed has to be equal to the speed of the engine. To determine the brake power at the engine flange, the required propeller power should be divided by the transmission efficiency η_{TRM} to take transmission losses into account, the brake power is:

$$P_B = \frac{P_p}{\eta_{TRM}} \qquad\qquad \text{ref. (3.41)}$$

The obtained brake power should lie within the operating envelope of the chosen engine, and go through MCR. If this is not the case select another operating envelope, or select another propeller.

In a geared drive the gearbox becomes part of the matching process. The prime mover in a geared drive has a higher speed than the speed required by the propeller, so a reduction gearbox is found. The gearbox ratio is defined as:

$$i \overset{\text{def}}{=} \frac{n_e}{n_p}$$
ref. (3.40)

In practice the gearbox introduces a degree of freedom as will be shown next. Propeller selection has been treated in Chapter 10. There we stated that for a geared drive the propeller could be matched to the prime mover by means of the gearbox. So we chose the largest diameter possible and determined the optimum speed of the propeller. The propeller load curve can be determined as a function of propeller speed.

In Figure 11.7 the dotted line represents the brake power required from an engine if it drives the propeller directly. To match this propeller load with the operating envelope that has also been shown in the figure, maximum power should be delivered at the MCR speed of the engine. The gearbox ratio should therefore be:

$$i = \frac{n_{e,0}}{n_{p,0}}$$

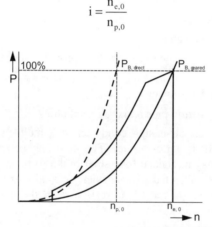

Figure 11.7   Choosing a gearbox ratio to match propeller load and operating envelope.

So in general, to compare the propeller load to the operating envelope of a prime mover, not only transmission efficiency needs to be taken into account, but also the gearbox ratio.

$$\left.\begin{array}{l} P_B = \dfrac{P_p}{\eta_{TRM} \cdot k_e} = \dfrac{c_4}{\eta_{TRM} \cdot k_e} \cdot n_p^{\,3} = \dfrac{c_4}{\eta_{TRM} \cdot k_e} \cdot \dfrac{n_e^{\,3}}{i^3} \\[3mm] c_9 = \dfrac{c_4}{\eta_{TRM} \cdot k_e \cdot i^3} \end{array}\right\} \rightarrow P_B = c_9 \cdot n_e^{\,3} \qquad (11.19)$$

where k_e is the number of identical engines per shaft and $i = 1$ for direct drive and $i > 1$ for geared drive. The most general form also includes PTO, see equation (11.20):

$$P_B = \left(\frac{P_p}{\eta_{TRM}} + P_{PTO} \right) \cdot \frac{1}{k_e} \qquad (11.20)$$

11.4 Off-design conditions

The propulsion plant will often operate under off-design conditions. It is necessary to determine those off-design conditions and check whether the propulsion plant still functions satisfactorily or not. The main off-design conditions are:

1). The ship sails at a speed other than design speed.

2). The hull resistance has changed due to:

  – Hull fouling, which increases with time

  – Change of displacement compared to the design displacement

  – Sea state other than design sea state

  – Sailing in restricted water depth.

  The resistance that needs to be overcome by a propeller also changes when:

  – Towing another ship or dragging equipment (for instance array behind a warship or a net behind a fish-trawler.)

  – Dredging with a suction pipe and drag head ploughing through the seabed.

3). Non-driven shaft(s): an off-design condition in a multi-shaft configuration occurs when one of the shafts is out of service. The shaft may be trailing, i.e. running freely at low speed, or it may be locked by a shaft brake so its speed is zero. Not only are the remaining shafts subjected to a heavier load, also the total load, i.e. the ship resistance, increases due to the added resistance of the non-driven shaft(s) and the necessary rudder corrections.

4). Change of pitch in case of CP propeller.

5). Disconnected engine(s): an off-design condition of a multi-engine configuration may be the change of the number of engines connected to a propeller shaft. The remaining engines on the shaft are subjected to an increased load at the same ship speed.

6). Power take off (PTO): in case the plant is provided with a power take-off a change of required power of the PTO results in a change of total engine load.

7). Change of gear ratio of the gearbox in a geared drive.

When investigating off-design conditions, it is essential to distinguish between two categories of off-design conditions:

▪ Off-design conditions that influence the operational point of the propeller. They should be studied by using the open water propeller characteristics. As a rule of thumb, all off-design conditions that are a result of changes that take place outside the ship's hull belong to this category: for example change of speed, change of resistance, change of driven shafts and change of propeller pitch.

• Off-design conditions that do not change the operational point of the propeller, so they can be solved without the open water diagrams. As a rule of thumb, the off-design conditions that are the result of a change inside the ship's hull belong to this category: for example change of number of connected engines, change of power to PTO and change of gear ratio.

In the following sections, a number of off-design conditions will be studied. The off-design condition will always be compared with the design condition. All variables in the design condition will be indicated with index *0*. So in the design condition, speed is $v_{S,0}$, resistance is R_0, propeller speed is n_0 and propeller power is $P_{p,0}$.

The power plant under consideration is a CODAD-configuration, see Figure 11.8. It has two propeller shafts each driven by two identical diesel engines. The cruise speed of 20 knots is developed by one diesel engine per propeller, and full speed of 28 knots by four diesels. See also Table 11.1.

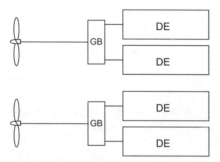

Figure 11.8   Diagram of CODAD configuration with four identical engines.

11.4.1 Effect of off-design speed

Assume that we want to investigate the effect of ship speed v_S, which is different from the design speed $v_{S,0}$. Further assume that wake factor and thrust deduction factor (and consequently the hull efficiency) have also changed. Other variables (pitch, number of shafts, number of engines, PTO and gearbox ratio) have not changed and will be left out of the investigation. The parameters are given in Table 11.3.

The resistance–speed relation in the design point has, in section 11.3, been transformed to the thrust coefficient of a ship as a function of the advance ratio:

$$K_{T,ship,0} = c_{7,0} \cdot J_0^2 \qquad\qquad \text{ref. (11.9)}$$

Likewise, this relationship exists for any off-design resistance–speed relation:

$$K_{T,ship} = \frac{1}{\rho \cdot D^2} \cdot \frac{c_1}{k \cdot (1-t) \cdot (1-w)^2} \cdot J^2$$

$$K_{T,ship} = c_7 \cdot J^2 \qquad\qquad \text{ref. (11.9)}$$

Parameters	Design condition	Off-design condition
v_s	$v_{s,0}$	v_s
c_1	$c_{1,0}$	c_1
R	$R_0 = c_{1,0} \cdot v_{s,0}^2$	$R = c_1 \cdot v_s^2$
w	w_0	w
t	t_0	t
η_H	$\eta_{H,0}$	η_H
$c_7 = \dfrac{K_{T,ship}}{J^2}$	$c_{7,0}$	c_7

Table 11.3   Design condition parameters versus off-design condition variables: off-design speed.

As explained in Chapter 3, the resistance increases more rapidly at increased speed, hence a change of ship speed has an effect on resistance R but also on the coefficient c_1. In case the off-design speed is lower than the design speed, it may be expected that in general, the coefficient c_1 has decreased relative to $c_{1,0}$ due to Froude effects. Consequently, it may be assumed that coefficient c_7 has decreased because c_1 is the most important factor in equation (11.10). These considerations explain why the off-design ship curve will lie below the design ship curve in the open water propeller diagram, as shown in Figure 11.9. (On the other hand, if the off-design speeds considered are higher than the design speed the off-design ship curve will lie above the design ship curve.)

The input parameters for the off-design speeds are given in Table 11.1. Intersection of the off-design ship curve with the thrust coefficient curve of the propeller leads to a new operational point for a particular off-design condition. If we assume that the design speed is the maximum ship speed, it implies that decreasing ship speed results in a blur of off-design intersection points between $K_{T,ship}$ and $K_{T,\,propeller}$. See Figure 11.9.

Parameters	Design condition	Off-design condition I	Off-design condition II
v_s	28 knots =14.4 m/s	20 knots = 10.3 m/s	12 knots =6.2 m/s
$c_1 = \dfrac{R}{v_s^2}$	5.35×10^3	4.14×10^3	3.59×10^3
w	0.04	0.06	0.07
t	0.06	0.08	0.09
$c_7 = \dfrac{1}{\rho \cdot D^2} \cdot \dfrac{c_1}{k \cdot (1-t) \cdot (1-w)^2}$	0.209	0.172	0.154

Table 11.4   Overview of input variables for off-design speed.

The figure shows that decreasing ship speed leads to increasing advance ratio, decreasing thrust coefficient, decreasing torque coefficient and increasing open water propeller efficiency because c_1 is speed-dependent. In the table below two points from the blur are used to calculate $P_{p,load}$ and n_p.

Parameters	Design condition	Off-design condition I	Off-design condition II
J	0.992	1.035	1.055
K_T	0.206	0.184	0.174
K_Q	0.0457	0.0416	0.0396
η_O	0.710	0.730	0.738
$c_3 = \dfrac{1-w}{J \cdot D} = \dfrac{n_p}{v_s}$	0.255	0.239	0.232
$c_4 = \dfrac{2\pi \cdot \rho \cdot D^5}{\eta_R} \cdot K_Q = \dfrac{P_p}{n_p^3}$	236×10^3	214×10^3	204×10^3
$P_{p,load}$	11624 kW	3189 kW	599 kW
n_p	220 rpm	148 rpm	86 rpm

Table 11.5   Calculation table off-design speed.

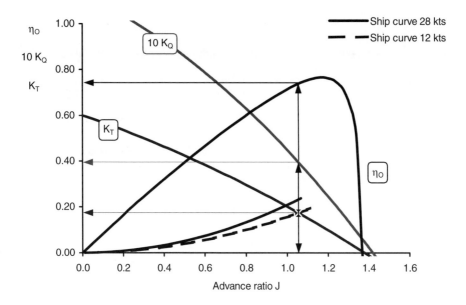

Figure 11.9   Open water diagram showing the effect of off-design speeds on operational points of the propeller.

The relationship between propeller speed and ship speed, and between propulsion power and shaft speed can be shown if the calculations in Table 11.5 are repeated for the entire range of ship speeds. The results are shown in Figure 11.10 and Figure 11.11.

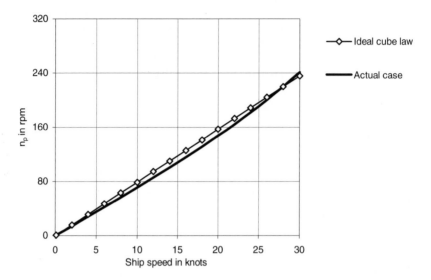

Figure 11.10   Propeller speed versus ship speed: *propeller law* and actual case.

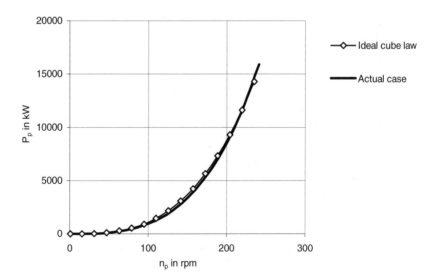

Figure 11.11   Propulsion power versus shaft speed: *propeller law* and actual case.

Figure 11.12 and Figure 11.13 show the required propeller power and the propulsive efficiency respectively, as a function of ship speed.

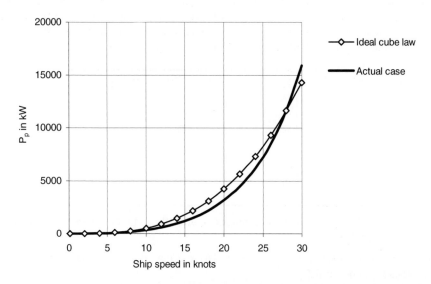

Figure 11.12   Propulsion power versus ship speed: *propeller law* and actual case.

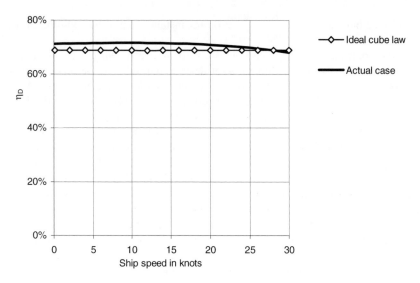

Figure 11.13   Propulsive efficiency versus ship speed: *propeller law* and actual case.

11.4.2 *Effect of added resistance*

Assume that the resistance at the design speed is higher than the resistance under the design condition, for whatever reason; see section 11.4 *Off-design conditions*. Further assume that wake factor and thrust deduction factor (and consequently the hull efficiency), pitch, number of shafts, number of engines, PTO and gearbox ratio have not changed and their influence will be left out of the investigation. So:

Parameters	Design condition	Off-design condition
v_s	$v_{S,0}$	$v_{S,0}$
c_1	$c_{1,0}$	c_1
R	$R_0 = c_{1,0} \cdot v_{S,0}^2$	$R = c_1 \cdot v_{S,0}^2$
w	w_0	w_0
t	t_0	t_0
η_H	$\eta_{H,0}$	$\eta_{H,0}$
c_7	$c_{7,0}$	c_7

Table 11.6   Design condition parameters versus off-design parameters for added resistance.

As shown in section 11.4.1, it is possible to derive a new thrust coefficient curve for the ship in off-design conditions:

$$K_{T,ship} = c_7 \cdot J^2 \qquad\qquad \text{ref. (11.9)}$$

If the resistance has increased, $\dfrac{R}{R_0} = \dfrac{c_1}{c_{1,0}} > 0$, for instance due to hull fouling or a heavy

sea state, the coefficient c_1 has increased, as well as coefficient c_7. The ship curve at higher resistance lies above the ship curve at design condition, so the intersection of the thrust coefficient curves for ship and propeller will be at a lower advance ratio. As will be shown in the next example, added resistance results in decreased advance ratio, increased thrust and torque coefficients, and decreased open water efficiency.

As an example, assume a ship for which the effects of change of resistance are shown in two off-design conditions: a heavy and a light off-design condition. In an ideal resistance–speed curve coefficient c_1 does not depend on speed and is equal to the service margin y as defined by equation (11.1) multiplied by the coefficient c_0 (equation (3.4)).

Wake factor, thrust reduction factor, hull efficiency, ship speed, pitch, number of shafts, number of engines, PTO and gearbox ratio are assumed the same in all conditions. In the design condition resistance R_0 is 1111 kN. In a light off-design condition, resistance is lower: due to less fouling than at design conditions, less displacement volume and calm seas the service margin is lower. In a heavy off-design the service margin has increased due to the effects of four years of fouling and rough seas.

$$SM = y_1\left(fouling\right) \cdot y_2\left(hull\,form\right) \cdot \left(\frac{\Delta}{\Delta_{nom}}\right)^{\frac{2}{3}} \cdot y_3\left(sea\,state\right) \cdot y_4\left(water\,depth\right)$$

This example continues with the example ship used in section 11.2 and described in Table 11.1. The service margin at design condition SM_0 was determined to be 1.22. The service margin for the heavy and light conditions are specified below:

- Heavy condition
  - Hull fouling after 4 years with 3% increase per year: $y_1 = 1.13$ (was 1.06)
  - Displacement remains full load: $y_2 = 1.04$ (was 1.04)
  - Sea state 8: $y_3 = 1.76$ (was 1.10)
  - Total added resistance: $SM_H = 2.05$ (was 1.22)
- Light condition
  - Hull fouling after 0 years: $y_1 = 1.0$ (was 1.06)
  - Displacement 3100 tonne (instead of 3500 tonne): $y_2 = 0.96$ (was 1.04)
  - Sea state 0 (still water): $y_3 = 1.0$ (was 1.10)
  - Total added resistance: $SM_L = 0.96$ (was 1.22)

$$\left.\begin{array}{l} SM_0 = \dfrac{P_{E,design}}{P_{E,trial}} = \dfrac{R_0}{R_{trial}} \\[2em] SM = \dfrac{R}{R_{trial}} \end{array}\right\} \Rightarrow R = R_0 \cdot \dfrac{SM}{SM_0}$$

Table 11.7 gives an overview of the input variables:

Parameters	Off-design: light	Design condition	Off-design: heavy
v_s	28 knots	28 knots	28 knots
SM	0.96	1.22	2.05
$c_1 = \dfrac{R}{v_s^2}$	4.22×10^3	5.36×10^3	9.00×10^3
w	0.04	0.04	0.04
t	0.06	0.06	0.06
c_7 (ref. (11.10))	0.165	0.209	0.351

Table 11.7   Overview of input variables of example for added resistance.

The influencing factor c_7 has been determined with equations (11.9) and (11.10):

$$K_{T,ship} = c_7 \cdot J^2 \qquad\qquad \text{ref. (11.9)}$$

$$c_7 = \frac{1}{\rho \cdot D^2} \cdot \frac{c_1}{k_p \cdot (1-t) \cdot (1-w)^2}$$ ref. (11.10)

So, the three ship thrust coefficient curves can be drawn in the open water diagram, see Figure 11.14, from which the variables in Table 11.8 can be found.

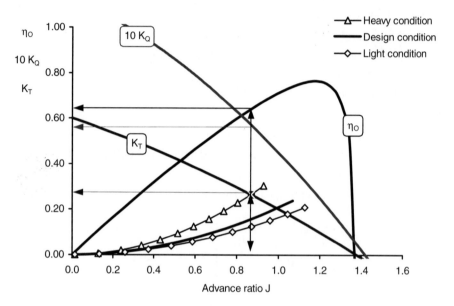

Figure 11.14   Example added resistance.

Parameters	Off-design: light	Design condition	Off-design: heavy
J	1.044	0.992	0.868
K_T	0.180	0.206	0.265
K_Q	0.0408	0.0457	0.0571
η_O	0.734	0.710	0.642
$c_3 = \dfrac{1-w}{J \cdot D} = \dfrac{n_p}{v_s}$	0.242	0.255	0.291
$c_4 = \dfrac{2\pi \cdot \rho \cdot D^5}{\eta_R} \cdot K_Q = \dfrac{P_p}{n^3}$	210×10^3	236×10^3	294×10^3
$P_{p,load}$	8906 kW	11624 kW	21688 kW
n_p	209 rpm	220 rpm	252 rpm

Table 11.8   Calculation table added resistance.

Figure 11.15 and Figure 11.16 show propeller speed and propeller power as a function of the ship speed.

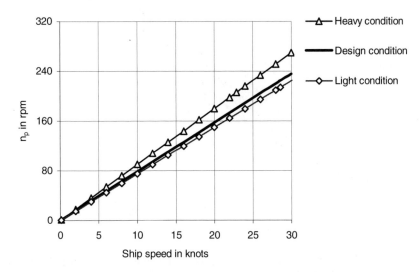

Figure 11.15   Propeller speed versus ship speed for three conditions with different resistance in normal, heavy and light condition.

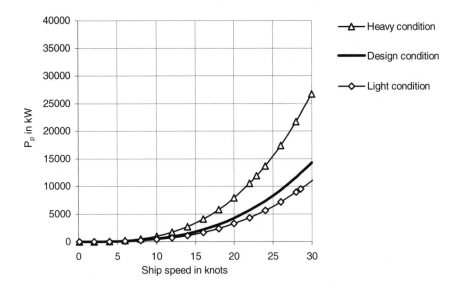

Figure 11.16   Propeller power versus ship speed for normal, heavy and light condition.

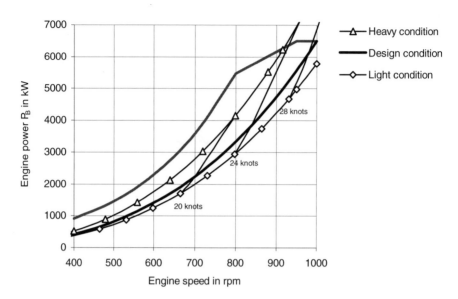

Figure 11.17   The brake power required by the propeller in the operating envelope for
                    the diesel engine.

Figure 11.17 shows the brake power required by a propeller in the operating envelope for the engine. Note how the design speed of 28 knots can no longer be achieved in the heavy condition. To show the direct relationship between power and ship speed, lines of constant ship speed are indicated.

11.4.3 *Effect of change of number of driven shafts*

In a multi-shaft configuration one or more of the shaft lines may be non-driven: trailing or blocked. In those cases, the load of the driven propeller(s) changes because the thrust required to propel the ship at a certain speed has to be delivered by a smaller number of shafts. For instance, when a twin-shaft configuration sails on only one shaft the remaining one has to deliver twice the thrust at the same ship speed, thus its load has doubled.

Additionally, the non-driven shafts add to the appendage drag of the hull, thus increasing the ship's resistance. Also, the rudder increases the total resistance because it has be at an angle to compensate for the asymmetric thrust. So, in effect the load of the remaining propeller not only increases because it has to take over the task of the non-driven shafts, but also because the total resistance increases. The increase of resistance is captured in the constant c_1, whereas the increased thrust that the propeller has to generate due to the change of number of propeller shafts k_p follows from the definition of the influencing factor c_7.

Take for example a power plant which consists of two identical shaft lines that has been designed for twin-shaft operation: $k_{p,0} = 2$ and $k_{e,0} = 2$. In the off-design condition that we will study, only one shaft is operating and the disconnected shaft is trailing, see

Figure 11.18. The speed in the off-design condition is equal to the design speed and the resistance is proportional to the ship speed squared.

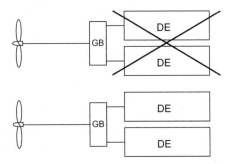

Figure 11.18   Diagram of CODAD configuration: single shaft operation.

If the additional resistance that is generated by the trailing shaft, i.e. appendage drag, is assumed to be 10 to 15 percent of the resistance overcome by that propeller, the total resistance that has to be overcome by the remaining propeller, is:

$$R = \frac{R_0}{2} + 1.15 \cdot \frac{R_0}{2} = c_1 \cdot v_{S,0}^2 = 1.075 \cdot c_{1,0} \cdot v_{S,0}^2$$

Under the assumption that wake factor and thrust reduction factor are constants the influencing factor changes from $c_{7,0}$ to c_7:

$$\left. \begin{array}{l} c_7 = \dfrac{1}{\rho \cdot D^2} \cdot \dfrac{c_1}{(1-t) \cdot (1-w)^2} \dfrac{1}{k_p} \\[4mm] c_1 = 1.075 \cdot c_{1,0} \\[2mm] k_p = \frac{1}{2} k_{p,0} \end{array} \right\} \Rightarrow c_7 = 2.15 \cdot c_{7,0}$$

The off-design ship curve can now be drawn in the open water propeller diagram:

$$K_{T,ship} = c_7 \cdot J^2 \qquad\qquad \text{ref. (11.9)}$$

Table 11.9 gives an overview of the input variables that result in the diagram in Figure 11.19.

Parameters	*Design condition*	*Off-design: single shaft*
v_s	28 knots	28 knots
$c_1 = \dfrac{R}{v_s^2}$	5.36×10^3	5.76×10^3
k_p	2	1
$c_7 = \dfrac{K_{T,ship}}{J^2}$	0.209	0.449

Table 11.9   Overview of input variables for single-shaft operation (non-driven shaft is trailing).

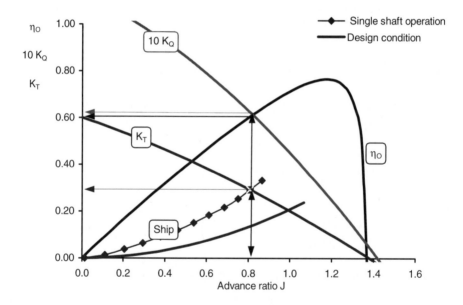

Figure 11.19   Open water propeller diagram with ship curves for twin-shaft and single-shaft operation.

In the new operational point of the propeller, the propeller load has to be determined, see Table 11.10:

Parameters	Design condition	Off-design: single shaft
J	0.992	0.808
K_T	0.206	0.293
K_Q	0.0457	0.0624
η_O	0.710	0.605
$c_3 = \dfrac{1-w}{J \cdot D} = \dfrac{n_p}{v_s}$	0.255	0.313
$c_4 = \dfrac{2\pi \cdot \rho \cdot D^5}{\eta_R} \cdot K_Q = \dfrac{P_p}{n_p^{\,3}}$	236×10^3	322×10^3
$P_{p,load}$	11624 kW	29383 kW
n_p	220 rpm	270 rpm

Table 11.10   Calculation table change of number of shafts.

Note that the factor c_4 has increased by a factor 1.36, which is the ratio of K_Q to $K_{Q,0}$, whereas the thrust that has to be generated by the propeller has increased by a factor of 2.15. This is a result of the higher propeller loading and the increased slip at the propeller. It implies that, for the loading of the engine, the propeller acts as an attenuator.

Figure 11.20 shows propeller speed as a function of ship speed, and Figure 11.21 shows delivered propulsion power as a function of shaft speed.

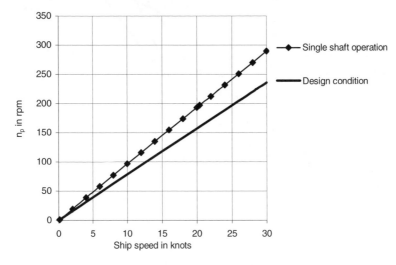

Figure 11.20   Propeller speed versus ship speed for normal 2-shaft and 1-shaft operation.

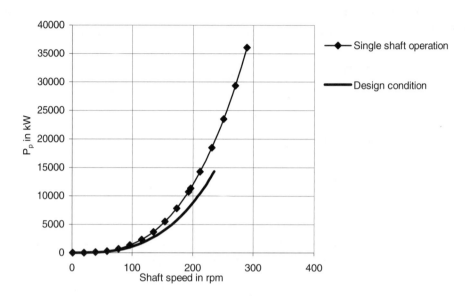

Figure 11.21   Propeller power versus propeller speed for 2-shaft and single shaft operation.

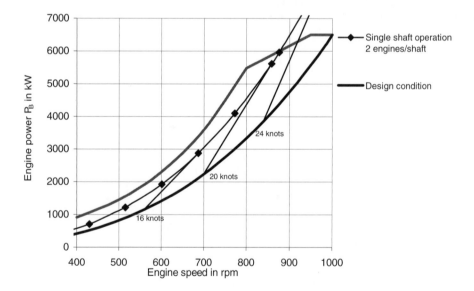

Figure 11.22   Operating envelope of a diesel engine for twin-shaft and single shaft operation.

If a realistic operating envelope for a diesel engine is matched with the propellers this could lead to an unacceptable situation. See Figure 11.22. In the design condition, the operating point of the propeller and the engine lies in the top right-hand corner: the MCR point. During single shaft operation the resistance curve moves up and it is hardly possible to drive the ship: the propeller load has moved closer to the limits of the operating envelope leaving hardly any room for acceleration, increased resistance or other off-design conditions. An acceptable situation might be obtained if a CP propeller or a 2-speed gearbox is used, or if a diesel engine with a much wider operating envelope is adopted.

If, on the other hand, the propeller load curves are matched with the operating envelope of a gas turbine, the off-design condition may be fully acceptable. See Figure 11.23. The operating point of the single shaft condition shifts to the left, but because the shape of the operating envelope is much wider than that of the diesel engine, the available turbine power is still high. Although design speed will not be reached, the speed might still be acceptable

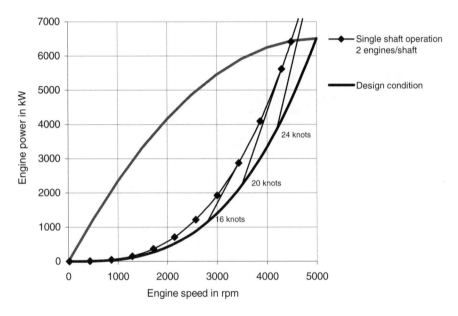

Figure 11.23   Operating envelope of a gas turbine for twin-shaft and single shaft operation.

11.4.4 *Effect of change of propeller pitch*

If a CP propeller is fitted the effect of change of the propeller pitch has to be studied. If the pitch changes, the ship curve as given by equation (11.9) is the same in design and off-design conditions. The thrust coefficient curve of the propeller, however, has changed. So, in the open water propeller diagram the propeller shifts to another operational point. For the new operational point, a propeller load curve can be determined as a function of propeller speed. The result is an array of curves (one for every pitch ratio), from which it is clear that by changing the pitch the matching with an engine can be improved.

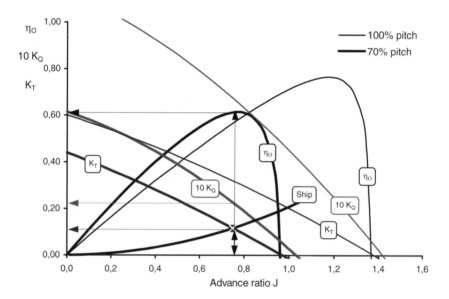

Figure 11.24   Open water propeller diagram for a CP propeller (2 pitches indicated) intersecting with the design ship curve.

The lines that were representing the thrust and torque coefficients of a FP propeller in Figure 11.6 are now lines of a CP propeller at the design pitch ratio P/D. Lines of reduced (off-design) pitch have been added in Figure 11.24. Table 11.11 gives the calculation table needed to obtain Figure 11.25 and Figure 11.26.

Parameters	Design condition	Off-design: change of pitch
P/D	1.30	0.86
θ	30.6° (100%)	21.4° (70 %)
J	0.992	0.749
K_T	0.206	0.117
K_Q	0.0457	0.0227
η_O	0.710	0.613
$c_3 = \dfrac{n_p}{v_s}$	0.255	0.337
$c_4 = \dfrac{P_p}{n_p^3}$	236×10^3	117×10^3
$P_{p,load}$	11624 kW	13419 kW
n_p	220 rpm	292 rpm

Table 11.11   Calculation table for the effect of pitch reduction.

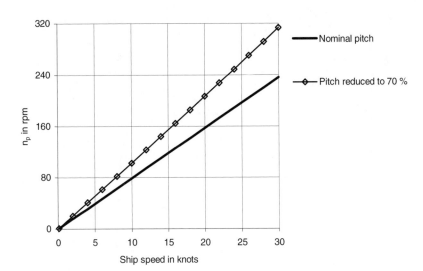

Figure 11.25   Propeller speed versus ship speed for design condition and reduced pitch.

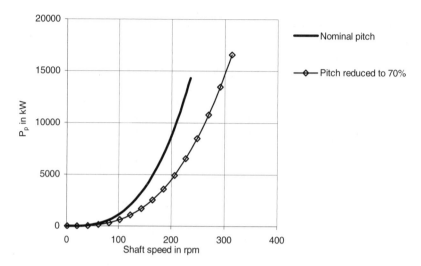

Figure 11.26   Propeller power versus propeller speed for design condition and at
                    reduced pitch.

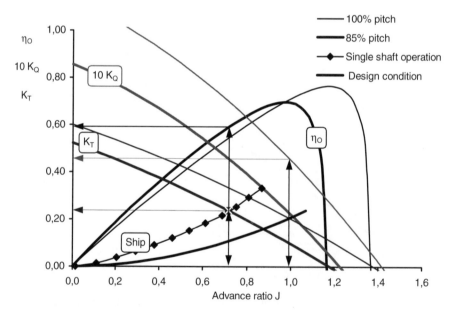

Figure 11.27   Open water propeller diagram for a CP propeller with ship curves for
                    design and single shaft operation.

To explain the use of pitch control, the example of the previous section is continued. It has been shown that, in case of single FP propeller operation, the propeller load line and the limit of the operating envelope lay close together, so an unacceptable situation arose because there was not enough room for additional resistance or acceleration, heavy seas, etc. We will now study single-shaft operation at reduced pitch and the second shaft trailing.

The ship curve in off-design condition is the same as for the off-design condition in section 11.4.3: the ship's thrust requirement has not changed. At every off-design pitch ratio the propeller has an operational point for which advance ratio, thrust and torque coefficient have to be determined.

For optimum engine operation the propeller load curve should go through the MCR point. So, to determine the required pitch ratio, the new operating point of the propeller should have the same torque coefficient as the design condition. This is shown in Figure 11.27. Table 11.12 is the calculation table of this case.

Figure 11.28 gives the new propeller load curve in the operating envelope for a diesel engine. Note that the lines of constant speed in this diagram are different from the lines of constant speed in Figure 11.22.

Parameters	Design condition	*Off-design: single shaft & reduced pitch*
P/D	1.30	1.07
θ	30.6°	26° (85%)
J	0.992	0.715
K_T	0.206	0.237
K_Q	0.0457	0.0457
η_O	0.710	0.591
$c_3 = \dfrac{1-w}{J \cdot D} = \dfrac{n_p}{v_s}$	0.255	0.353
$c_4 = \dfrac{2\pi \cdot \rho \cdot D^5}{\eta_R} \cdot K_Q = \dfrac{P_p}{n_p^3}$	236×10^3	236×10^3
$P_{p,load}$	11624 kW	31123 kW
n_p	220 rpm	305 rpm

Table 11.12 Calculation table effect of change of number of shafts and propeller pitch.

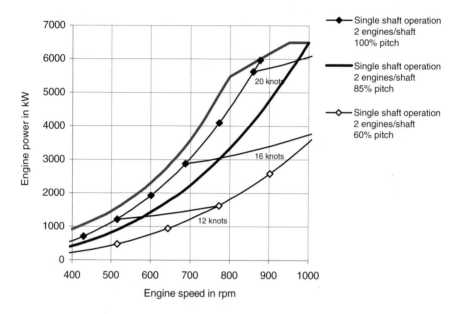

Figure 11.28   Operating envelope for a diesel engine with CP propeller load-lines.

11.4.5 Effect of change of number of engines per shaft

In case of configurations with multiple engines per shaft, the effect of shutting down one engine on a shaft is essentially different from shutting down one shaft, see Figure 11.29. By changing the number of driving engines the operating point of the propeller is not changed: the propeller is not affected by changing the source of power.

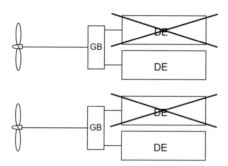

Figure 11.29   CODAD configuration : twin-shaft operation, one engine per shaft.

In off-design condition, the propeller is driven by a single engine, so the engine must produce twice the power at the same engine speed. That this is a very hard task for any engine but in particular for the diesel engine is shown in Figure 11.30. Analytically, this can be shown with the equations from section 11.3.3:

$$P_{B,0} = \frac{P_{p,0}}{\eta_{TRM,0} \cdot k_{e,0}} \qquad\qquad \text{ref. (11.20)}$$

Where $k_{e,0} = 2$. If $k_e = 1$, and transmission efficiency is assumed constant in design and off-design condition then:

$$P_B = \frac{P_{p,0}}{\eta_{TRM,0} \cdot k_e} = 2 \cdot P_{B,0}$$

The load curve for operation of one engine per shaft normally lies completely outside the power speed envelope of a modern turbocharged diesel engine. Pitch reduction or variable reduction gearbox must be used to bring the operating line within the envelope again. A wider engine envelope as for instance possible with sequential turbocharging might also offer a solution.

On the other hand, a gas turbine does not have a problem delivering (almost) maximum power at a somewhat lower output speed when shutting off one engine of two on a shaft. In fact this is done in practice on COGAG frigates. Figure 11.31 shows the operating envelope of a gas turbine with the two propeller loads that were also shown in Figure 11.30. Note that the lines of constant speed are vertical lines.

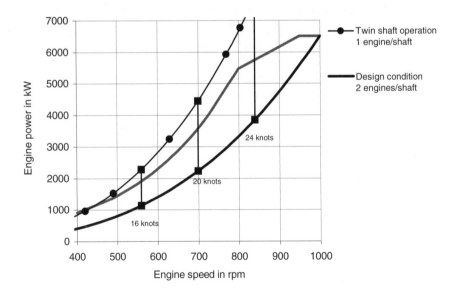

Figure 11.30   Operating envelope for a diesel engine showing propeller load in design and off-design condition: twin-shaft operation, one engine per shaft.

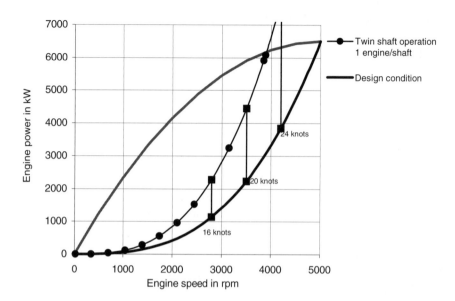

Figure 11.31   Operating envelope for a gas turbine showing propeller load in design
                    and off-design condition: twin-shaft operation, one engine per shaft.

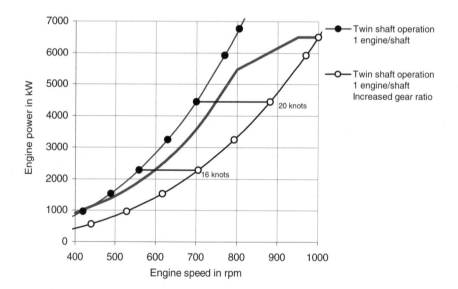

Figure 11.32   Operating envelope for a diesel engine showing the effect of increased
                    gear ratio.

11.4.6 Effect of change of gear ratio

In case of a geared drive with a two-speed gearbox, the effect of change of the gear ratio should be examined. Consider two identical engines on one shaft without PTO. As in section 11.4.5 one of the engines is disconnected, as a result the brake power as required by the load becomes unacceptably high. If gear ratio i is also changed, the brake power can be changed to fit the operating envelope as shown by the diagram in Figure 11.32.

The gear ratios which ensure that the load curve of the propeller intersects the operating envelope of the engine at MCR when two engines are connected, and when one engine is connected, can be determined as follows. First consider the propeller power as a function of propeller speed as determined in Table 11.2:

$$P_p = 236 \times 10^3 \cdot n_p^3$$

With the transmission efficiency of 0.95, the brake power as required by the propeller of one engine (in case of two ($k_e = 2$) equally loaded engines) is:

$$P_{B,load} = \frac{P_p}{\eta_{TRM} \cdot k_e} = 124 \times 10^3 \cdot n_p^3 \qquad (11.21)$$

Consequently, if one engine would be disconnected, the load required by the propeller from the remaining engine is:

$$P_{B,load} = 248 \times 10^3 \cdot n_p^3 \qquad (11.22)$$

Both load curves should pass through the MCR point of the engine envelope. The engine has an MCR of 6500 kW at 1000 rpm engine speed. For normal operation of two-engines per shaft, the load curve reaches 6500 kW at a propeller speed of $n_p = 3.74$ s^{-1} = 225 rpm (refer to equation (11.21)). In the off-design condition in which one engine drives one shaft, the load curve reaches 6500 kW at a propeller speed of $n_p = 2.97$ s^{-1} = 178 rpm (refer to equation (11.22)).

As the engine runs at a speed of 1000 rpm in the MCR point, the gear ratios which are required for the design condition and the examined off-design condition are respectively:

$$i_{design\ k_e=2} = \frac{1000}{225} = 4.45$$

$$i_{off\text{-}design\ k_e=1} = \frac{1000}{178} = 5.61$$

Note that the design condition, as described by Table 11.2, is associated with the CSR of the engines:

$$P_{CSR} = \frac{P_{p,0}}{\eta_{TRM} \cdot k_e} = \frac{11624}{0.95 \cdot 2} = 6115$$

So, the engine margin in this example proves to be rather small:

$$EM = \frac{P_{CSR}}{P_{MCR}} = \frac{6115}{6500} = 0.94$$

This rather low margin is acceptable considering that the example ship is a naval vessel which sails its maximum design speed only for a limited part of the time.

Also note that the gear ratios as determined in this example are based on the assumed squared resistance curve and the resulting cubic propeller load curve. In case the gear ratios need to be determined for a situation in which the resistance curve is not quadratic, the data of the power-speed relation in section 11.4.1 should be used. Assume the same transmission efficiency as above of 0.95. If the engine has an MCR power of 6500 kW, the maximum propeller power is still 6115 kW. With Figure 11.11, the propeller speed can be determined as n_p = 181 rpm. Consequently, the gear ratio in the off-design condition is slightly smaller because the propeller speed is higher than for the ideal cube law:

$$i_{design\,k_e=2} = \frac{1000}{225} = 4.45$$

$$i_{off\text{-}design\,k_e=1} = \frac{1000}{181} = 5.52$$

11.4.7 Effect of change of PTO

The change of the PTO-load is another off-design condition that does not affect the propeller load but changes the brake power required from an engine. If the load of the PTO is higher during an off-design condition, the brake power required in the off-design condition should still fit in the operating envelope of the engine. If this is not the case measures should be taken: for example, the added load should not be fed from the PTO but from the electric power plant, or other loads should be switched off.

$$P_{B,0} = \left(\frac{P_D}{\eta_{TRM}} + P_{PTO,0} \right) \cdot \frac{1}{k_e} \qquad\qquad \text{ref. (11.20)}$$

Figure 11.33 shows the brake power required by the propeller in design condition and the brake power required by the propeller and the PTO in off-design. The PTO is assumed to be constant over the range of speeds. Note that for low speeds the margin between the load curve and the limit of the operating envelope is small. This may be a reason to switch off the shaft generator at low engine speed. Another reason to switch the generator off is that the speed is too low to obtain the rated voltage.

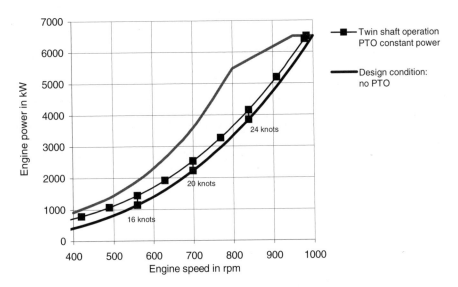

Figure 11.33   Operating envelope for a diesel engine with the design load and the off-design load which includes PTO.

Note that this is a hypothetical case. Usually, if PTO is considered, it will be considered in the design condition and not as an off-design condition. In the design condition, the combined load curve of the propeller and the PTO will intersect the drive curve at the MCR point. It will often be found that PTO is not possible in the low speed range for the same reasons as above.

11.5 A simplified method of calculation

In case only a few calculations with regard to matching and off-design have to be made, this can be done with the method explained in the previous section. It will, however, be more efficient to have a (spreadsheet) computer program, in which all relevant equations are included. In such a program the propeller's K_T, K_Q and J relations may be described by polynomial functions as for instance published by Marin for the Wageningen series of propellers.

If a suitable program is not available and the calculations have to be done manually, a lot of effort can be saved by using the method described in this section. This method relates the off-design condition variables to the corresponding variables of a known nominal condition: usually this is the design condition indicated with index *0*. All variables are expressed as a fraction of the corresponding design value. These *normalised variables* are indicated with a star and defined as:

$$X^* = \frac{X}{X_0}$$

(11.23)

The calculation by means of ratios is attractive, because the variables that do not change are left out of the equations.

For instance, the normalised variables for ship resistance, ship speed, propeller speed and propeller open water torque are respectively:

$$R^* = \frac{R}{R_0}, \quad v_s^* = \frac{v_s}{v_{s,0}}, \quad n_p^* = \frac{n_p}{n_{p,0}} \quad \text{and} \quad Q^* = \frac{Q}{Q_0} \qquad \text{ref. (11.23)}$$

Later in this section the star notation will be used to determine the new operational point when resistance increases.

Assume that the propeller–hull interaction parameters may be regarded as unchanged: so, w, t and η_H are assumed to remain constant. The calculation using normalised variables now proceeds as follows:

$$\left. \begin{array}{c} R = c_1 \cdot v_S^2 \rightarrow R^* = c_1^* \cdot v_S^{*2} \\ c_1 = constant \end{array} \right\} \rightarrow R^* = v_S^{*2} \qquad (11.24)$$

$$\left. \begin{array}{c} v_A = (1-w) \cdot v_S \\ w = constant \end{array} \right\} \rightarrow v_A^* = v_S^* \qquad (11.25)$$

$$\left. \begin{array}{c} J = \dfrac{v_A}{n_p \cdot D} \\ D = constant \end{array} \right\} \rightarrow J^* = \dfrac{v_A^*}{n_p^*} \qquad (11.26)$$

$$\left. \begin{array}{c} T = \dfrac{R}{(t-1)} \\ t = constant \end{array} \right\} \rightarrow T^* = R^* \qquad (11.27)$$

$$\left. \begin{array}{c} K_T = \dfrac{T}{\rho \cdot n_p^2 \cdot D^4} \\ \rho = constant \end{array} \right\} \rightarrow K_T^* = \dfrac{T^*}{n_p^{*2}} \qquad (11.28)$$

$$K_Q = \dfrac{Q}{\rho \cdot n_p^2 \cdot D^5} \rightarrow K_Q^* = \dfrac{Q^*}{n_p^{*2}} \qquad (11.29)$$

This section will also show analytical approximations of the K_T, K_Q and J-relations in the open water propeller diagram. A linear and a parabolic function will be derived. These approximations requires only a few parameters of the open water propeller diagram. The approximations are reasonably accurate and do not require a large amount of constants for polynomial functions.

11.5.1 Linear and parabolic approximations of open water propeller curves

For a fixed pitch propeller, the thrust and torque coefficient are a function of the advance ratio:

$$K_T = f(J)$$

$$K_Q = f(J)$$

In case of a controllable pitch propeller both these characteristics consist of a set of curves: for each pitch angle another curve, so K_T and K_Q are function of the advance ratio and the pitch angle:

$$K_T = f(J, \theta)$$

$$K_Q = f(J, \theta)$$

We will confine ourselves to the FP propeller and determine a linear and a parabolic approximation for K_T and K_Q for a given open water propeller diagram.

Linear approximation of K_T and K_Q

First assume linear relationships for K_T and K_Q:

$$K_T = K_{T,0} + \left(\frac{dK_T}{dJ}\right)_0 \cdot (J - J_0) \tag{11.30}$$

$$K_Q = K_{Q,0} + \left(\frac{dK_Q}{dJ}\right)_0 \cdot (J - J_0) \tag{11.31}$$

In Figure 11.34 the linear approximation of K_T is shown. (K_Q has been left out for clarity.)

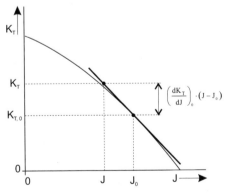

Figure 11.34   Linear approximation of K_T around the design point.

Divide by the values at the design condition to obtain normalised variables:

$$\frac{K_T}{K_{T,0}} = 1 + \frac{J_0}{K_{T,0}} \cdot \left(\frac{dK_T}{dJ}\right)_0 \cdot \left(\frac{J}{J_0} - 1\right) \tag{11.32}$$

$$\frac{K_Q}{K_{Q,0}} = 1 + \frac{J_0}{K_{Q,0}} \cdot \left(\frac{dK_Q}{dJ}\right)_0 \cdot \left(\frac{J}{J_0} - 1\right) \tag{11.33}$$

This can be written in a compact way using the star notation:

$$K_T^* = 1 + a \cdot \left(J^* - 1\right) \tag{11.34}$$

$$K_Q^* = 1 + b \cdot \left(J^* - 1\right) \tag{11.35}$$

The parameters a and b are *relative inclinations* of the propeller characteristic which can be estimated with the tangent of the K_T-curve in the design point:

$$a = \frac{J_0}{K_{T,0}} \cdot \left(\frac{dK_T}{dJ}\right)_0 \tag{11.36}$$

$$b = \frac{J_0}{K_{Q,0}} \cdot \left(\frac{dK_Q}{dJ}\right)_0 \tag{11.37}$$

Parabolic approximation of K_T and K_Q

Another possibility is to assume parabolic functions for K_T and K_Q. To determine these functions from an open water diagram, three points on each curve are necessary. In Figure 11.35 those points are indicated: on each curve the design point and the intersection points with the J– and K–axes are indicated. The coordinates of these points have been normalised in Table 11.13. The resulting K_T^* and K_Q^* curves are shown in Figure 11.36.

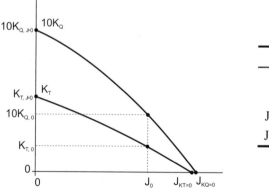

J	K_T	K_Q
0	$K_{T, J=0}$	$K_{Q, J=0}$
J_0	$K_{T,0}$	$K_{Q,0}$
$J_{KT=0}$	0	-
$J_{KQ=0}$	-	0

Figure 11.35 K_T– and K_Q–curves, each with three points to fit a parabolic function.

$J^* = \dfrac{J}{J_0}$	$K_T^* = \dfrac{K_T}{K_{T,0}}$	$K_Q^* = \dfrac{K_Q}{K_{Q,0}}$
0	$\dfrac{K_{T,J=0}}{K_{T,0}} = k_T$	$\dfrac{K_{Q,J=0}}{K_{Q,0}} = k_Q$
1	1	1
$\dfrac{J_{K_T=0}}{J_0} = j_T$	0	-
$\dfrac{J_{K_Q=0}}{J_0} = j_Q$	-	0

Table 11.13   The co-ordinates of the three points used to fit a parabolic function in star-variables.

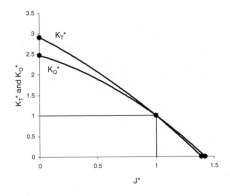

Figure 11.36 K_T^* and K_Q^* curves as parabolic functions.

The following parabola can be derived for K_T^*:

$$K_T^* = 1 + a \cdot (J^* - 1) + b \cdot (J^* - 1)^2 \qquad (11.38)$$

Using basic algebra and the coordinates in Table 11.13, a and b can be determined as:

$$a = \frac{j_T - 2}{j_T - 1} - k_T \cdot \frac{j_T - 1}{j_T}$$

$$b = \frac{k_T}{j_T} - \frac{1}{j_T - 1} \qquad (11.39)$$

Such a parabola can also be determined for the $K_Q{}^*$–J^* relation.

It is suggested to use the linear approximation in case the new operational point of the propeller is expected to be close to the design condition, and to use the parabolic approximation in case the new operational point lies further away.

11.5.2 Application: new operating point with added resistance

We will now use this method of calculation to determine the new operating point when ship resistance increases relative to a fully known (design) operational point. Assume that the new condition involves an increase of ship resistance with a factor c (>1) at a constant ship speed, so:

$$c > 1 \quad and \quad v_S = v_{S,0}$$

(This is in fact one of the off-design conditions that were mentioned in section 11.4 under points (2) and (3) and was discussed in detail in section 11.4.2.) The relationships between the normalised variables can be determined:

$$R = c \cdot R_0 \rightarrow R^* = c \tag{11.40}$$

$$v_S = v_{S,0} \rightarrow v_S{}^* = 1 \tag{11.41}$$

$$v_A{}^* = v_S{}^* = 1 \tag{ref. (11.25)}$$

$$J^* = \frac{v_A{}^*}{n_p{}^*} = \frac{1}{n_p{}^*} \tag{11.42}$$

$$T^* = R^* = c \tag{11.43}$$

$$K_T{}^* = \frac{T^*}{n_p{}^{*2}} = \frac{c}{n_p{}^{*2}} \tag{11.44}$$

With equations (11.42) and (11.44) the $K_{T,ship}$–J relationship can be found in normalised variables, without any calculation:

$$K_{T,ship}^* = \frac{c}{n_p{}^{*2}} = c \cdot J^{*2} \tag{11.45}$$

As shown graphically in section 11.4, the new operational point of the propeller can be found by intersecting the altered $K_{T,ship}$-curve with the K_T-curve of the propeller. Consequently, in this calculation the $K_T{}^*$ functions are equal.

$$K_{T,ship}^* = K_{T,propeller}^* \tag{11.46}$$

In this example the square $K_{T,propeller}{}^*$-function will be used, so:

$$c \cdot J^{*2} = 1 + a \cdot \left(J^{*} - 1\right) + b \cdot \left(J^{*} - 1\right)^{2} \tag{11.47}$$

Two roots can be solved for J^{*}; the positive root is the sought solution for the new operational point (index N):

$$J^{*} = J_{N}^{*}$$

This J_{N}^{*} leads to the new $K_{T,N}^{*}$ and $K_{Q,N}^{*}$, with the aid of the derived parabolic K_{T}^{*} and K_{Q}^{*}–functions. All other variables can now be determined.

Equation (11.42) defines J^{*} for $v_{S}^{*} = 1$:

$$J^{*} = \frac{1}{n_{p}^{*}} \tag{ref. (11.42)}$$

So, the propeller speed in the new operational point is:

$$n_{p,N} = \frac{n_{p,0}}{J_{N}^{*}}$$

In words: the propeller speed has to be increased reverse proportional to J to maintain ship speed at the design speed $v_{S,0}$.

The required propeller torques and delivered power should also be written in star notation to determine the effect of added resistance to the engine load:

$$K_{Q}^{*} = \frac{Q^{*}}{n_{p}^{*2}} \tag{ref. (11.29)}$$

$$Q_{N} = K_{Q,N}^{*} \cdot n_{p,N}^{*}{}^{2} \cdot Q_{0} \tag{11.48}$$

$$M_{D,N} = K_{Q,N}^{*} \cdot n_{p,N}^{*}{}^{2} \cdot M_{D,0} \tag{11.49}$$

$$P_{D,N} = K_{Q,N}^{*} \cdot n_{p,N}^{*}{}^{3} \cdot P_{D,0} \tag{11.50}$$

In words: the propeller power required to maintain the design speed $v_{S,0}$, has to be increased with a factor of the K_{Q} ratio and the third power of the propeller speed ratio. It also becomes clear that, if propeller speed is maintained at its original design speed $n_{p,0}$, i.e. $n_{p}^{*} = 1$, the delivered power has increased only with the ratio of K_{Q}. Of course in that case the ship speed would not be maintained at the original ship speed, $v_{s,0}$, but would decrease.

We can continue this example to find out what the new maximum ship speed will be at the increased ship resistance. Assume that the ship resistance is a square function of ship speed. This leads to the conclusion that for every ship speed on the square resistance curve, the operational point of the propeller (K_Q, K_T and J) remains constant (as established in section 11.3.2). For the new propeller power–speed relation this means:

$$P_D = K_{Q,N}{}^* \cdot n_p^{*3} \cdot P_{D,0} \qquad (11.51)$$

Where $K_{Q,N}{}^*$ is now a constant and $n_p{}^*$ may vary. If a constant transmission efficiency (η_{TR}) is also assumed, the propeller load, as experienced by the propulsion engine, is:

$$P_{B,load} = K_{Q,N}{}^* \cdot n_e^{*3} \cdot P_{B,0} \qquad (11.52)$$

This is a cube power–engine speed relation which can be drawn in the engine's operational envelope. An example is shown in Figure 11.37. In this figure the load curve for the design condition is shown as well as the new load curve. The new load curve lies a factor $K_{Q,N}{}^*$ above the design curve.

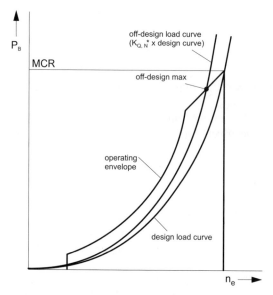

Figure 11.37   Intersection of the off-design ship curve with the operating envelope.

The intersection with the limit of the operating envelope leads to the maximum engine speed in the new condition. From this, the new maximum ship speed can be determined.

11.6 Matching a propulsion engine and a waterjet

Although it is not common practice to use open water diagrams for waterjets, as it is for screw type propellers, it is possible to present waterjet propulsion characteristics in non-dimensional diagrams that are comparable to the open water propeller diagrams. The waterjet thrust, torque and ship speed are made non-dimensional:

$$K_T = \frac{T}{\rho \cdot n^2 \cdot D^4}$$

$$K_Q = \frac{M_P}{\rho \cdot n^2 \cdot D^5}$$

$$J = \frac{v_s}{n \cdot D}$$

Note the slight differences in the definitions of the torque coefficient (M_P instead of Q) and of the advance ratio (v_S instead of v_A) when compared with the definitions of these coefficients for the screw type propeller. The thrust and torque coefficients can be shown as functions of the advance ratio. In order to compare with the K_T and K_Q curves of a propeller, these are also shown in Figure 11.38.

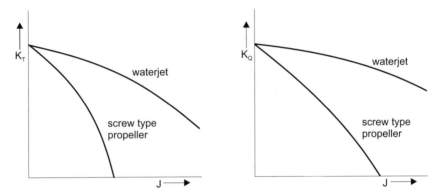

Figure 11.38 K_T and K_Q curves for a waterjet.

From the figure it can be concluded that the K_T and K_Q curves of a waterjet are much flatter than those of the screw type propeller. This implies that thrust and torque are hardly affected by ship speed. This is a result of the fact that the entrance speed of the water into the waterjet is hardly affected by ship speed, but is much more determined by the impeller speed. For screw type propellers this is quite different due to the location of the propeller, underneath the hull, as the water entrance speed into the propeller disc is directly proportional to the ship speed.

The resulting effect is that with an increase of ship resistance the required torque of a waterjet increases only slightly. This is attractive for the driving engine. It is outside the scope of this book to extensively treat the propulsion characteristics of waterjets and the interaction with the ship's hull. For a thorough discussion of the topic, reference is made to [van Terwisga, 1997].

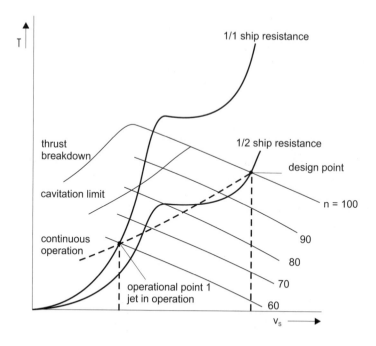

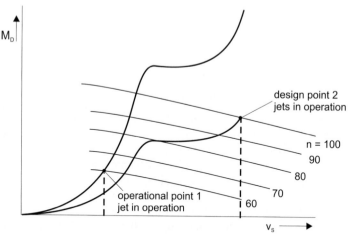

Figure 11.39   Thrust and torque characteristics for a waterjet: in design condition, two
                waterjets are in operation, in off-design one.

Design condition

In this book, we will use the diagrams as discussed in section 6.4.3 to match a water jet and a prime mover qualitatively. Assume a high-speed ship propelled by two identical waterjets. Figure 11.39 shows the thrust and torque characteristics as a function of ship speed. In the design condition, both waterjets are in operation and each propulsor has to develop half the ship resistance.

The maximum ship speed is obtained at 100% impeller speed and the design point lies just below the continuous operation limit. Due to the hump in the ship resistance curve the waterjet will operate in the zone between continuous operation and the cavitation limit during acceleration of the ship. By transferring the intersection points of the ship resistance with the impeller speed curve in the thrust diagram to the torque diagram, the torque–ship speed relation can be found. From this diagram the relationship between required impeller power and speed can be determined. Next, the diagram of required brake power versus engine speed can be drawn in the operating envelope of a diesel engine; see Figure 11.40.

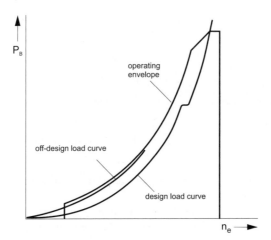

Figure 11.40   Brake power required by the waterjet in the operating envelope for a diesel engine.

This qualitative example shows that such a torque speed relation can be met even by a highly turbocharged diesel engine, without special measures to improve the torque capabilities at reduced engine speeds. Refer to the torque limits 3, 4 and 5 in Figure 7.14.

Off-design condition

Consider an off-design condition in which the ship is propelled by one waterjet instead of two. The waterjet has to supply a thrust that compensates for the full ship resistance. This means that at constant ship speed, the thrust to be delivered increases with a factor 2 or slightly more due to the eccentric thrust in this case. The increase of ship resistance, as experienced by the waterjet is however, less than in case of a ship with two screw-type propellers. (In that case ship resistance as experienced by the single driving propeller increases with more than a factor two due to the trailing resistance of the other propeller.)

As shown in Figure 11.39 operation with one waterjet is limited by cavitation. The maximum continuous speed is found by intersection of the full ship resistance curve with the continuous operation limit. This means that far less than maximum engine output can be used as shown in Figure 11.40.

11.7 Exercises

Exercise 1

A cargo ship will be provided with a propulsion plant consisting of a two-stroke low-speed diesel engine, which directly drives a fixed pitch propeller. The propulsion engine also drives a shaft generator during sea operation. In the design condition of the ship the following data are valid:

- ship speed $\quad\quad\quad\quad\quad\quad\quad\quad\quad$ $v_s = 20\ knots = 10.29\ m/s$
- ship resistance $\quad\quad\quad\quad\quad\quad$ $R = 777.5\ kN$
- effective power $\quad\quad\quad\quad\quad\quad$ $P_E = 8000\ kW$
- wake fraction $\quad\quad\quad\quad\quad\quad\quad$ $w = 0.2$
- thrust deduction $\quad\quad\quad\quad\quad$ $t = 0.12$
- relative rotative efficiency $\quad\quad$ $\eta_R = 0.99$
- propeller power $\quad\quad\quad\quad\quad\quad$ $P_P = 11480\ kW$
- propeller speed $\quad\quad\quad\quad\quad\quad$ $n_P = 125.6\ rpm = 2.093\ 1/s$
- shaft efficiency $\quad\quad\quad\quad\quad\quad$ $\eta_s = 0.977$

It may be assumed that the ship has a square resistance curve and that the hull-propeller interaction data (w, t and η_R) are constant.

The power required to drive the shaft generator: $P_{SG} = 1000\ kW$. The power required by the shaft generator is constant independent of engine speed. The shaft efficiency may be regarded as constant.

The open water characteristics of the propeller are:

J	K_T	K_Q	η_o
0	0.497	0.0774	0
0.2	0.438	0.0692	0.201
0.4	0.360	0.0588	0.390
0.6	0.270	0.0462	0.558
0.8	0.170	0.0321	0.674
1.0	0.064	0.0163	0.625
1.12	0	0.0065	0
1.20	-	0	-

The propeller has 5 blades, a pitch-diameter ratio P/D = 1.06, a blade area ratio of 0.75 and a diameter of 5.5 m. In the design condition the propellers operational point is:

$$J_0 = 0.715 \quad and \quad K_{T,0} = 0.215 \quad and \quad K_{Q,0} = 0.0382 \quad and \quad \eta_{o,0} = 0.640$$

The ship owner wishes to install a diesel engine with an engine margin of 0.85. Besides the design condition, he wishes to investigate 3 off-design conditions, as follows:
Light running: the ship sails in ballast condition, in which case the resistance will be 550 kN at v_s = 20 knots. The shaft generator requires 500 kW.
Normal service condition without shaft generator.
Heavy running: the ship sails in heavy seas, in which case the resistance has increased with a factor 1.5 compared to normal service condition.

A). Determine the required maximum continuous rating (MCR) of the propulsion diesel engine and its rated speed. (This will be the contract MCR and speed on which basis the engine will be ordered from the manufacturer.)
B). Determine the performance of the propulsion plant in the 3 defined off-design conditions: For every off-design condition, calculate the maximum ship speed, the corresponding engine brake power and propeller rpm.
   With regard to the operational envelope of the diesel engine three limitations apply:
   – The maximum engine speed $n_{e,max}$ = 1.03 n_{MCR}

   – For $n_e \leq n_{MCR}$: $P_B = \dfrac{n_e}{n_{MCR}} \cdot P_{MCR}$

     (This is effectively constant-torque behaviour.)
   – For $n_{MCR} \leq n_e \leq n_{e,max}$: $P_B = P_{MCR}$

Solution exercise 1

A). The engine brake power required to sail the design speed and to drive the shaft generator follows from the given data:

   – $P_B = \dfrac{P_P}{\eta_s} + P_{SG}$

   – $P_B = \dfrac{11480}{0.977} + 1000 = 11750 + 1000 = 12750 \ kW$ at $n_e = n_p$ = 125.6 rpm.

   The required MCR of the engine follows from:

   – $EM = \dfrac{P_{B,csr}}{P_{B,MCR}} = 0.85$

   – $P_{B,MCR} = \dfrac{12750}{0.85} = 15000 \ kW$

The corresponding engine speed has to match with the load curve as defined by the propeller load curve and the shaft generator load. As the ship has a square resistance curve and a cubic propeller load curve, the following is valid for engine brake power:

$$- \quad P_B = P_{B,propeller} + P_{SG} = c \cdot n_p^3 + P_{SG}$$

The constant c follows from $P_{B,propeller} = 11750$ kW at $n_P = 2.093$ 1/s $= 125.6$ rpm $\Rightarrow$ $c = 1281.5$ kWs^3.

Consequently, the load curve as experienced by the engine in design condition is:

$$- \quad P_B = 1281.5 \cdot n_p^3 + 1000$$

So, at $P_{B,MCR} = 15000$ kW the propeller speed follows as $n_p = 2.217$ 1/s $= 133$ rpm. The contract MCR is consequently defined by: $P_{MCR} = 15000$ kW at $n_{MCR} = 133$ rpm.

B). Plot the open water characteristics in a diagram to solve the following problems.
   Light running

To find the new propeller load curve it is necessary to determine the new operational point of the propeller in the open water diagram. For R $= 550$ kN at $v_s = 20$ knots $= 10.29$ m/s a $K_{T,ship}$ can be derived as:

$$- \quad K_{T,ship} = c_7 \cdot J^2 = \frac{1}{\rho \cdot D^2} \cdot \frac{c_1}{k_s \cdot (1-t) \cdot (1-w)^2} \cdot J^2$$

k_s, ρ, D, w, and t are the same as in the given design condition and c_1 follows from: $c_1 = \dfrac{R}{v_s^2} = \dfrac{550 \cdot 10^3}{(10.29)^2} = 5194$

Consequently: $K_{T,ship} = 0.2975 \cdot J^2$ (In   the   design   condition   the $K_{T,ship}$ *was* $0.4205 \cdot J^2$)

–   Intersecting the $K_{T,ship}$-curve with the $K_{T,propeller}$-curve leads to the propeller operational point as follows:

$$J = 0.780 \quad K_T = 0.181$$

From which can be found in the open water diagram:

$$K_Q = 0.0336 \quad \eta_o = 0.669$$

As can be expected with a lower resistance, the advance ratio as well as the open water efficiency have increased. The propeller speed for a ship speed of 20 knots $= 10.29$ m/s follows from the advance ratio

$$- \quad n_p = \frac{v_s \cdot (1-w)}{J \cdot D} = 1.919 \ s^{-1} = 115 \ rpm$$

The propeller power now follows from:

$$- \quad P_P = \frac{K_Q \cdot \rho \cdot n_p^{\;2} \cdot D^5 \cdot 2 \cdot \pi \cdot n_p}{\eta_R} = 7770 \; kW$$

The engine brake power to drive the propeller and the shaft generator now becomes:

$$- \quad P_B = \frac{P_P}{\eta_s} + P_{SG} = \frac{7770}{0.977} + 500 = 8453 \; kW$$

As the propeller has a cubic load-curve (in this case), brake power can be expressed as:

$$- \quad P_B = c \cdot n_p^3 + P_{SG}$$

$$- \quad P_{B,load} = 1125.4 \cdot n_p^3 + 500$$

When this line is drawn in the engine operating envelope, one can conclude that the engine will be limited by its maximum engine speed:

$$n_{e,max} = 1.03 \cdot n_{MCR} = 1.03 \cdot 133 = 137 \; rpm$$

In this case, the engine will develop $P_B = 13897$ kW. The maximum ship's speed in light running condition follows from the propeller rpm and advance ratio as:

$$- \quad v_s = \frac{J \cdot n_P \cdot D}{(1-w)} = \frac{0.78 \cdot 2.283 \cdot 5.5}{1-0.2} = 12.24 \; m/s = 23.8 \; knots$$

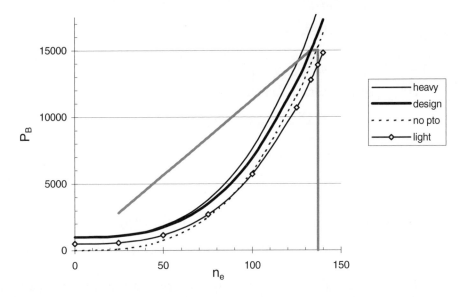

Figure 11.41   The operating conditions of Exercise 1 in the envelope for the engine.

Service condition, without shaft generator

In this case, only the shaft generator has been switched off. This means that the propeller loading is not affected by this change. The propeller remains in the design operational point $J = 0.715$, $K_T = 0.215$ and $K_Q = 0.0382$. The load-curve as experienced by the engine now consists only of the design propeller load:

$$P_B = 1281.5 \cdot n_p^3$$

The MCR power of 15000 kW will be reached at $n_p = 2.271$ s^{-1} = 136.2 rpm. This lies within the operating envelope, but above $n_{MCR.}$

– The maximum ship speed is now (speed and propeller rpm are proportional):

$$v_s = \frac{136.2}{125.6} \cdot 20 = 21.7 \; knots$$

This is a condition which might be used when the ship is behind schedule.

Heavy condition

The propeller's operational point shifts to a lower advance ratio, due to the increased resistance.

$$K_{T,ship} = \frac{1}{\rho \cdot D^2} \cdot \frac{c_1}{k_s \cdot (1-t) \cdot (1-w)^2} \cdot J^2$$

with $c_1 = \dfrac{1.5 \cdot 777500}{10.29^2} = 11014$ and the other variables as before:

$$K_{T,ship} = 0.6307 \cdot J^2$$

The operational point of the propeller follows from intersecting $K_{T,ship}$ with $K_{T,propeller}$ at: $J = 0.634$, $K_T = 0.254$ and $K_Q = 0.0438$ and $\eta_o = 0.585$.

– The propeller speed for a ship speed of 20 knots is now:

$$n_p = \frac{v_s \cdot (1-w)}{J \cdot D} = 2.361 \; s^{-1} = 141.6 \; rpm$$

– The propeller power in this condition is:

$$P_D = \frac{K_Q \cdot \rho \cdot n^2 \cdot D^5 \cdot 2 \cdot \pi \cdot n}{\eta_R} = 18860 \; kW$$

– The load as experienced by the diesel engine is defined by:

$$P_B = \frac{P_P}{\eta_s} + P_{SG} \rightarrow P_B = \frac{18860}{0.977} + 1000 = 20304 \; kW \; at \; n_e = 141.6 \; rpm$$

This point lies outside of the operating envelope of the engine. Consequently a ship speed of 20 knots cannot be achieved.

– The load-curve as experienced by the diesel engine is now:

$$P_{B,load} = c \cdot n_p^3 + P_{SG} \rightarrow P_{B,load} = 1433 \cdot n_p^3 + 1000$$

When this line is drawn in the operational envelope it can be concluded that the engine torque limitation is the limiting factor. For the engine torque limit the following relation applies:

$$P_{B,drive} = 15000 \cdot \frac{n_p}{2.217} = 6766 \cdot n_p$$

- In the intersection point, $P_{B,drive}$ is equal to $P_{B,load}$:

$$6766 \cdot n_p = 1433 \cdot n_p^3 + 1000 \rightarrow n_p = 2.095 \ s^{-1} = 125.7 \ rpm \ \text{and} \ P_B = 14175 \ kW$$

- The maximum deliverable ship speed follows with the advance ratio:

$$v_s = \frac{J \cdot n_p \cdot D}{(1-w)} = \frac{0.634 \cdot 2.095 \cdot 5.5}{(1-0.2)} = 9.13 \ m/s = 17.8 \ knots$$

So, the maximum speed in heavy condition is considerably lower than design speed, even with the engine running on its torque limit.

Alternative Solution for B

This exercise, with regard to off-design conditions can also be solved with the simplified method of calculation as described in section 11.5.

Light running

- The calculation is performed in ratios:

$$R^* = \frac{550}{777.5} = 0.7074 \ at \ v_s^* = 1$$

because w and t are assumed constant, this leads to:

$$K_{T,ship}^* = 0.7074 \cdot J^{*2}$$

- The K_T-J-relation with a linear approximation through the design point and a point at a higher advance ratio:

$$K_T^* = 1 + a \cdot (J^* - 1) \ \ where \ \ a = \frac{J_0}{K_{T,0}} \cdot \left(\frac{dK_T}{dJ} \right)_0$$

$$a = \frac{0.715}{0.215} \cdot \left(\frac{0.170 - 0.215}{0.8 - 0.715} \right) = -1.7606$$

Note that it is not the tangent in the design point that has been used but the slope of the K_T curve between the J-values of $J_0 = 0.715$ and $J = 0.8$. This is done because the expected ship curve of a light running condition will lie lower than the design curve. This will improve the approximation.

- By intersection of $K_{T,ship}$ with $K_{T,propeller}$ it follows:

$$0.7074 \cdot J^{*2} = 1 - 1.7606 \cdot \left(J^* - 1\right)$$

$$\rightarrow J^* = 1.090 \quad and \quad K_T^* = 0.841$$

- For K_Q^* can be derived:

$$K_Q^* = 1 + b \cdot \left(J^* - 1\right) \quad where \quad b = \frac{J_0}{K_{Q,0}} \cdot \left(\frac{dK_Q}{dJ}\right)_0$$

$$b = \frac{0.715}{0.0382} \cdot \left(\frac{0.0321 - 0.0382}{0.8 - 0.715}\right) = -1.3432$$

$$\rightarrow with \quad J^* = 1.090 \quad it \ follows \ that \quad K_Q^* = 0.879$$

Again the approximation is a straight line between the values for $J=J_0$ and a lower point.
- The new propeller load, as experienced by the engine, is now:

$$P_{B,prop}^* = K_Q^* \cdot n_p^* \rightarrow P_{B,prop} = K_Q^* \cdot P_{B,prop,0} \cdot n_p^{*3}$$

$$P_{B,prop} = 0.879 \cdot 11750 \cdot \left(\frac{n_p}{2.093}\right)^3 = 1126 \cdot n_p^3$$

- The total required brake power now becomes:

$$P_{B,load} = 1126 \cdot n_p^3 + 500$$

- This curve will intersect with the maximum speed limit of the operating envelope:

$$P_B = 13900 \ kW \ at \ n_p = 2.283 \ s^{-1} = 137 \ rpm$$

- The ship's speed follows from:

$$v_S = v_S^* \cdot v_{S,0} = J^* \cdot n_p^* \cdot v_{S,0} = 1.090 \cdot \frac{137}{125.6} \cdot 20 = 23.8 \ knots$$

Heavy condition

The linear approximation of the propeller curve will go through the design point and a point with a lower advance ratio:

$$K_T^* = 1 + a \cdot \left(J^* - 1\right) \quad where \quad a = \frac{J_0}{K_{T,0}} \cdot \left(\frac{dK_T}{dJ}\right)_0$$

$$a = \frac{0.715}{0.215} \cdot \left(\frac{0.215 - 0.270}{0.715 - 0.6}\right) = -1.5905$$

Again it is not the tangent of the design point that has been determined but the slope of the K_T-curve between two consecutive point: here J_0 and a smaller $J = 0.6$ because the ship curve is expected to lie higher.

- $R^* = 1.5$ at $v_s^* = 1$, so $K_{T,ship}^* = 1.5 \cdot J^{*2}$

- Intersection with $K_{T,propeller}^*$ leads to: $J^* = 0.887$ and $K_T^* = 1.180$

- Consequently

$$K_Q^* = 1 + \frac{0.715}{0.0462} \cdot \left(\frac{0.0382 - 0.0462}{0.715 - 0.6} \right) \cdot \left(J^* - 1 \right) = 1.122$$

- So, the engine brake power for propulsion:

$$P_{B,prop}^* = K_Q^* \cdot n_p^{*3}$$

$$P_{B,prop} = 1.122 \cdot 11750 \cdot \left(\frac{n_p}{2.093} \right)^3 = 1438 \cdot n_p^3$$

- The total engine load:

$$P_{B,load} = 1438 \cdot n_p^3 + 1000$$

- Drawing this curve in the operational envelope and intersecting with $P_{B,drive} = 6766 \cdot n_p$ leads to $P_B = 14140$ kW at $n_p = 2.091$ $s^{-1} = 125.5$ rpm

- The new ship speed follows from:

$$v_s = v_s^* \cdot v_{s,0} = J^* \cdot n_p^* \cdot v_{s,0} = 0.887 \cdot \frac{125.5}{125.6} \cdot 20 = 17.7 \; knots$$

11.8   References and further reading

van Terwisga, 1997
>   T. J. C. van Terwisga: *"A parametric propulsion prediction method for waterjet driven craft"*, Fast 97, March 1997

Chapter 12
Ship fuel consumption and exhaust emission

12.0 Learning goals

After studying this chapter, the student must be able to:

- *Calculate the energy demand, amount of fuel and exhaust emission, ship range and maximum number of days at sea during a mission or voyage.*

- *Calculate the energy demand, amount of fuel and exhaust emission over a year of operation based on the ship's operational profile.*

12.1 Introduction

This chapter will use the methods to determine power requirements on board for propulsion and auxiliary purposes that were developed in Chapter 3, in order to arrive at a prediction of the total brake power required from the prime movers. With the engine characteristics of fuel consumption, as given in Chapters 7 and 8 for diesel engines and gas turbines respectively, the required amount of fuel can be established both per unit time and distance. Given the fuel oil stored on board, the range and endurance of the ship can be calculated. It will turn out that fuel per mile has a minimum for a certain ship speed and consequently range has a maximum at that same speed.

This "fuel optimum" speed must not be confused with the economical speed even though there is a relation. Obviously, at the "fuel" optimum speed fuel cost will be minimal. Fuel costs however are only part of the total costs. In particular crew costs and the costs associated with the depreciation of the investment need to be added. These costs increase at lower speed, when related to distance covered. Then in conjunction with the freight rate the economic speed can be established. This, however, lies outside the scope of this chapter.

Exhaust emissions are associated with the combustion of fossil fuel. The amounts exhausted in the atmosphere will be quantified for SO_x and NO_x. Finally, mission profiles will be introduced and annual fuel consumption and exhaust emission will be estimated.

12.2 Energy balance for a certain ship speed

The energy demand from propulsion and auxiliary systems and the energy supply by main and auxiliary engines will be determined as a function of ship speed. The losses in the transmission of the propulsion system and the losses in the generators in the electric power plant will be included.

12.2.1 Propulsion power

First consider the power delivered to the propellers as defined in section 3.4:

$$P_D = C_D \cdot \rho^{1/3} \cdot \Delta^{2/3} \cdot v_S^{\,3}$$

ref. (3.28)

The delivered power coefficient C_D is not a constant but a function of speed, displacement, hull fouling, hull form, propeller geometry, sea state and water depth. C_D usually increases with increasing ship speed, in particular for advanced ship types and naval ships with a high Froude number. See Figure 12.1 for a typical example.

The net effect is that the power–speed relation of a ship is usually steeper than the cube of speed. Figure 12.2 shows the power delivered to the propellers of a 4000 tonne frigate. This ship will be used as the *example ship* throughout this chapter.

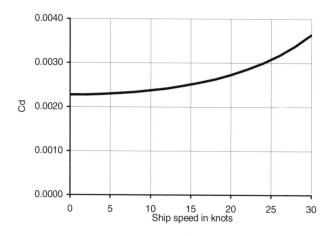

Figure 12.1   Delivered power coefficient C_D that increases with ship speed.

12.2.2 Auxiliary electric power

The auxiliary electric power has been studied in Chapters 3 and 4. The electric power consists of:

- the auxiliary machinery load (pumps etc).
- hotel load (air conditioning, cool and cold stores, lighting etc).
- operational load /the weapon electronics.

In principle the electric power of a ship is a function of ship speed, time of the day and operating condition. It can be determined by means of an electrical load analysis as introduced in section 3.5. In this chapter, mean values have been assumed for the operating condition and daytime dependency, and speed dependency has been neglected. As a result the electric power demand is a constant as indicated Figure 12.2. At zero speed, a harbour condition can be defined, in which the auxiliary power is normally lower.

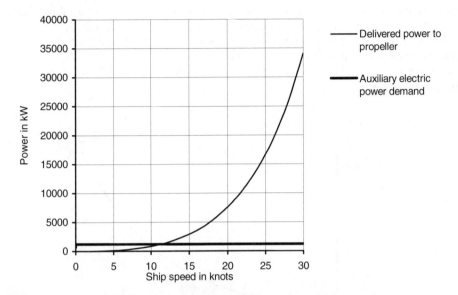

Figure 12.2   Propulsion and auxiliary power demand as functions of ship speed for a frigate of 4000 metric tons displacement.

12.2.3 *Transmission and generator losses*

The power demands determined in the previous section need to be related to engine brake power of main (propulsion) and auxiliary engines. Some losses need to be taken into account:

- transmission losses, which must be added to the power delivered to the propeller.

- generator losses, which must be added to the electric power supplied to the auxiliary systems.

The mechanical transmission losses consist of shaft bearing and seal losses (typically 0.5% to 1% at nominal power), and gearbox losses (3% to 5% for complex gearboxes with two or three reduction stages and 1% to 2% for single stage reduction gearboxes).

The shaft losses will have the character of a constant torque; so, the loss power varies with shaft speed. For the off-design behaviour of the gearbox losses, it is assumed that part of the losses is proportional to the transmitted power, that another part is proportional to the transmitted torque and that the balance is proportional to shaft speed. For an analytic model of these losses refer to [Stapersma, 94] and [Stapersma, 97]. Figure 12.3 shows a typical curve of the transmission loss at decreasing shaft speeds.

Although the transmission losses drop at low ship speeds, they do so at a much lower rate than the delivered power. This can be seen in Figure 12.4, in which the transmission losses are shown as a percentage of transmitted power: now the curve increases at low power and low ship speed. This relative increase of the losses partly counteracts the better delivered power coefficient C_D at low speeds. A refined model for transmission losses therefore is necessary to correctly estimate required power at low ship speeds.

For the constant auxiliary power assumed in the example ship, a constant generator efficiency can be assumed of 95%. If auxiliary power is varying, analytic models for generator efficiency at part load are necessary and these can also be found in [Stapersma, 94] and [Stapersma, 97].

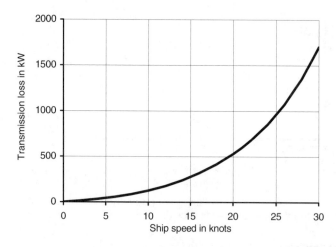

Figure 12.3   Typical transmission losses in the mechanical driven propulsion installation of the example ship.

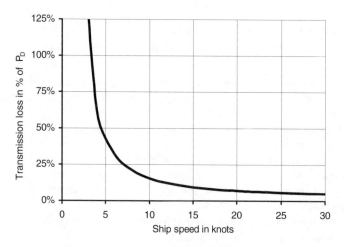

Figure 12.4   Transmission losses of Figure 12.3 as percentage of transmitted power.

12.2.4 Total power and energy demand

Figure 12.5 shows the required brake power from propulsion and auxiliary engines. The upper line in the figure represents the total brake power, i.e. the sum of all engines.

Most vessels require more auxiliary power than propulsion power at low speeds, and more propulsion power than auxiliary power at high speeds. This also applies to the example ship: the brake power for propulsion (i.e. propeller power including transmission losses) dominates the brake power for auxiliary electric demand at all speeds higher than 12 knots. At low speeds, however, the auxiliary power is higher than the power required for propulsion.

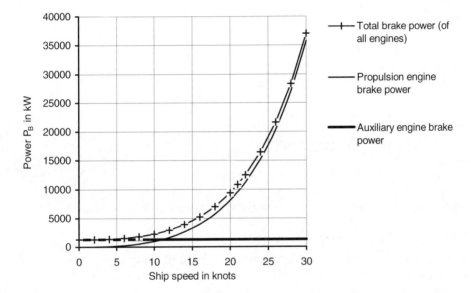

Figure 12.5   Total brake power (i.e. including transmission and generator losses) for the example ship.

The relative importance of the auxiliary power at low speeds is demonstrated if brake power is divided by speed, which effectively is the (brake) energy consumption per mile:

$$ecm = \frac{P_B}{v_S} = \frac{P_B \cdot \Delta t}{d} = \frac{E}{d} \tag{12.1}$$

Where:

   E = *energy required*
   d = *distance travelled during time interval* Δt *at speed* v_S.

The energy per mile for a constant auxiliary power of course increases strongly at low speeds. For the example ship, it dominates the scene below 12 knots: see Figure 12.6. As a result the total brake power has a bathtub shape with a minimum value at about 8 knots. From an energy point of view this is *an* optimal speed, but *the* optimal speed is defined by lowest fuel consumption; this will prove to be a slightly different speed.

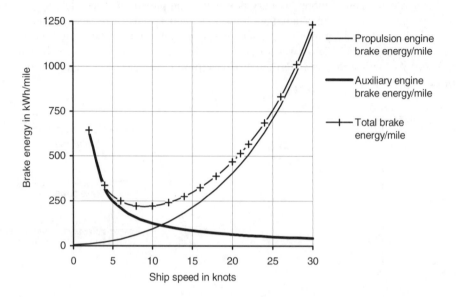

Figure 12.6   Required energy per mile for the example ship.

12.2.5 *Distribution over prime movers*

In order to obtain insight into the fuel consumption of the different prime movers onboard, it is important to know how the power is divided amongst the different prime movers. Assuming there are propulsion engine(s) and auxiliary engines, the propulsion engines deliver their power to the propulsion train and the PTO, if present. The auxiliary engines drive generators which, possibly in combination with the shaft generator(s), deliver power to the auxiliary distribution system.

The example ship has a two-shaft CODOG propulsion system: the propulsion power up to 20 knots is shared between the two cruise engines, and above that speed the power is shared between the two main engines. Their contribution to the required power is shown in Figure 12.7.

The auxiliary power is delivered by two generator sets, both running at maximal 80%: in case one unit fails, the other can be overloaded to 110%. The excess power demand (160% - 110% = 50% of one generator) must be switched off (these are the less important consumers or the so-called *non-preferent* groups).

For an integrated electrical concept, there is of course more flexibility in power generation. The optimum fuel consumption at a particular speed can be reached by combining the different generators in a certain way. In practice however, it is not practical to change to the optimum engine combination in case of frequent changes of ship speed: the advantage of optimum fuel consumption must be weighted against more frequent starting and stopping of the engines.

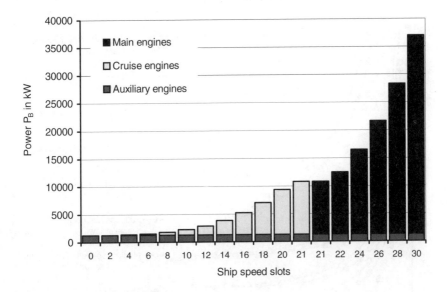

Figure 12.7   Total power and distribution over prime movers for the example ship.

12.3 Fuel consumption and exhaust emission

12.3.1 *Engine fuel & emission characteristics*

Specific fuel consumption has been introduced in Chapter 7. The definition of (brake) specific fuel consumption is:

$$\text{sfc} \stackrel{\text{def}}{=} \frac{\dot{m}_f}{P_B} \qquad\qquad \text{ref. (7.32)}$$

The nominal value (i.e. at nominal power) is different for different types of prime mover. Figure 12.8 gives typical specific fuel consumptions in g/kWh for several prime movers. It shows both the difference at nominal power (MCR = Maximum Continuous Rating) and the different shapes of the part load curve.

If fuel consumption would decrease linearly with power and be zero in case of zero power, the *specific* fuel consumption would be constant over the power range. Normally, however, there is a certain *idle* fuel flow (4% to 5% for diesel engines and 13% to 18% for gas turbines) which causes the specific fuel flow to go up steeply at low power. Also there is a difference between the idle fuel flow at zero power but nominal speed (generator load), and that for zero power and minimum speed (approximately propeller law). The latter is often lower resulting in a slightly better specific fuel consumption at part load. Hence for each type of engine, Figure 12.8 gives two curves: one propeller load (cube law) and another for generator load (constant speed).

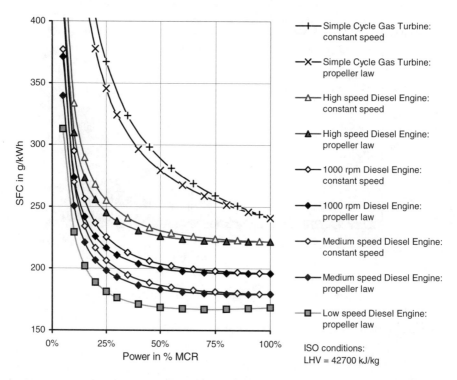

Figure 12.8   Specific fuel consumption of prime movers.

Every kilogram of fuel burned is associated with the emission of pollutants, as discussed in section 7.4.6 for the diesel engines. This is expressed by the pollutant emission ratio introduced in the same section:

$$\text{per} \overset{\text{def}}{=} \frac{\dot{m}_{pe}}{\dot{m}_f} \qquad \text{ref. (7.46)}$$

For some pollutant emissions, such as SO_x (the total of SO_2 and SO_3) and CO_2 the emission ratio is completely determined by the fuel composition. Only the emission of SO_x will be discussed in more detail as an example of this group of emissions: 20 grams SO_x per kilogram fuel for 1% sulphur (S) in the fuel. So, assuming for the example ship a low-sulphur light distillate fuel with 0.2% S, then the SO_x emission ratio (soxer) is 4 g/kg fuel.

For other pollutant emissions, such as NO_x (the total of NO and NO_2 and other nitrogen oxides), HC and unburnt particles, the emission ratio depends on load and speed of the engine as well as on ambient conditions. So, the emission ratio is not a constant value. For this group of pollutant emissions, NO_x will be discussed in more detail.

Often the NO_x emission ratio (noxer) of a diesel engine increases with decreasing load, as shown in Figure 12.9. The reason for this trend is that the amount of NO_x in parts per million (ppm) does not vary much and the air excess ratio increases at part load, as explained in [Stapersma, 1998]. Furthermore, observe that NO_x emissions are smaller for high-speed engines than for low-speed engines. The reason for this is the fact that the formation of NO_x takes time and is therefore more easily accomplished in low-speed engines. To simplify matters, the dependency on off-design speed and ambient conditions has been neglected.

For a simple cycle gas turbine, the NO_x formation "freezes" at low load due to the rapidly falling temperatures in the combustion chamber at part load (which by the way also causes the bad off-design specific fuel consumption). Also, the NO_x emission ratio of a gas turbine is substantially lower than the emission ratios of the diesel engines; even lower than the *noxer* of the high-speed diesel engine.

Having established a constant (SO_x) and a varying (NO_x) emission ratio, the specific pollutant emission (spe in g/kWh generated power) is simply:

$$spe = per \cdot sfc \qquad\qquad \text{ref. (7.47)}$$

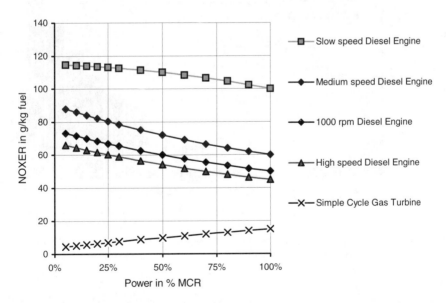

Figure 12.9 NO_x emission ratio for prime movers.

12.3.2 Ship fuel consumption and exhaust emission per hour

By multiplying the specific fuel consumption with the power, the fuel consumption of the ship per unit time can be obtained:

$$\dot{m}_f = sfc \cdot P_B \qquad\qquad \text{ref. (7.32)}$$

Multiplying this with the emission ratio gives the exhaust emission per unit time:

$$\dot{m}_{pe} = per \cdot sfc \cdot P_B \qquad\qquad (12.2)$$

Figure 12.10 shows the fuel consumption of each engine of the example ship. As for the power, this is a steep increasing curve. Note the step when changing to the main engines, this is caused by the higher *sfc* of the main engine at part load compared to the *sfc* of the cruise engine at full load.

Due to the constant emission ratio the SO_x emission follows the same trend as the fuel consumption but of course is substantially smaller: see Figure 12.11. The NO_x emission of the example ship is given in Figure 12.12. Note the relatively low amount coming out of the main gas turbines of the CODOG propulsion, considering the high power required for the high speeds.

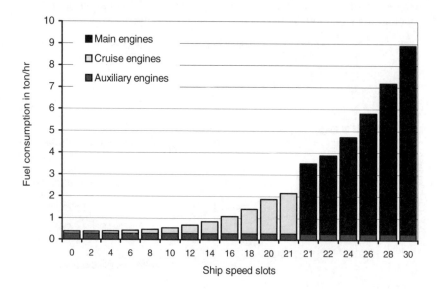

Figure 12.10   Fuel consumption per hour of the mechanically driven CODOG installation of the example ship.

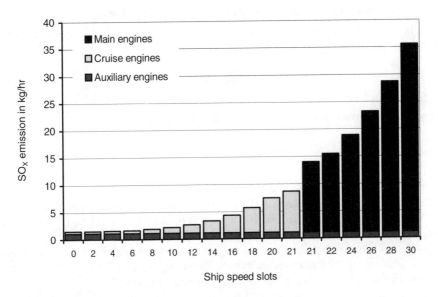

Figure 12.11 SO_x emission of the CODOG installation of the example ship.

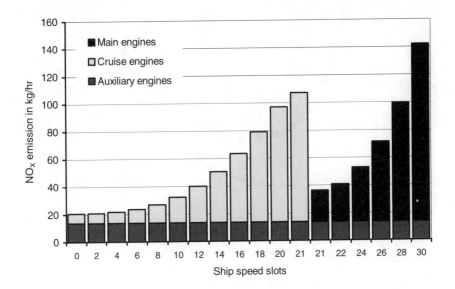

Figure 12.12 NO_x emission of the CODOG installation of the example ship.

12.3.3 *Ship fuel consumption and exhaust emission per mile*

The fuel consumption per mile covered can be found by dividing the fuel consumption per hour by the speed:

$$\mathrm{fcm} \overset{\mathrm{def}}{=} \frac{\dot{m}_f}{v_S} \tag{12.3}$$

Fuel per mile is linked with the energy per mile introduced earlier:

$$\mathrm{fcm} = \frac{\dot{m}_f}{v_S} = \frac{\mathrm{sfc} \cdot P_B}{v_S} = \mathrm{sfc} \cdot \mathrm{ecm} \tag{12.4}$$

Figure 12.13 shows a typical curve of the fuel consumption per mile of the example ship as a function of speed. Two things are notable. First, there is the sharp decrease when switching to cruise engines at around 20 knots; this is caused by the change from part load *sfc* of gas turbines to nominal load *sfc* of diesel engines. Secondly, at lower speeds, there is an optimum value of the fuel consumption per distance covered. Note that this optimum speed is different for the two cases: sailing on diesel engines (for the example ship around 10 knots) and sailing on the main gas turbines (around 14 knots).

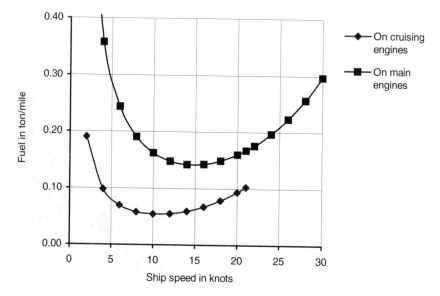

Figure 12.13   Fuel consumption per mile of the example ship.

The same calculation can be carried out for the exhaust emissions. The pollutant emission per mile is found as:

$$\text{pem} \overset{\text{def}}{=} \frac{\dot{m}_{pe}}{v_S} \qquad (12.5)$$

This has been calculated for the example ship for both SO_x and NO_x, refer to Figure 12.14. Now it is clear that the switch from main gas turbines to cruising diesel engines, apart from being advantageous for fuel consumption, also improves the SO_x emission. The low sulphur fuel that was assumed for the example ship caused the SO_x emission to be low anyway. On the other hand, the NO_x emission increases when switching to the diesel engines.

Like fuel consumption, the emissions exhibit a minimum value for a certain ship speed, albeit for NO_x at a slightly lower value (8 versus 10 knots) when sailing on cruising engines and at a slightly higher speed (16 versus 15 knots) when sailing on main gas turbines. The minima are flat anyway, in particular for the SO_x emission, making low emission operation possible as long as speed is not too high or too low.

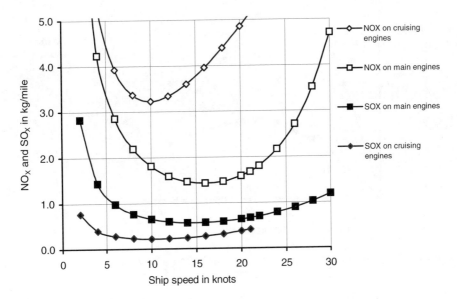

Figure 12.14 NO_x and SO_x emission per mile.

12.4 Range and endurance

Given the amount of fuel F onboard and the fuel consumption per mile and the fuel consumption per hour as a function of ship speed the following can be determined:

- Range: How far can the ship get as a function of speed?
- Endurance: How long can the ship sail as a function of speed?

12.4.1 Range

If the amount of fuel available on board is F then the range is the inverse of fuel consumption per mile:

$$R = \frac{F}{fcm} = \frac{F}{sfc \cdot ecm} = \frac{F \cdot v_S}{sfc \cdot P_B} = \frac{F \cdot v_S}{\dot{m}_f} \tag{12.6}$$

Figure 12.15 shows a typical curve of the range of the example ship as a function of speed. Of course the range also makes a step change when switching from main to cruise engines. Range is the inverse of fuel consumption per mile, so if there is an optimum for fuel consumption, there is an optimum for range as well.

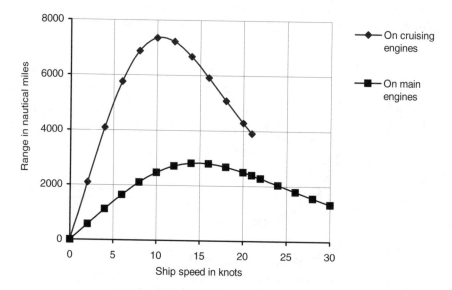

Figure 12.15   Range of a typical frigate of 3300 tonne displacement with mechanically driven CODOG installation.

The range is decreasing at low speeds because:

- the energy per mile increases steeply at low speeds because of the more or less constant bottom load of the auxiliary power: see Figure 12.6.
- the idling fuel of the engines at low load (another bottom value) causes a high specific fuel consumption and consequently a shorter range: see Figure 12.8.

When calculating the range of a ship, it is necessary to take into account that not the full fuel storage capacity can be used, because a small part of the fuel cannot be pumped out of the tanks. Further, some fuel will be lost in the separators of the fuel cleaning system. These losses can be in the order of 5% of the storage tank capacity.

12.4.2 Endurance

Endurance is important in case a ship has to stay present in a certain area. It is linked to range as follows:

$$T = \frac{R}{v_S} \tag{12.7}$$

Endurance can be calculated alternatively as:

$$T = \frac{F}{sfc \cdot P_B} = \frac{F}{\dot{m}_f} \tag{12.8}$$

Figure 12.16 gives the endurance of the example ship for which the previous figure gave the range. Again there is a step when changing from main to cruise engines. A marked difference with the range is that endurance always increases when ship speed decreases. In fact the maximum occurs exactly at zero ship speed.

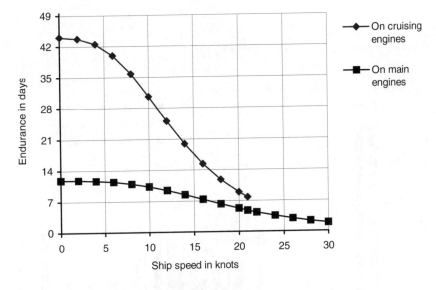

Figure 12.16   Endurance of the example ship.

12.5 Annual fuel consumption and exhaust emission

Having established the range and endurance of a ship depending on the fuel onboard, the next step is to calculate the fuel consumption on a mission or voyage or over a year. With specific fuel consumption a function of power, and power a function of ship speed, it seems obvious that the speed distribution of the ship during a mission or during a year has to be known. The speed distribution is given in the operational profile.

12.5.1 Operational profile

The operational profile of a ship gives the time intervals that a ship sails at a certain speed. In a formal way, the speed profile could be given as:

$$\Delta t_i \quad at \quad v_i \tag{12.9}$$

The time intervals, can either be specified in hours in order to define the distribution of speeds of one voyage, or in days to define the speed distribution of the total of voyages during for instance a year. A naval vessel may have different speed profiles for the different missions that a ship may carry out (e.g. general purpose, towed array and escort) as will be shown in Figure 12.17.

The summation of time intervals either gives the duration of a voyage if a voyage profile has been given, or is a year if the operational profile is an annual profile.

$$T = \sum_i \Delta t_i \tag{12.10}$$

Where,

$T = duration\ of\ voyage,\ or\ one\ year$

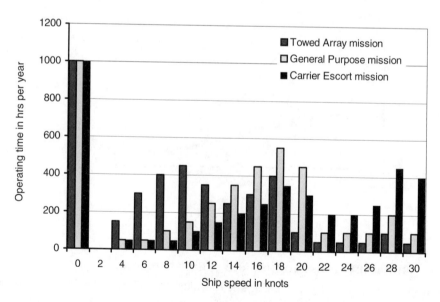

Figure 12.17   Typical speed profiles for frigates with different missions.

In Figure 12.17, annual speed profiles are shown for typical naval missions; these often show a local peak for high speed and a broad area of cruising or lower speeds. Figure 12.18 gives examples of annual speed profiles for some merchant ship types. The profiles show the characteristic peak around one or more service speeds.

A normal mission of a frigate or submarine is 4 to 8 weeks, i.e. about 30 to 60 days or approx. 700 to 1400 hours. During peacetime the total sailing time of a frigate is not more then 125 days or 3000 hours; that is less than 35% of the year. This percentage could be named *duty factor*; it is low compared to the merchant navy where missions may require operation for 4500 hours to 7500 hours (50% to 85% a year).

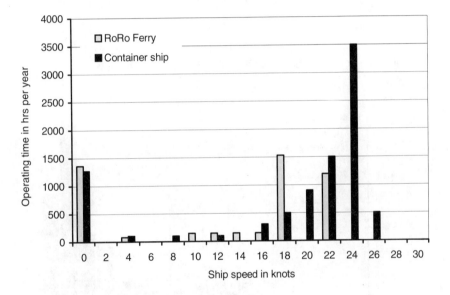

Figure 12.18   Speed profiles for a roll-on roll-off ferry and for a container ship.

In the preceding figures, the mean speed of the operational profile can be determined by dividing the total distance covered during a voyage or a year by the duration of the voyage or the sailing time during a year respectively:

$$\overline{v} \stackrel{def}{=} \frac{D}{T} = \frac{\sum_i v_i \cdot \Delta t_i}{\sum_i \Delta t_i} \qquad (12.11)$$

For frigates with top speeds of around 30 knots, the mean speed for general missions is around 17 knots, for towed array missions it would be in the order of 13 knots and for carrier escort it could be as high as 21 knots. Therefore, the mean speed is only 40 to 70% of the maximum speed capability; for merchant ships this ratio is normally around 80%.

The duty factor and the mean speed ratio are characteristic parameters of an operational profile.

12.5.2 Ship fuel consumption and exhaust emission per year

For a discrete formulation of the mission profile, the required energy (for instance in kWh) for a particular speed is:

$$E_i(v_i) = P_i \cdot \Delta t_i = C_D(v_i) \cdot \rho^{1/3} \cdot \Delta^{2/3} \cdot v_i^3 \cdot \Delta t_i \qquad (12.12)$$

The fuel consumed at that speed during a year is:

$$M_{f_i} = sfc(P_i) \cdot P_i \cdot \Delta t_i \qquad (12.13)$$

This is shown in Figure 12.19 for all speed values of the example CODOG frigate. Note the enormous amount of fuel that is required for 200 hours at 28 knots.

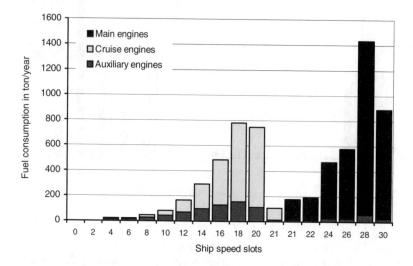

Figure 12.19   Annual fuel consumption, distributed over the ship speeds, of the example ship.

The same can be done for the emissions. The total amount of SO_x, as it is produced during a year, is presented in Figure 12.20. The profile over the different speeds is the same as for the fuel but of course the absolute value is smaller in proportion with the (constant) emission ratio of SO_x.

The NO_x emission for all ship speeds contributing to the sailing profile over a year is given in Figure 12.21. Now the combined effect of the high proportion of running hours at cruising speeds and the relative high NO_x emission of the diesel engines compared to the gas turbines make that, contrary to fuel consumption and SO_x emission, high speed operation on the gas turbines does not dominate.

When the contributions of all speed slots in Figure 12.19, Figure 12.20 and Figure 12.21 are added, total fuel consumption and exhaust emission can be calculated. For the example frigate with the assumed mission profile, the fuel consumption is 6700 tonne/year, the SO_x emission is 27 tonne/year while the NO_x emission is 210 tonne/year.

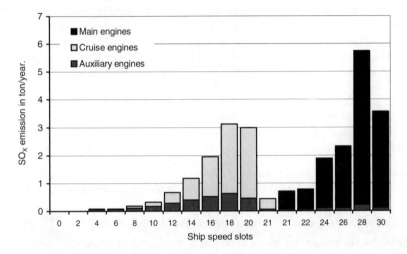

Figure 12.20   Annual SO_x exhaust emission of the example ship.

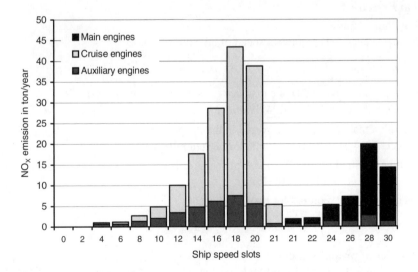

Figure 12.21   Annual NO_x exhaust emission of the example ship.

12.6 Exercises

Exercise 1

A CODOG frigate has 3500 tonne displacement. The specific delivered power coefficient is 0.030 and may be assumed independent of ship speed. For gearbox and transmission a 4% power loss may be assumed, independent of shaft speed and power. Auxiliary power for this type and size of frigate is estimated to be 0.3 kW/tonne displacement.

Main power is delivered by two gas turbines for which brake power matches the top speed of 30 knots. Cruising power is delivered by two high-speed 1000 rpm cruise diesel engines for which brake power matches a cruise speed of 20 knots. During the missions considered the ship sails on both shafts. Auxiliary power is supplied by two high-speed diesel generators that are matched such that in the normal conditions that are considered in this case they run at 80% power. Generator efficiency may be taken as 95%.

Fuel consumption and NO_x emissions may be estimated from Figure 12.8 and Figure 12.9 in this chapter. The seawater density is 1025 kg/m^3. 1 nautical mile is 1852 m.

A journey is planned where a distance of 528 nautical miles must be covered in 24 hours. Two alternatives are considered. For both scenarios fuel consumption must be calculated as well as total NO_x emission:

- *Alternative I:* One speed of advance for the complete journey

- *Alternative II:* Fast sailing at 28 knots for 8 hours and the remaining time at a lower speed such that the time of arrival is exactly 24 hours after departure

---

Solution Exercise 1

Specification of mission.

The first scenario (I) requires a speed of advance of:

$$v_S = \frac{D}{T} = \frac{528}{24} = 22 \ knots = 11.31 \ m/s$$

In the second scenario (II), the distance covered during the 1st phase is:

$$D_1 = T_1 \cdot v_{s,1} = 8 \cdot 28 = 224 \ nautical \ miles$$

Then the remainder must be covered in the 2nd phase:

$$D_2 = D - D_1 = 528 - 224 = 304 \ nautical \ miles$$

The time required for that 2nd phase of scenario II is:

$$T_2 = T - T_1 = 24 - 8 = 16 \ hrs$$

Speed of advance required for that 2nd phase:

$$v_{S,2} = \frac{D_2}{T_2} = \frac{304}{16} = 19 \ knots = 9.77 \ m/s$$

Rated power of propulsion plant

Required power follows from the definition of the delivered power coefficient plus an allowance of 4% for gearbox losses.

$$P_B = 1.04 \cdot C_D \cdot \rho^{\frac{1}{3}} \cdot \Delta^{\frac{2}{3}} \cdot v_S^{\ 3} = 1.04 \cdot 0.031 \cdot 1025^{\frac{1}{3}} \cdot \left(3500 \cdot 10^3\right)^{\frac{2}{3}} \cdot v_S^{\ 3} = 7.5 \cdot 10^3 \cdot v_S^{\ 3}$$

(Note that since C_D is non-dimensional, displacement must be in kg and power comes out in Watt).

Rated power of two gas turbines is equal to required power at 30 knots = 15.43 m/s:

$$P_{B,GT,full} = 7.5 \cdot 10^3 \cdot 15.43^3 = 27500 \ kW$$

Rated power of two cruising diesel engines is equal to the required power at 20 knots (= 10.29 m/s):

$$P_{B,DE,full} = 7.5 \cdot 10^3 \cdot 10.29^3 = 8200 \ kW$$

Alternative I

Part load power for **propulsion** at 22 knots on gas turbines is:

$$P_{B,GT,22} = 7.5 \cdot 10^3 \cdot 11.31^3 = 10850 \ kW$$

This is 40% of rated gas turbine power. From Figure 12.8 the sfc at this part load can be read from the gas turbine curve for propeller load (this is the lower of the two gas turbine curves):

$$sfc = 300 \ g/kWh$$

NO_x emission ratio can be estimated by reading Figure 12.9 at 39.5% part load:

$$noxer = 8.5 \ g/kg \ fuel$$

from which the specific NO_x emission can easily be determined:

$$sne = noxer \cdot sfc = 8.5 \cdot \frac{300}{1000} = 2.55 \ g/kWh$$

Then fuel consumption and NO_x emission are:

$$\dot{m}_f = sfc \cdot P_{B,GT,22} = 300 \cdot 10850 = 3.26 \cdot 10^6 \ g/hr = 3.26 \ tonne/hr$$

$$\dot{m}_{NOx} = sne \cdot P_{B,GT,22} = 2.55 \cdot 10850 = 27.7 \cdot 10^3 \ g/hr = 27.7 \ kg/hr$$

So during 24 hours:

$$m_f = \dot{m}_f \cdot T = 3.26 \cdot 24 = 78.2 \ tonne$$

$$m_{NOx} = \dot{m}_{NOx} \cdot T = 27.7 \cdot 24 = 665 \ kg$$

Auxiliary power is specified in relation to the size of the ship. For the 3500 tonne frigate under consideration auxiliary power is:

$$P_{aux} = 0.3 \cdot 3500 = 1050 \ kW$$

Allowing for the generator efficiency of 95%, the auxiliary diesel engine power is:

$$P_{aux,DE} = \frac{1050}{0.95} = 1105 \ kW$$

At this mean value of the auxiliary power demand two diesel generators are running at 80% power (so installed diesel engine power for these two sets together is 1105/0.8 = 1380 kW).

Specific fuel consumption for a high speed diesel running at 80% load at constant speed can be read from Figure 12.8:

sfc = 220 g/kWh

(note that the curve is very flat and that the difference between propeller load and generator load is marginal)
and NO_x emission ratio from Figure 12.9:

noxer = 47 g/kg fuel

from which the specific NO_x emission can easily be determined:

$$\text{sne} = \text{noxer} \cdot \text{sfc} = 47 \cdot \frac{220}{1000} = 10.35 \ \ g/kWh$$

Then fuel consumption and NO_x emission are:

$$\dot{m}_f = \text{sfc} \cdot P_{B,DE,Aux} = 220 \cdot 1105 = 0.24 \cdot 10^6 \ \ g/hr = 0.24 \ \ tonne/hr$$

$$\dot{m}_{NOx} = \text{sne} \cdot P_{B,GT,22} = 10.35 \cdot 1105 = 27.7 \cdot 10^3 \ \ g/hr = 11.4 \ \ kg/hr$$

So during 24 hours:

$$m_f = \dot{m}_f \cdot T = 0.24 \ \cdot 24 = 5.8 \ \ tonne$$

$$m_{NOx} = \dot{m}_{NOx} \cdot T = 11.4 \ \cdot 24 = 275 \ \ kg$$

Total required for scenario I:

$$m_f = 78.2 + 5.8 = 84 \ \ tonne$$

$$m_{NOx} = 665 \ + 275 = 940 \ kg$$

Alternative II

In the 1st phase the ship sails for 8 hours at 28 knots on gas turbines. Part load power for **propulsion** at 28 knots = 14.4. m/s on gas turbines is:

$$P_{B,GT,28} = 7.5 \cdot 10^3 \cdot 14.4^3 = 22400 \ \ kW$$

This is 79% of rated gas turbine power. From Figure 12.8 the sfc at this part load can be read from the gas turbine curve for propeller load:

sfc = 255 g/kWh

NO_x emission ratio can be estimated by reading Figure 12.9 at 78.6% part load:

noxer = 13 g/kg fuel

from which the specific NO_x emission can easily be determined:

$$\text{sne} = \text{noxer} \cdot \text{sfc} = 13 \cdot \frac{255}{1000} = 3.32 \ \ g/kWh$$

Then fuel consumption and NO_x emission are:

$$\dot{m}_f = \text{sfc} \cdot P_{B,GT,22} = 255 \cdot 22400 = 3.26 \cdot 10^6 \ \ g/hr = 5.71 \ \ tonne/hr$$

$$\dot{m}_{NOx} = \text{sne} \cdot P_{B,GT,22} = 3.32 \cdot 22400 = 27.7 \cdot 10^3 \ \ g/hr = 74.4 \ \ kg/hr$$

So during 8 hours:

$$m_f = \dot{m}_f \cdot T = 5.71 \ \cdot 8 = 45.7 \ \ tonne$$

$$m_{NOx} = \dot{m}_{NOx} \cdot T = 74.4 \ \cdot 8 = 595 \ \ kg$$

In the 2nd phase the ship sails at 19 kts = 9.77 m/s on cruising diesel engines. Part load power for propulsion now is:

$$P_{B,DE,19} = 7.5 \cdot 10^3 \cdot 9.8^3 = 7000 \ kW$$

This is 85% of rated diesel engine power. From Figure 12.8 the sfc at this part load can be read from the 1000 rpm (nominal speed) diesel engine curve for propeller load (but propeller curve and generator curve almost coincide here)

$$sfc = 195 \ g/kWh$$

NO_x emission ratio can be estimated by reading Figure 12.9 at 78.6% part load:

$$noxer = 55 \ g/kg \ fuel$$

from which the specific NO_x emission can easily be determined:

$$sne = noxer \cdot sfc = 55 \cdot \frac{195}{1000} = 10.7 \ g/kWh$$

Then fuel consumption and NO_x emission are:

$$\dot{m}_f = sfc \cdot P_{B,GT,22} = 195 \cdot 7000 = 1.37 \cdot 10^6 \ g/hr = 1.37 \ tonne/hr$$

$$\dot{m}_{NOx} = sne \cdot P_{B,GT,22} = 10.7 \cdot 7000 = 27.7 \cdot 10^3 \ g/hr = 74.9 \ kg/hr$$

So during 16 hours:

$$m_f = \dot{m}_f \cdot T = 1.37 \cdot 16 = 21.9 \ tonne$$

$$m_{NOx} = \dot{m}_{NOx} \cdot T = 74.9 \cdot 16 = 1198 \ kg$$

Auxiliary power is the same as for scenario I and continues over the full 24 hours, so the total amount of fuel and emission for auxiliary power are the same as for scenario I. Total required for scenario II:

$$m_f = 45.7 + 21.9 + 5.8 = 73.4 \ tonne$$

$$m_{NOx} = 595 + 1198 + 275 = 2068 \ kg$$

Conclusions

The difference in fuel consumption between scenario I and II is 84 − 73.4 = 10.6 tonne. In other words, scenario II uses only 87% fuel compared to scenario II. Normally a "flat scheme" i.e. a constant speed results in the lowest fuel consumption. Sailing at 28 knots (well above the mean required speed of advance) requires so much more fuel that it cannot be compensated by sailing at 19 knots during the other part. However, in this case sailing at low speed is not on the "thirsty" gas turbine, with its inherent high sfc at part load, but at an economical diesel engine with a flat sfc curve. This implies a discontinuity in the fuel consumption, which is sufficient to allow running at high speed for a while, although required power is disproportionally large. Also, it is clear that a ship speed of 22 knots, close to the switch point from main to cruise, is a rather unfavourable ship speed with respect to fuel consumption and must be avoided.

For NO_x emission, however, the conclusions are even stronger in favour of scenario II: the difference between scenario I and II is 2068 - 940 = 1128 kg. In other words, NO_x emission of scenario II is only 45% of that of scenario I. This can mainly be attributed to the lower NO_x profile of a gas turbine compared to a diesel engine.

12.7 References and further literature

The method described in this chapter forms the basis of the program SHIPPROGNOSIS, available at the RNLNC. Method and results were published in:

[Stapersma, 1994]

      D. Stapersma: *"The importance of (e)mission profiles for naval ships"*, INEC94 conference: Cost effective Maritime Defence, Plymouth, 31 Aug- 2 Sept 1994

[Stapersma, 1997]

      D. Stapersma, J.D. Wilgenhof: *"Savings in installed power, fuel consumption and emissions?"*, AES 97: 2nd All Electric Ship conference, Paris, March 1997

[Stapersma, 1998]

      D. Stapersma, H. Knoll: *"Practical Emission Research for a Navy"*, 22nd CIMAC International Conference on Combustion Engines, Copenhagen, May 1998

Index

Index

Index

Index

Index

Index

Index

Index

Index